G000123733

# THE ILLUSTRATED BOOK OF
# ANIMAL LIFE

# THE ILLUSTRATED BOOK OF
# ANIMAL LIFE

By Jana Horáčková and colleagues

TREASURE PRESS

Text: J. Horáčková, J. Čihař, J. Felix, V. Hanák, J. Lellák,
J. Moucha, I. Novák, J. Zahradník

Illustrations: A. Čepická, K. Hísek, J. Malý, P. Rob,
B. Vančura

Translated by D. Coxon, M. Hejlová, E. Kovanda,
O. Kuthanová, I. Pokorný, S. Pošustová

English version first published 1980 by
Reed International Books Ltd

This 1991 edition published by
Treasure Press
Michelin House
81 Fulham Road
London SW3 6RB

© 1990, Aventinum, Prague
(First edition 1980 by Artia, Prague)
All Rights Reserved. No part of this publication may be
reproduced or transmitted in any form or by any means,
electronic or mechanical, including photocopy, recording, or any
information storage and retrieval system, without permission in
writing from the copyright owner.

ISBN 1 85051 697 9
Printed in Czechoslovakia by Neografia, Martin
3/13/04/51-08

# Contents

# The Evolution of Animals

How, when and why was life created on Earth? How, when and why were plants and animals created? What caused their variety of form? What were their ancestors like? Men have wanted to know answers to these questions for ages past. Even today, only some can be answered. Scientists have only theories regarding the remotest past and the nearer they get to the present the more likely they are to find reasonable explanations to some of the questions.

Nobody has yet succeeded in discovering and producing evidence about the beginning of life on Earth, just as nobody has yet found the real cause of its creation. Man's knowledge is poor in this respect, for it is based on few facts. Palaeontologists, who can sometimes back their knowledge by findings of fossil remains, mainly of the hard parts of animals and plants, are in a somewhat easier situation. But such evidence is rarely abundant and the farther we go into the past the rarer it becomes. Through the collaboration of researchers from different fields of science it has been possible to identify some major events in the historical development (phylogenesis) of animals and, on this basis, to derive some of their inter-relationships. It is interesting to consider and speculate about the process which results in the evolution of the most advanced forms even though our knowledge is sometimes patchy.

It is always important to bear in mind that the evolution of living things has proceeded in accord with the environment and that it was subject to the following laws. Animals have different characteristics and abilities; in nature we cannot find two identical specimens of the same species. Therefore when they face the same kind of stresses, or when they compete for the same resources, they do not respond in the same way. Though each individual tries, according to its ability, to find the best food, to secure the most favourable site, to protect itself and its young against enemies, and to shelter itself against cold, water, heat, or competition, only some can succeed. This effort to survive is the struggle for existence. Those which are able to cope with the external conditions, and adapt themselves, survive. Other individuals, though, are so disturbed by the environmental factors that they are unable to adapt themselves and perish. In other words members of the same species are differently viable, hence they react in varying degrees to pressures of the environment. This force − known as natural selection − is the sieve through which the fittest pass while the less able are held back. The biological differences between members of the same species is the basic prerequisite for the working of natural selection. Natural selection materializes through the struggle for existence and is the driving force of evolution.

On the basis of the latest scientific research, it is currently assumed that life on Earth appeared 2,500 million to 3,000 million years ago. The age of the Earth is estimated at 4,000 million to 5,000 million years. However, our answers on the creation of life are based only on theories. It is assumed that the formation of simple organic compounds was essential for the beginning of life. From these compounds and with the aid of various physical factors, more and more complex substances formed and the most significant among them were proteins, which enabled further development to take place. Proteins agglomerated into structures of ever increasing complexity until they reached the form of coacervates, that is droplets surrounded by a membrane. The first manifestation of living matter — metabolism — probably appeared in these coacervate clusters of proteins. The process of metabolism developed over the course of millions of years and where the process of synthesis predominated over the process of breakdown the organization of living matter improved. The originally undifferentiated, that is non-cellular, living matter ultimately became differentiated into cells composed of a nucleus and protoplasm. The cell became the basic functional and structural unit from which the great diversity of animal and plant species has evolved. All animals, from the simplest unicellular protozoans up to the highest forms of life, go through a stage when they consist of only one cell. Cellular organization represents a new, higher degree of development. Cells were also the first independent living organisms (prokaryotes). After their differentiation, about 1,500 million years ago, the most primitive plant (autotrophic) and animal (heterotrophic) organisms emerged.

Green plants do not depend on other living beings for their nutrition, but are able to synthesize complex organic substances from simple inorganic matter. This phenomenon is known as autotrophy. Animals, and plants that are not green, draw energy mainly from organic substances (other plant and animal bodies or their decomposition products). In other words, they are heterotrophic.

The next stage in the development of living matter was connected with the agglomeration of separate cells into colonies. The individual cells gradually lost their independence and became parts

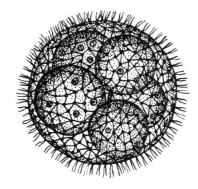

*Volvox globator* — a colony with daughter colonies inside

of a new many-celled whole — a colony. The evolution of such colonies was apparently the starting point for the formation of multicellular organisms — Metazoa. Within the colonies, the different cells specialized in performing certain functions — digestion, excretion, reproduction. The specialized cells are then grouped to form multicellular tissues of different shapes and with different specific functions.

The formation of new cells, and their growth and differentiation are the basic processes of growth, development and reproduction of multicellular animals. Sexual reproduction was the next important point in evolution. It is characterized by fertilization — the uniting of two parental sex cells (gametes) to form a single cell (zygote). This single cell is the starting point in the development of every new living organism. Thus, in the process of sexual reproduction, even the many-celled animals go through the unicellular stage — the fertilized egg. The gametes have different heritable properties which, after the union, are combined in the zygote. Hence zygotes have enhanced heritable variation and greater adaptability to changing living conditions. Only zygotes with properties most suitable for particular living conditions survive. Fertilization on the one hand extends the range of heritable properties of the zygote and on the other it activates the egg into development. The fertilized egg grows into an embryo. The early stage of embryonic life includes several significant phases. First comes cleavage of the egg, resulting in the formation of a large number of cells; then comes gastrulation with the formation of primordial layers, followed by the third phase when the organs begin to develop. Especially important is the process of gastrulation when the outer primordial layer, the ectoderm, differentiates from the inner primordial layer, the endoderm, so that the original one-layered embryo becomes two-layered. The endoderm connects with the outside of the gastrula through an opening called the blastopore. Gastrulation takes a different course in different groups of animals. It is accompanied by cell division and by the rearrangement of cell complexes. In some animals it is connected with the development of the third primordial layer, the mesoderm. The rearrangement of cell complexes is related to the formation of future organs. During this rearrangement various parts of the embryo acquire new positions and their mutual contacts affect each

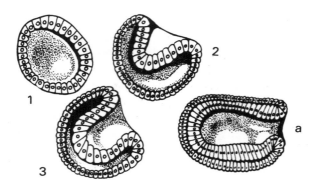

Cross section of several developmental stages of *Branchiostoma lanceolatum:* 1 — blastula, 2—4 — gastrulation, a — blastopore

other and influence further formation of the embryo. There are specific relations between the primordial layers and the creation of organs; in vertebrates the skin surface, the nervous system, many sense organs, the eye lens, and several of the endocrine glands, originate from the ectoderm whereas the alimentary canal, liver, pancreas, the notochord (around which the vertebrae form) and the respiratory system are formed from the endoderm; the packing and connective tissues, bones, cartilage, muscles and blood corpuscles develop from the mesoderm.

From a comparative study of cleavage and gastrulation in different animals, scientists have been able to draw some conclusions regarding the evolution of multicellular animals and the basic phylogenetic relationships between the different animal phyla.

How advanced an animal is at birth depends on the length of its embryonic life, which in turn depends on the quantity of nutritional substances (yolk) in the egg. The development of animals with little yolk is short and a simple larva which differs considerably from the adult animal hatches from the egg. It changes into an adult in the course of its larval life either by gradual development or by sudden changes (by dissolving the larval organs and creating new organs of an adult). This phenomenon is known as metamorphosis. From eggs with a larger yolk content the animal hatches after a longer period. In some groups the young are similar to adults in most respects except proportions and size. The larval stage is missing. The same applies to the development of the embryo inside the mother's body. This is direct development. Nevertheless some groups of animals with a large

amount of yolk, such as insects and amphibians, develop indirectly. The body organization of their larvae is perfect but very different from that of the adults. These larvae, too, undergo gradual or radical metamorphosis.

The originally primitive forms of mutlicellular animals (Metazoa) developed into various forms and reached different degrees of perfection. An important stage of evolution was the creation of the embryonic membranes. Embryonic membranes are an adaptation to life on dry land. They contain a liquid which replaces the aquatic medium for the embryo; the liquid protects the embryo mechanically from the effects of the environment and sometimes assists its metabolism. Embryonic membranes occur in insects and higher vertebrates.

One important development in land animals was the evolution of tracheae. These distribute gases throughout the body. They transfer oxygen directly to the cells of the body and account for the so-called external respiration. The vascular system thus became less concerned with the distribution of gases. Breathing through tracheae is used by the most numerous group of invertebrates, the Mandibulata (or Tracheata), that is the land arthropods, as well as by the Onychophora.

An important event which signified the appearance of vertebrates was the creation of the internal body support structure — the notochord. The notochord precedes the spine in the course of evolution and is one of the main characteristics of the animal phylum to which we ourselves belong, the Chordata.

The next steps were the evolution of a hard case protecting the brain, the development of jaws and the evolution of paired limbs. The development of jaws is an important leap in evolution for they permit an active approach to food. At this point vertebrates definitely abandoned the passive way of acquiring food until then so common in the animal kingdom and typical of the lower chordates which are mainly filter-feeders.

Paired limbs — fins — were of prime importance for the formation of "modern" fins of higher fish and for the formation of walking limbs of terrestrial vertebrates or tetrapods.

An immensely important stage which influenced the direction of further development of vertebrates was the movement from water to land. Dry land provided new and rich sources of food. Fish could reach them while basking in shallow water and even crawled after food on the banks. Moreover, waters in which the ancestors of terrestrial vertebrates used to live dried up at regular intervals. For the water inhabitants it was vital to be able to move into other water reservoirs which remained filled. Thus the new sources of food and the periodical drying up of water reservoirs were apparently the main reasons leading to the conquering of dry land by the ancestral amphibians.

The longer periods spent on dry land, and eventually the permanent terrestrial life of land vertebrates required some important changes in anatomy and in body construction. The respiratory organs had to adapt to utilizing atmospheric oxygen, and so the gill apparatus was replaced by air sacs and lungs. Directly connected with the rearrangement of the respiratory apparatus was the change in the system of blood circulation. The paired fins were transformed into walking limbs. The head had to become more mobile, and the neck vertebrae differentiated and connected by joints. In connection with changes in respiration and in the mobility of the head, the skull bones underwent some changes. The body which was no longer supported by water had to be reinforced by a strong skeleton, especially by the breastbone. The fish scales were gradually replaced by other forms of body covering.

Of almost the same evolutionary significance as the transfer from water to dry land was the change in egg structure and of the way of reproduction of the first exclusively terrestrial vertebrates, the reptiles, compared with their amphibian ancestors. While the eggs of amphibians hatch only in water, eggs of reptiles (and later of birds and monotreme mammals) always develop on dry land. The eggs of reptiles are self-contained units, the properties of which allow for safe development on dry land. The egg has its own source of nutrition (the yolk), its own watery medium (the amniotic fluid), embryonic membranes which assist the metabolism of the embryo, and a strong protective case within which the whole development of the embryo takes place. The egg is fertilized inside the mother's body. From the aspect of phylogenesis we can say that only after this adaptation was dry land definitely conquered.

Other important moments in evolution took place in the class of mammals. They are connected with viviparity, the development of the mammary glands and the evolution of the placenta which allows for perfect and long-term embryonic development within the maternal body.

Absolutely essential for the development of the whole chordate phylum was the development of the nervous system. While the notochord is common to all chordates, the brain is a specific organ of the vertebrates. In the course of evolution the brain gradually increased in volume and became differentiated. The cortex (pallium) evolved and developed until eventually it gave rise to the neopallium in some reptiles. The highest nervous functions and, in man, the acquisition of speech and language, is connected with the extraordinary development of the neopallium.

Let us now make a general summary of the main stages in the development of life on Earth. The first stage was the origin of complex molecules arranged in coacervate droplets and possessing the twin properties of metabolism and reproduction. These we can assume to be the first living things. The complex molecules were proteins, which were responsible for the metabolism, and nucleic acids, which were the carriers of information and had the property of being able to duplicate themselves. The primitive coacervates and molecular agglomerations eventually acquired a surrounding fat-and-protein membrane and became a cell.

These primeval cells were very much at the mercy of the external conditions. It is likely that they began to differentiate into different species, some of which were colonial — the oldest known fossils of living organisms, found in Precambrian rocks, are simple cells linked in chains.

The simple cells gave rise to a new kind of cell, with a nucleus and also the possibility of sexual reproduction. Most retained the ability to synthesize their own food and, in doing so released oxygen into the environment. The proliferation of these plants radically changed the environment and paved the way for a new mode of metabolism — that of animals, feeding on plants or even on each other.

These early, single-celled or colonial animals and plants eventually gave rise to multicellular forms and the ancestors of the various phyla we know today — and also some which have become extinct — but now, as then, the animal kingdom is ultimately dependant on the plant kingdom.

The evolution of life on Earth may be said to have culminated in the origin of Man who occupies a unique place in the web of life.

# The Zoological System

Knowledge about living organisms accumulated over the generations and became increasingly confusing. It was necessary to arrange the information so that natural scientists could find some order in the mass of facts and use the knowledge for further research and practical purposes. In the past, scientists have made many attempts to introduce a logical system of classification. The creation of a so-called natural system was found to be best. Such a system must reflect the conditions in nature as accurately as possible, and therefore be more than just a system of classification. It should reflect the phylogenetical (historical) development of organisms from the simplest and most ancient forms to the most recent and most advanced ones and, at the same time, include their mutual relationships. The word "should", however, is the main problem. For over the long period of development very complex relationships have been created and the clarification of these is slow and laborious. There is but little evidence on which a more detailed reconstruction of the past could be based. It is thus apparent that all the systems established so far have been built on incomplete sets of information and are necessarily simplified. The natural system is the ideal which the current system more or less approaches. The zoological system thus cannot be considered perfect or final. It is a flexible summary of available data, gradually to be supplemented as new information is discovered.

Karl Linné (usually known by the Latin version of his name — Linnaeus), a Swedish naturalist of the 18th century, is considered to be the founder of modern classification and nomenclature. This genius of a scientist classified all the plants and animals he knew according to their mutual similarities. He formulated his system in a treatise "Systema naturae" which was first published in 1735. The 10th edition of "Systema naturae", published in 1758, became the basis which was further developed by generations of scientists and upon which even the current system is based.

Modern systematics — taxonomy — deals with the classification of animals, with problems of variability and the origin of species as well as with problems of formulating systematic units. In order to understand more readily the multiplicity of animal species, a number of categories have been introduced to denote different ranks in the hierarchy of classification. Examples are phylum, class and order. Taxa (singular — taxon) are specific groups of animals within some category, for example Primates, Anseriformes and Diptera are all taxa with the rank of order.

The framework of the system is a succession of basic systematic categories — kingdom, phylum, class, order, family, genus and species. The kingdom is the highest category in the system and includes several phyla, a phylum includes one or more classes, and so on. This basic hierarchy is enriched by a number of intermediate categories which allow for a better description of the relationships. The succession of currently used categories is as follows: kingdom, subkingdom, phylum, subphylum, superclass, class, subclass, infraclass, cohort, superorder, order, suborder, infraorder, superfamily, family, subfamily, tribe, subtribe, genus, subgenus, species, subspecies.

Some systematic categories may be immediately identified according to the suffixes added to the root of the Latin name. The endings commonly used are:

—idae for a family (Viverridae, Vespidae),

—inae for a subfamily (Antilocaprinae),

—oidea or —acea are used, but not universally, for a superfamily (Dasyuroidea, Muricacea),

—ptera or —formes for an order in insects and birds (Heteroptera, Pelecaniformes).

The higher categories are more abstract than the lower ones, but allow for clearer expression of evolutionary relationships. Some species with certain similar features (such as dentition, shape of the skull, internal organs etc.) are placed in the same genus. The genera, again based on common similarities, are grouped into a family, families into an order, and so on. The limitation of these categories depends on the importance assigned by each scientist to the different features and on which he considers decisive. The only real unit which objectively exists in nature is the species. Many scientists have made attempts (and presented many definitions) to characterize a species faithfully. According to currently recognized definitions we may regard a species to be a group of populations, the members of which have a common genetic origin. These individual populations may be more or less separate but are able to interbreed with each other (actually or potentially). At the same time they are reproductively isolated from other populations which represent other species.

Even the species is a variable unit which continues to develop under the influence of internal and external factors. Individuals of some species do not differ very much from each other — in other words, those species have little variability. Less variable species are, as a rule, more ancient; they live in an almost unchanging environment or in places without competition from other species. Therefore their features became stabilized in the course of evolution. Species which are of more recent origin are usually much more variable, either because they are still seeking the most suitable way of adapting to the conditions of the environment or because their environment is neither unchanging nor uniform. Within the species there are often populations which differ from other populations of the same species in particular minor characteristics, but they can mate with each other without difficulty. These different populations we denote as subspecies. A species which is divided into several subspecies is described as polytypic; a species without subspecies is monotypic.

Variability must be taken into account when new species are being described. Each newly described species is represented by a holotype (single specimen) and by paratypes (a group of specimens used by the author to represent variability).

The placing of an actual species into the schedule of the zoological system and defining its systematic affiliation can best be seen from the following two examples:

| Kingdom: | Animalia | |
|---|---|---|
| Phylum: | Arthropoda (arthropods) | Chordata (chordates) |
| Class: | Insecta (insects) | Aves (birds) |
| Order: | Diptera | Anseriformes |
| Family: | Muscidae | Anatidae |
| Genus: | Musca | Cygnus |
| Species: | *Musca domestica* (Common Housefly) | *Cygnus olor* (Mute Swan) |

From highest to lowest the categories of the zoological system are decreasingly comprehensive — there is just one kingdom, 27 phyla, many more classes, even more orders, etc. The following list demonstrates this phenomenon. The system presented includes all extant (living) phyla, important subphyla, classes and orders, the members of which are included in this book. In these cases, for purposes of clarity we also use the auxiliary taxa.

As this book deals exclusively with multicellular animals the brief characteristics refer only to the higher metazoan taxa starting from sponges. The subkingdom Protozoa is not included in this list.

Kingdom: **ANIMALIA**

Subkingdom: **METAZOA**
6. Phylum: Porifera
    class: Calcarea
    class: Silicea p. 312
7. Phylum: Cnidaria (Coelenterata)
    class: Hydrozoa
    class: Scyphozoa
    class: Anthozoa p. 312
        order: Gorgonaria p. 312
        order: Actiniaria p. 312
8. Phylum: Ctenophora (Acnidaria)

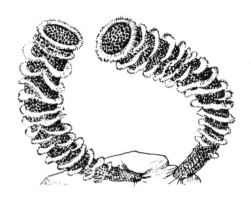

*Euplectella aspergillum* (Porifera)

## Phylum: PORIFERA (sponges)

The lowest multicellular organisms, with about 5,000 species, inhabiting fresh and salt water. Adult sponges are sedentary, the larva being the mobile stage. The body of sponges is composed of two layers of cells with a gelatinous substance in between. The gelatinous substance — the mesogloea — contains morphologically different cells which fulfil the basic functions of the organism, and supporting elements which form the skeleton. A primitive digestive tract is developed; water with plankton enters the system through small pores (ostioles) on the surface of the body and through small canals. Filtered water is expelled from the body through larger openings.

Calcareous sponges (Calcarea) form clusters, often of many individuals. They have a pipe-like shape. The mesogloea is reinforced by simple, triaxial or quadriaxial calcareous spicules.

Siliceous sponges (Silicea) live singly or in clusters. Their mesogloea contains either a skeleton of siliceous spicules, often ornamentally shaped, or needles covered with sponginous fibres. In some species the skeleton is formed almost exclusively by spongin, a fibrous protein.

## Phylum: CNIDARIA
(sea anemones, jellyfish, corals etc.)

Cnidarians comprise 9,000 or so species of aquatic, more or less mobile animals that live independently or in colonies. The body is formed by the ectoderm (outer layer) and endoderm (inner layer of cells), with a supporting layer in between. Muscle cells are

13

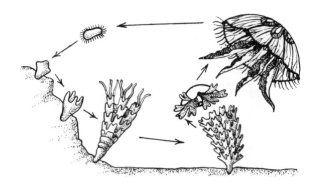

Development of a medusa (Cnidaria)

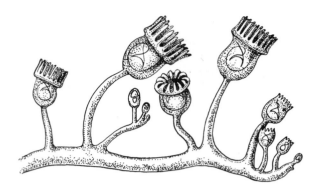

*Pedicellina cernua* (Entoprocta)

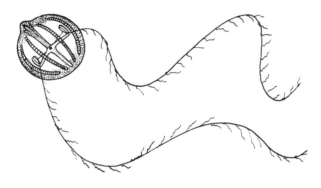

*Pleurobrachia pileus* (Ctenophora)

developed as well as scattered nerve cells. The ectoderm has a large number of cells containing a poisonous substance and an eversible filament through which the poison penetrates the body. The extensive digestive tract has a single opening for both intake and expulsion, and is surrounded by one or more rings of tentacles.

Cnidaria exist in two different body types which either alternate at regular intervals or one may predominate. The sexually mature type is the medusa (the mobile stage), the asexual type is the polyp (the sedentary stage) which develops from

*Planaria gonocephala* (Platyhelminthes)

eggs laid by the medusa. In general the development of cnidarians is as follows: a ciliate larva, the planula, hatches from the egg and after settling it develops into a polyp from the body of which medusae separate and later lay new eggs. In the Hydrozoa the polyp stage often predominates or the two forms regularly alternate. The digestive system is simple. In the Scyphozoa the medusoid stage predominates. The diameter of the saucer-shaped body sometimes even exceeds one metre, and on the underside it has marginal tentacles for hunting prey. The digestive tract is covered with numerous bulges. Anthozoa exist only as the polyp stage, either solitarily or in colonies, and are especially common in warm seas. The bodies of some are soft, for example sea anemones (Actiniaria), whereas others (corals) form a hard calcareous skeleton, often conspicuously coloured. The digestive tract is divided by cross folds or mesenteries.

Phylum: CTENOPHORA (comb jellies)
These are pelagic (ocean-inhabiting) animals which range from a few milimetres to over one metre in size, without sting cells but with sticky cells (callocytes) on the tentacles. The body is bilaterally symmetrical, ciliate, and has a pair of tentacles; the tentacles and cilia are used for locomotion. The phylum includes some 80 species.

Phylum: PLATYHELMINTHES (flat worms)
About 12,000 both independent and parasitically living species. The body, which is mostly flat, is composed of three primordial layers (ecto-, endo- and mesoderm); the muscles, sexual, nervous, digestive and excretory organs are developed. Vascular and respiratory systems are absent. The

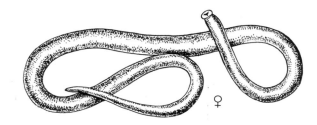

*Tetrastema quadrilineata* (Nemertini)

Pig-worm — *Ascaris lumbricoides* (Nemathelminthes)

platyhelminths are hermaphrodite and lay large numbers of eggs. The parasitic species often undergo complex development in the course of which they invade different hosts.

Phylum: ENTOPROCTA (moss animals)
A small phylum comprising aquatic species which live mostly in colonies. The body is cup-shaped and is always carried on a stem. The cup contains the body organs, and its upper end is rimmed with tentacles that cannot be withdrawn. In the hollow of the cup the anal and oral openings are adjacent. Members of this phylum reproduce both sexually and asexually.

Phylum: NEMERTINI (ribbon worms)
Mostly marine animals with an unsegmented muscular body from a few milimetres to several metres in length. A protrusible proboscis on the front part of the body is in some species equipped with a stylet and a poison gland. The intestine is pouch-like with an anus, and vascular and excretory systems are present. Ribbon worms have separate sexes (dioecious); marine species go through a larval (pilidium) stage. They live on various tubicolous worms which they draw from the tubes with their proboscides. They have remarkably great reproductive capacity.

Phylum: NEMATHELMINTHES
(roundworms and their allies)
The body is unsegmented, the parenchyma (connective tissue) is little developed so that a false body cavity (pseudocoel) is formed inside the body. A vascular system is absent. Many species live in water, soil, excrements, etc.; many others live parasitically in plant tissues, or in various organs of other animals. Nemathelminths are dioecious. About 12,000 species are contained in six classes,

the most numerous of which is the nematode class. Some well-known parasites belong among the nematodes — the pinworm *(Enterobius vermicularis)*, pig roundworm *(Ascaris lumbricoides)* as well as *Parascaris equorum* and eelworms (Rhabditoidea) which live in plant tissues.

Phylum: PRIAPULIDA
The smallest phylum with only one class and order including four species. Priapulids grow to be 8 cm at most. They are predators and live in the mud of cooler seas. The body is covered by a strong warty cuticle; the front part is extended to form a spiny proboscis. The mouth is equipped with chitinous teeth. The body cavity is large, filled with a liquid which contains pigmented cells. A vascular system is not developed. Members of this phylum are dioecious. The eggs are fertilized in the water outside the female's body and their development includes a larval stage.

Phylum: MOLLUSCA
(snails, slugs, bivalves, squids etc.)
After the arthropods, the molluscs form the most numerous animal phylum with about 130,000 described species. They can be small, medium sized or extremely large. The body of molluscs is unseg-

*Priapulus caudatus* (Priapulida)

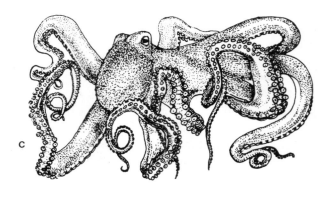

Molluscs (Mollusca):  a − *Cepea nemoralis*,
b − *Astarte borealis*,  c − *Octopus vulgaris*

mented, soft and may be slimy. It consists of a foot, visceral pouch and mantle. The foot is a muscular organ of locomotion − used for crawling, swimming and digging. The mantle is formed by folds of different sizes which often embrace the whole body and, together with the foot, they delimit the mantle cavity. Excretory openings are situated within this cavity and in aquatic species, the sex organs, gills and digestive systems are also housed there. The surface of the mantle secretes calcium carbonate and an organic substance from which shells of different texture are produced. The shell often consists of three layers − the inner layer (hypostracum) is mother-of-pearl, the middle one (ostracum) is strong and calcareous, and the outer layer (periostracum) is organic and often coloured or patterned. Mollusc shells are very variable and need not be visible from the outside. The typical gastropod shell is composed of a single piece, twisted into a spiral shape and often sculpted. In other species (bivalves) the shell consists of two valves of the same size, or one may be larger than the other. The shell of a chiton is built from overlapping plates. Some cephalopods *(Nautilus)* have an external shell while in others it is internal and may be reduced or even lost.

The nervous, vascular and excretory systems and the sensory organs are well developed in molluscs. Members of the phylum are carnivorous, omnivorous or herbivorous, and either dioecious or hermaphrodite. They live on land and in water.

Chitons have a muscular foot and an inconspicuously developed head. The dorsal side of the body is arched and covered with loosely joined plates which allow the animal to curl up into a ball. They live in the tidal zone firmly attached to stones, feeding on algae. Their sexes are separate and the females lay eggs.

Gastropods (Gastropoda) have a muscular, often flattened, foot adapted for crawling; the foot of some marine species has fin-like lobes. The visceral pouch is usually spirally-coiled within the shell. The shell is usually dextral (that is, the spire turns to the right); less often it is sinistral (turning to the left). Its opening is frequently closed by a permanent or temporary lid. The external shell is absent in some species. Gastropods have a well-developed radula (tongue-like organ). They live in most habitats but they are always found in humid places. They form the most numerous group of molluscs.

The body of scaphopods (Scaphopoda) is encased in a tapering tubular shell open at both ends; the dorsal side is concave, the ventral one is convex. The anterior opening of the shell is the larger of the two. The shell is obliquely buried in the sand so that the posterior end projects above the sea bed. Scaphopods breathe through the surface of the mantle; they have no gills. A radula is present. They live on microorganisms found in deeper water deposits.

Bivalves (Bivalvia) have a bilaterally symmetrical body, flattened from the sides and covered by a mantle between two shell valves. The shells are joined dorsally by a hinge and are drawn together by muscles acting perpendicularly to the hinge. The head is not developed, and the radula is absent.

The foot is wedge-shaped and extends from the mantle cavity at the anterior edge. There are two siphons in the rear end of the mantle. Water containing dispersed plankton enters through the lower siphon and washes over the extensive gills, while the undigested residue and exhaled water are expelled through the upper siphon. Bivalves are exclusively aquatic animals. They move along the bottom and sometimes anchor themselves by byssus filaments. They are most often dioecious, the females laying a large number of eggs which develop into larvae known as veligers in the case of marine species, and as glochidia in the case of freshwater species.

The most advanced group of molluscs are the cephalopods (Cephalopoda). The body is sac-shaped and bilaterally symmetrical, with a clearly defined head, peculiarly large eyes and arms which may be covered by suckers. There are eight arms in octopuses, ten in cuttlefish and squid, and many (which lack suckers) in *Nautilus*. The mantle is a single pouch with a foot modified to form a muscular funnel. The shell is usually reduced and hidden under the skin; only in nautiloids (Nautiloidea) is it external. The sexes are separate and young hatch straight from the eggs. The largest mollusc species are found among the cephalopods. They are squid of the genus *Architeuthis* which, according to some authors, reach up to 30 metres in size (including arms). Cephalopods are exclusively marine predators.

## Phylum: SIPUNCULIDA (peanut worms)

This phylum includes some 250 marine species which live buried in the sand and mud of the sea bed. The first third of their naked and muscular body narrows into a retractile introvert. The border of the mouth carries ciliate tentacles. The intestine is spirally-folded and the anus opens on the dorsal surface in the anterior half. The sexes are separate; the females lay eggs from which larvae hatch and swim amidst the plankton, growing within a few weeks into mature individuals.

## Phylum: ECHIURIDA (spoon worms)

This phylum comprises some 70 marine species. They live hidden in the sea bed or in the crevices of rocks. They have a long nonretractile proboscis (prostomium) with a ciliated groove on the ventral surface. By moving the cilia they concentrate microscopic food around the mouth. The sexes of some

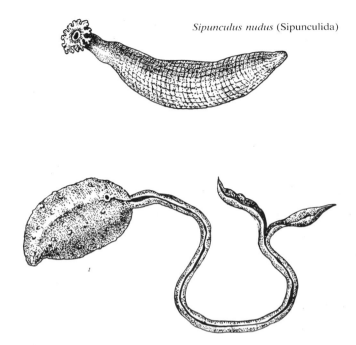

*Sipunculus nudus* (Sipunculida)

*Bonellia viridis* (Echiurida)

species, for example *Bonellia viridis,* are clearly separated; the males are 1 to 3mm long and live on or in the bodies of the much larger females.

## Phylum: ANNELIDA (segmented worms)

Some 9,000 species live in water and on dry land. They have a worm-like body which is segmented both inside and outside. The different segments are divided by walls (septa). The excretory and sometimes even the sexual system is segmented. They have a paired ventral nervous system with an oesophageal ring. The vascular system is not segmented and is highly developed. There is a closed blood circulation through a system of longitudinal and circular veins. Blood runs through the dorsal vein toward the head and in the reverse direction through the ventral vein (that is the opposite way to chordates). The blood pigment is haemoglobin or chlorocruorin.

*Piscicola geometra* (Annelida)

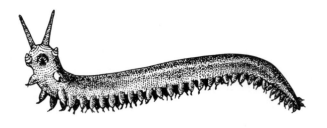

*Heteroperipatus engelhardi* (Onychophora)

Polychaetes (Polychaeta) are almost exclusively marine animals. Many species swim freely, others live in large groups buried in sand or hidden in small tubes which they secrete and to which sand particles, shells, etc. adhere. Swimming polychaetes hunt their prey actively while the sedentary species live on whatever food the water happens to bring. The body of polychaetes is elongate, sometimes flattened and often conspicuously ciliated. The body segments sometimes carry unjointed appendages along the sides (parapodia) with tufts of bristles and sensory organs — eyes and tactile processes. Tentacles are present on the first segment (prostomium). Polychaetes have separate sexes, the females laying up to several thousand eggs. They have a larval stage known as a trochophore.

Members of the Clitellata have the typical worm-like segmented body without tentacles or parapodia. The segments usually carry tufts of bristles (for example earthworms) or suckers (for example leeches). A typical feature is the saddle (clitellum), a glandular organ formed on several segments on the front part of the body. The saddle produces a mucous secretion from which the egg cases are made. The skin of terrestrial members of this class contains numerous slime glands. The slime facilitates movement and assists respiration because atmospheric oxygen dissolves in it. The species are hermaphrodite, and they develop directly from the eggs.

## Phylum: ONYCHOPHORA (velvet worms)

The phylum includes just one class with some 70 species which are distributed in warm regions. Onychophora have their body covered with papillae arranged into numerous rings, a pair of antennae on the head and several forked, hooked claws on the unjointed legs which are adapted to walking. At first glance they resemble caterpillars. Their vascular system is open, the blood freely bathes the organs of the body. They breathe through branching tracheae and are the most primitive phylum in which tracheae occur. The sexes are separate. In most species the fertilized eggs are retained in the oviducts of the female during the development of the embryo. Velvet worms frequent humid places under fallen wood, foliage, etc. and are predaceous on soft-bodied invertebrates.

## Phylum: TARDIGRADA (water bears)

Miscroscopic inhabitants of moss and humid soil or sand as well as stagnant water. The body is cylindrical with a suctorial mouth and four pairs of retractile stubby legs with claws. External segmentation is only slightly visible, while internal segmentation is absent. Vascular and respiratory systems are absent. The sexes are separate; the females lay eggs from which the young hatch directly. Tardigrades are able to survive over periods of drought and extreme temperatures (frost or heat) in anabiosis — a state of suspended animation.

## Phylum: PENTASTOMIDA (tongue worms)

Members of this phylum live in the respiratory passages, sinuses and lungs of reptiles and mammals (even Man) and in the air-sacs of birds. They show features characteristic of their parasitic way of life. The body is flattened, unsegmented, covered by a cuticle, and on the sides of the mouth there are two pairs of small pouches used for attachment. The digestive tract and anus are devel-

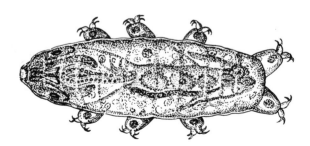

*Macrobiotus hufelandi* (Tardigrada)

*Armillifer armillatus* (Pentastomida)

oped but respiratory, vascular and excretory systems are absent. The reproductive organs are highly developed. The sexes are separate and development is complex. Larvae hatch from the eggs and then undergo characteristic stages of development in intermediate hosts before infecting the final host which is usually a carnivore.

## Phylum: ARTHROPODA (arthropods)

The most numerous animal phylum including many hundred thousand species. The species are mostly small, ranging from several millimetres to several centimetres in length. Extremely large species may have a leg span of a metre or more. Arthropods live all over the earth, and have adapted to a very wide range of habitats. Large numbers of species or huge numbers of individuals often occur together. The body is covered by a cuticle impregnated with chitin and sometimes calcium carbonate. It is divided into unequal segments which bear jointed appendages. Originally each segment carried one pair of appendages; in the course of evolution, however, some segments fused together to form larger units, the appendages became legs, antennae, mouth parts, etc., and the number of segments and appendages decreased.

The body regions in arthropods are: the head, thorax and abdomen. In some groups the head is fused with the thorax to form the cephalothorax. There may be a number of appendages on the thorax and abdomen. The cuticle covers the body segments and forms a hard external skeleton (exoskeleton). The segments are joined to each other either firmly or by flexible membranes and are mobile. The cuticle extends into the inside of the body to form attachment points for the muscles. Cuticle also provides a spiral reinforcement in the tracheal walls. The exoskeleton cannot increase its surface or volume, and if the arthropod is to grow, it must be discarded from time to time (moulted) and replaced with a larger one which is initially soft and expansive. Only this time can the arthropod increase in size; thus growth occurs at intervals and is not continuous. The time of moulting (ecdysis) is always a critical period in the life of an individual. Sometimes it occurs only during the period of larval development; adult insects (imagos), for example, do not grow, consequently they do not moult either.

The vascular system of arthropods is open, the heart is tubular and is perforated by paired pores (ostioles) through which blood is taken in. The blood is then expelled into the front part of the body from where it flows freely and bathes the body organs on its return to the heart. The nervous system is ganglionic.

Arthropods breathe by means of air-sacs, tracheae or gills. The tracheae form a system of pipes which branch throughout the body. Air enters the tracheae through small openings (spiracles) which are located on the sides of the body segments. Besides assisting in respiration, the tracheae

Arthropods (Arthropoda): a − *Trombidium holosericeum*, b − *Scapholeberis mucronata*, c − *Ergates faber*, d − Red admiral (*Vanessa atalanta*)

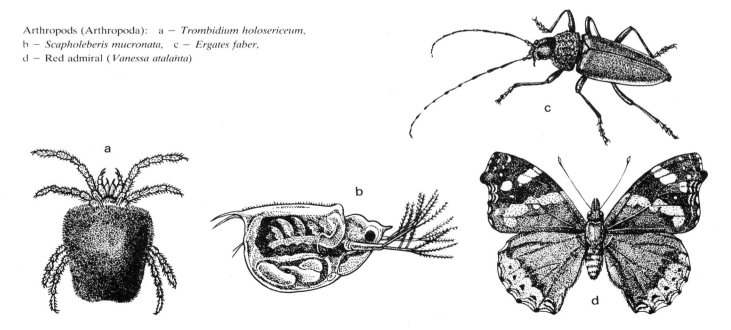

also serve to make the body lighter, and in aquatic species they act as a hydrostatic organ or air reservoir. The large air chambers can also act as resonators in sound production.

The sexes in arthropods are usually separate; the females lay eggs or give birth to fully developed miniature versions of the adult. A young individual, having hatched from the egg, may develop either directly (within the female's body) or indirectly; in the latter case there are several larval stages and only after some time is the adult form reached. Sometimes a quiescent pupal stage occurs between the last larval stage and the adult (imago). The larvae may strongly resemble the adult or be quite different in body form.

The arthropod phylum divides into four subphyla (including the extinct trilobites), many classes, orders, families, etc.

Arachnids (Arachnida) are mostly terrestrial animals. The body is divided into the prosoma (cephalothorax) and opisthosoma (the posterior part of the body). They have six pairs of appendages located on the prosoma. The first pair are the chelicerae, adapted for grasping and crushing, which comprise at least three segments and are located in front of the mouth. They bear small pincer-like claws. The second pair (pedipalps) are next to the mouth and vary in form and size. The remaining four pairs are adapted for running, leaping, etc.

Scorpions (Scorpiones) are among the largest arachnids. They live in tropical and subtropical regions. The last segment of the long abdomen (telson) is pointed, with a pair of poisonous glands in the swollen part of the abdomen. Scorpions have claws on the pedipalps and chelicerae, those on the pedipalps being especially large as an adaptation for hunting prey. Sexual dimorphism is not pronounced. The females hold the fertilized eggs within the body until the time of hatching. The young stay on the back of the mother for some time.

Spiders (Araneae) have an unsegmented opisthosoma constricted into a narrow waist at the point of connection with the prosoma; the pedipalps resemble short legs. The chelicerae are connected to a pair of poison glands which sometimes reach into the cephalothorax. They have spinnerets near the anus and on each of these there are numerous spinning glands. Spiders use the viscid fluid which hardens into silken threads to make webs, hiding places, cocoons, to faciliate move-

ment, etc. Some species build webs for trapping their prey, others do not. The sexes are separate, often with conspicuous sexual dimorphism — the female is usually larger than the male. In the course of mating the female often devours the male. The young develop directly. The females of some species take care of the cocoon containing the eggs or of the hatched young.

The opisthosoma of opilionids (Opilionida) is segmented and joined by its whole width to the prosoma. The chelicerae have claws, and the pedipalps resemble short legs. The other limbs are thin and many times longer than the body.

Crustaceans (Crustacea) are mostly aquatic arthropods. They breathe by means of gills or over the whole body surface. Terrestrial crustaceans breathe through tracheae. The body of crustaceans is protected by a stratified cuticle impregnated with chitin and usually calcium carbonate. Sometimes it is protected by a strong shield on the back (carapace). The head is sometimes joined with several adjacent segments to form a cephalothorax. Segments of the head, thorax and abdomen bear paired appendages — antennae, mouth parts and legs. Gills are located on the legs. Crustaceans live on a variety of food depending on the environment; many species are parasitic. They are mostly dioecious and their development from eggs is either direct (for example crayfish — *Astacus*) or includes a larval stage, known as the nauplius (for example crabs — *Carcinus* and many other marine species).

The subphylum Mandibulata is the most numerous group of arthropods. Its members exhibit a great range of form and size. The head is usually clearly separated from the body and bears a pair of antennae. Mandibulates usually breathe through tracheae although some tiny species breathe through the whole surface of the body.

Millepedes (Diplopoda) are usually small, at most 30mm long. The body is bare or covered with bristles and often protected by a shield. Each segment, starting from the fifth, carries two pairs of legs. The legs are usually slender and their number is not constant even within a given species. Most millepedes have simple eyes but some are blind. They live mainly on vegetable food.

Centipedes (Chilopoda) have a body composed of up to several dozen flat segments and a large head. The head bears a pair of antennae and biting mouthparts, behind which is a modified pair of legs which bear large claws connected with poison glands. The feet have eight segments, the last one of which is not adapted to walking but to feeling. Centipedes are predators.

Insects (Insecta) form the most numerous group of the subphylum Mandibulata. They are noted for a variety of colours, forms and sizes (the smallest species is less than one millimetre in size while the largest can reach 20 to 30cm). They live all over the world. They are of immense importance for they are irreplaceable and are often essential to nature; for example, in the pollination of plants, in the breakdown of humus and other debris, and they can provide some commercially valuable substances, etc.

The body of an insect consists of three distinct parts: the head, thorax and abdomen. Each part has been formed through the fusion of a different numbers of segments. The head bears the antennae, the mouthparts, and a pair of compound eyes. The mouthparts are modified according to the type of food the insect lives on. Most common is the biting type of mouth, which consists of mandibles and below them the maxillae. The maxillae bear a pair of maxillary palps, and the lower lip (labium) is equipped with another pair of palps. The mouthparts are sometimes fused to form a proboscis adapted for piercing and sucking as in mosquitoes, or for licking as in house flies.

The thorax is composed of three segments, the prothorax, mesothorax and metathorax. Each bears a pair of legs, attached by flexible joints on the ventral side. Typically there are two pairs of wings, one pair on the mesothorax and the other on the metathorax. The legs consist of five segments, variously shaped according to their function — running, hunting, digging, etc. Though insects typically have two pairs of wings, some species have only one pair developed; some primitive groups are primarily wingless while others have secondarily lost their wings in the course of their evolution. The principal type of wing consists of a double membrane with a system of veins. The wing surface may be naked, hairy, scaly or with a fringe of down, etc. The front pair may differ from the hind wings in size, shape and design.

The largest part of the insect body is formed by the abdomen. Originally it consisted of eleven segments and it usually has various appendages at the posterior end.

The sexes are usually separate and sometimes the females reproduce without the participation of the males (parthenogenesis). Insects develop through either incomplete or complete metamorphosis. In case of complete metamorphosis larvae hatch from the eggs laid by the females, grow and moult several times and then pupate. Within the pupa the larval organs are reorganized and only then does the adult (imago) emerge. In the case of incomplete metamorphosis the larvae (sometimes known as nymphs) hatch from the eggs; they grow and moult several times and in the last developmental stage transform into the imago. The pupal stage is absent. The larvae often resemble the imago, except that they are smaller, the sexual organs are not developed, and the wing bases develop gradually. These principal types of metamorphoses are in some groups very complex with many stages.

Dragonflies (Odonata) are usually large, with a long, slim or bulky abdomen, large compound eyes and powerful mandibles. They live close to water. They have separate sexes and develop through incomplete metamorphosis; their larvae live in water.

Mantids (Mantodea) have typical seizing legs which function on the principle of a pocket knife. They live mostly in subtropical and tropical regions but extend into southern Europe.

Long-horned grasshoppers (Ensifera) and short-horned grasshoppers (Caelifera) have narrow, leathery front wings and the hind wings, which are folded under the front pair, have a fringe of hairs. The last pair of legs are often adapted to jumping and sound production.

The mouthparts of the true bugs (Heteroptera) are modified into a piercing organ. Two-thirds of the front pair of wings (hemielytrae) are tough, the last third and the whole of the hind pair of wings are membranous. After emerging the nymphs resemble the adults and they undergo five developmental stages.

Beetles (Coleoptera) have the first segment of the thorax in the form of a shield. The first pair of wings are modified into armoured elytra, which usually cover almost the whole abdomen, and protect the folded pair of membranous flying wings underneath. Beetles are found in most habitats. They can be herbivorous, omnivorous or carnivorous. They develop through complete metamorphosis, the larvae usually having a different way of life from that of the adults. The pupa is free (all the appendages have their individual cuticle cases) and partly mobile.

Ants, bees and wasps (Hymenoptera) have two pairs of membranous wings with a conspicuously sparse venation. The hind pair is usually smaller than the front pair. The abdomen is either broadly attached to the thorax or there is a stalk or waist between the front and hind parts of the body. The females of some species possess an ovipositor which in others is modified to form a sting. Many species live in well defined communities. They are important pollinators and many species are parasitic, mainly on other arthropods.

Butterflies and moths (Lepidoptera) usually have two pairs of wings (the front pair is usually the larger) covered with coloured scales. The head is furnished with a pair of antennae, and mouthparts which are in the form of a proboscis, adapted for sucking. Males and females often differ in appearance (sexual dimorphism). The metamorphosis of lepidopterans is complete. The larvae (caterpillars) are mostly vegetarian and the pupae are inactive, covered by a firm case on which the various body parts are apparent (in some moths the case of the

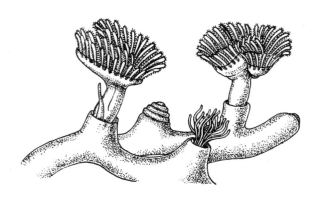

*Plumatella repens* (Ectoprocta)

*Balanoglossus clavigerus* (Hemichordata)

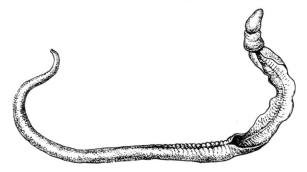

proboscis can be seen). Adults usually feed on plant juices, especially nectar.

The front membranous wings of true flies or two-winged flies (Diptera) are well developed, the second pair being modified into appendages known as halteres. The head is furnished with large and often colourful compound eyes and piercing or sucking mouthparts. Metamorphosis is complete.

Phylum: ECTOPROCTA
Members of this phylum are sedentary and live in seas and fresh water. They are either solitary or colonial. The body is enclosed in a case and the mouth is bordered with tentacles. They live on small animals and are hermaphrodite.

Phylum: HEMICHORDATA (acorn worms)
The worm- or pouch-like body is divided into the prosoma, mesosoma and metasoma. These animals live in the seas either solitarily or in colonies and may be either free or hidden in tubes. In species which burrow in mud (for example the Enteropneusta) the prosoma is reinforced from the inside by a ligament process.

Phylum: ECHINODERMATA
(starfish, sea-urchins etc.)
In ancient geological times this phylum included thousands of species but relatively few of their descendants are living today. The body shape of echinoderms is variable but the adults are fundamentally radially symmetrical. Usually they have a pentagonal symmetrical form (the number of arms or grooves (ambulacra) being five or a multiple of five). Under the skin there is a calcareous skeleton of plates, spikes etc. The internal body structure is complex, one of its most important components being the water vascular system. Water flows through a perforated plate (madreporite) on the back of the animal into a calcareous duct and from there into a circular network of canals. The branches of the canals communicate with the tube feet — organs of locomotion arranged in rows along the ambulacra. Each tube foot is an extensible muscular cylinder with a plate at the end. When the tube foot is filled with water it stretches out through an opening in the skeleton. On touching a strange object the muscles of the tube foot contract, the water runs out of it and the tube foot with the plate attaches itself by suction to the surface. By alternating the suction and release the animals

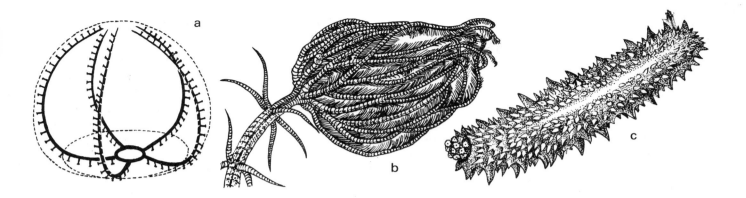

Echinodermata: a — ambulacral system of a sea urchin.
b — *Cenocrinus asteria*, c — *Holothuria tubulosa*

move along the sea bed. The water vascular system is also used for breathing and obtaining food. This phenomenon has no parallel in the animal kingdom. Echinoderms live on the sea bed. They have separate sexes or are hermaphrodite, and their development from eggs goes through a larval stage. The larvae are bilaterally symmetrical and before metamorphosis they are planktonic.

Sea lilies (Crinoidea) have a cup-shaped body attached mouth upwards to a stalk. The arms of the cup have a great capacity for regeneration. The anus lies near the mouth inside the cup.

Sea cucumbers (Holothuroidea) have an elongate body covered by a thick skin with spines. They either rest on the bottom or swim.

Starfish (Asteroidea) and brittle stars (Ophiuroidea) have a flattened body with a mouth on the under surface. Five radially disposed arms coalesce at the centre to form a disc. The skeleton consists of plates and the body is often covered with ossicles. They move with the help of the arms and tube feet. Starfish are dioecious. Their development is often direct, small starfishes emerging straight from the eggs. Starfish are predatory; they live mainly on bivalves which they force open by the pull of their arms. If shell valves do not yield they insert a part of the stomach pouch and inject their digestive juices. They then suck out the partly digested body of their prey. Brittle stars have long, often branching arms. The arms are flexible and the ambulacral tube feet are used for feeling, not for locomotion. There is no anus, waste passing out through the mouth, and the stomach is not protrusible. Ophiuroids develop through a larval (ophiopluteus) stage. They live in seas and river deltas.

Sea urchins (Echinoidea) have the mouth on the under surface. The body is spherical, heart- or disc-shaped and without arms. The anus is usually in the centre, on the opposite side to the mouth (Regularia); in some species the mouth is displaced to the edge and the body becomes bilaterally symmetrical (Irregularia). The skeleton is massive, often covered with spines. The mouth of some species is furnished with a special biting organ known as Aristotle's lantern. Sea urchins are dioecious with planktonic larvae (echinopluteus) hatching from the eggs. The larvae at first swim amidst the plankton, and later become sedentary.

Phylum: POGONOPHORA (beard worms)
Marine worms with long mobile arms. They live in deep seas in the muddy sea bed. They live buried in their tubes, the walls of which are of a cellulose-like substance. They are the most recently discovered animal phylum.

Phylum: CHAETOGNATHA (arrow worms)
Marine animals with an unsegmented transparent body. They form a part of the plankton. The body is bilaterally symmetrical with horizontal fins at the sides. A digestive system is present but vascular and excretory systems are lacking. Arrow worms are hermaphrodite and they develop directly.

Phylum: CHORDATA
Chordates have their own specific features, besides the features found in the other animal groups (bilaterally symmetrical body with a distinguishable head and tail end, segmentation, closed blood circulation and gill slits which may be present only in the embryonic stage of development).

Furthermore they have an internal body support in the form of a notochord which, evolutionarily, is the precursor of the spine. The notochord is a flex-

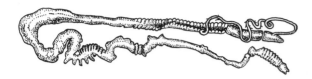

*Siboglinum fiordicum* (Pogonophora)

*Sagitta hexaptera* (Chaetognatha)

ible rod of turgid cells. It runs along the longitudinal axis of the animal below the hollow nerve cord. In the lower chordates it persists throughout their life but in the higher ones it occurs only in the embryos, being either partially or completely replaced in adults by the spine. The digestive tract runs between the notochord and the heart, and ends with an opening on the ventral side of the body. On the dorsal side of the vascular system blood flows from head to tail, and on the ventral side from tail to head, that is in the opposite direction to the blood in annelids, for example.

The chordates include some 42,000 species and are composed of three subphyla (tunicates with about 2,000 species, lancelets with 18 species and vertebrates with about 40,000 species).

The notochord of tunicates (Urochordata or Tunicata) is always present in the larvae but persists in the adult stage only in the class Larvacea. The tunicate body is not segmented and its skin secretes a gelatinous tunic consisting of a polysaccharide, tunicin, which is similar to cellulose. Tunicates live solitarily or in colonies in the seas. They are pelagic or sedentary and they feed on plankton. They are hermaphrodite, their development is often very complex and is characterized by heterogony, that is alternation of sexual and asexual generations and solitary and colonial forms.

Lancelets (Cephalochordata) are translucent animals up to 7 cm in length. Their muscles and sexual organs are conspicuously segmented, the notochord remains throughout their life and the vascular system is closed but the heart is absent. They live in the coastal regions in warm and temperate seas, usually at depths ranging from 10 to 50 metres. They usually live buried in the sandy sea bed, the head end pointing upwards. They swim by undulating movements of the body.

The subphylum of vertebrates (Vertebrata) is the most important group of chordates. The body of vertebrates has a head, body and tail, it is covered by several skin layers which produce hairs, scales or feathers, and is supported by a cartilaginous or bony skeleton. The limbs are very mobile and in most species serve as the major organ of locomotion. The central nervous system is composed of the brain and spinal cord. Vertebrates have highly developed sense organs (camera-like eyes, membranous ear labyrinths and an organ of smell are common to all groups). They have a high rate of metabolism, associated with their great mobility and active seeking of food.

Zoologists usually divide vertebrates into two groups according to the type of embryonic development. These groups, however, have no systematic value and therefore do not appear in the classification. Vertebrates that develop no amnion (Anamnia) lay their eggs into water and their embryos are not surrounded by the embryonic sacs (amnion and chorion). This group includes fish and amphibians. Vertebrates that do develop the amnion (Amniota) include reptiles, birds and mammals. If these lay eggs they do so only on land and the embryos develop within the embryonic sacs. The embryonic sacs (allantois, amnion and chorion) are specific embryonic organs which appear only along with the growing embryo. Vertebrates of the Amniota group always lay eggs on land or give birth to fully developed offspring.

The presence or absence of jaws is a basic feature according to which vertebrates are divided into superclasses. The cyclostomes are the only living class belonging to the group of jawless vertebrates (Agnatha). They have a sucking mouth with a strong tongue. The body is snake-like, edged with a continuous fin, and supported by a notochord. They are aquatic animals which live parasitically on fish. Adult freshwater species usually do not take food. The larvae live on organic particles.

All the other vertebrate classes belong to the Gnathostomata. The brain consists of five parts and is highly organized, characteristically there are two pairs of limbs (which are reduced or lost entirely in some forms) and in the inner ear there are always three semicircular canals. Vertebrates have invaded all habitats.

Cartilaginous fish (Chondrichthyes) live almost exclusively in warm seas, though a few species are cosmopolitan or reach into fresh waters. Sharks are pelagic predators, rays are benthic (bottom-dwelling) and chimaeras are deep-water cartilaginous fish. If not viviparous, cartilaginous fish lay eggs and in this case the young develop directly. The hatched young possess a large yolk sac on the contents of which they feed during the first days of life. After digesting it they begin to hunt for animal food independently. The skin of these fish is usually covered with placoid scales, only rarely is it naked. They possess a notochord. The skeleton is cartilaginous but the body of each vertebra is impregnated with calcium salts. Cartilaginous fish have no swim bladder. Large species predominate among this group.

Sharks (Lamniformes) have a fusiform body shape and they are fast and perfect swimmers. The skin is covered with placoid scales which reach the jaws and there form several rows of teeth which are usually large and sharp. Behind the head there are five to seven gill clefts. Sharks are mostly predatory, but the largest species among them (reaching up to 20 metres) live on plankton which they sieve through processes on the gill arches in a manner similar to that of whalebone whales. Some species are dangerous to Man.

The body of rays (Rajiformes) is dorso-ventrally flattened and often extended into a whip-like tail. The gill slits are located on the ventral surface. Pectoral fins are continuous along the margin of the head and body. Rays live mainly on molluscs.

Bony fish (Osteichthyes) are an outstandingly versatile group; their systematic classification is a frequent subject of discussion. Bony fish are exclusively aquatic vertebrates; the body is most often covered by bony scales (as an acquired feature it may be scaleless). The skeleton is bony and dermal bones (especially on the head) are present. The openings of the gill chambers are covered by opercula. Fertilization is usually external.

Lungfish (Dipnoi) live in shallow muddy waters of the tropics. They have two lungs which enable them to breathe atmospheric oxygen and move on land to some extent. Some species survive periods of drought in a torpid condition, buried in the ground in special cocoons.

The advanced bony fish (Teleostomi) breathe mainly oxygen, dissolved in water, through gills. In some groups breathing organs are developed which allow them to stay outside water for a short time. These fish live in fresh, brackish and sea water, and may be migratory. Some species (anadromous) ascend rivers from the seas for spawning (for example, salmon), while other species, such as eel, go to the sea to spawn, that is, they are catadromous.

One living order of bony fish has become secondarily cartilaginous. These are the sturgeons (Acipenseriformes). They have a fully developed notochord, cartilaginous skeleton, and the body is covered with bands of bony shields. The head protrudes into a snout (rostrum) equipped on the ventral side with tactile barbels round the mouth. They live in sea, brackish and fresh waters.

The Teleostei are, evolutionally, the most recent group of fish. Most have a bony skeleton with well developed vertebrae. The notochord is restricted by the vertebrae to the intervertebral spaces. They have paired pectoral and pelvic fins and single dorsal, caudal and anal fins. The fins sometimes merge to form a continuous border (for example, in eels). The body is covered with true bony scales. The lateral line is an important sense organ. Bony fish often lay large numbers of eggs which are fertilized in water.

The order Clupeiformes contains sea and freshwater fish and most are good swimmers. The fin rays are soft, the scales cycloid (the free edge is convex). Some groups, for example salmon and grayling have a characteristic adipose fin between the dorsal and tail fins. Other important species in this order are the herrings.

Members of the order Cypriniformes live almost exclusively in fresh water. On the edges of the fins there are several hard rays; the skin is covered with cycloid scales and usually there are small processes (pharyngeal teeth) on the gill arches. The main distinguishing feature is the Weberian apparatus, consisting of a series of small bones which connect the inner ear with the swim-bladder.

Members of the order Anguilliformes are migratory. They have a snake-like body with no pelvic fins and the dorsal, caudal and anal fins are fused to form a continuous border. The only freshwater species living in Europe is the European eel (Anguilla anguilla) but there are a number of marine species.

The most numerous and most advanced order of bony fish is the Perciformes. They live in both sea and fresh water. The scales are ctenoid (the free edge is toothed), the fins contain numerous bony rays, the pelvic fins are located in front of the pectoral fins and there are often two dorsal fins.

The Gadiformes are mainly marine fish with tiny scales, soft fin rays, and with pelvic fins located in front of the pectoral fins.

Amphibians (Amphibia) are generally confined to humid places. They live on the land, some species even in bushes and trees. They never inhabit seas, deserts and the polar regions. They represent a transitional stage between aquatic and entirely terrestrial vertebrates. Evolutionarily they are the first group of vertebrates with paired limbs adapted to movement on land. The adults breathe mainly through lungs while the larvae live in the water and breathe through gills. The skin of amphibians is bare, soft and contains numerous mucous glands; it also assists in respiration. The neck, trunk, sacrum and sometimes the tail part of the spine can be distinguished. Amphibians either lay eggs, or they are ovoviviparous, that is, they retain the eggs within the body until the time of hatching and produce fully developed offspring. The larvae (tadpoles) have a small tail and at first are legless, later developing first the hind legs and then the front legs which, initially, are covered by skin. Finally the tail is gradually absorbed and eventually disappears altogether. The metamorphosis of the tadpole into an adult is regulated by a hormone produced by the thyroid gland. Tadpoles live mostly on vegetable food. Species living in the temperate zone survive periods of adverse weather in a torpid state buried underground or in mud.

Frogs (Anura) live almost all over the world. In an evolutionary sense they are the most advanced amphibians. The body is shortened and lacks a tail. They have short front legs and powerful hind legs, a well developed middle ear, and large cavities filled with lymph under the skin. Fertilization is external. They are good swimmers and their way of swimming is unique among aquatic animals.

Members of the subclass Urodela have an elongated body with a tail, and limbs of equal length. The middle ear is partly atrophied and the skeleton is considerably reduced. Some species breathe through lungs but in others gills persist throughout their life. Fertilization is internal. Mating organs are absent in males which release spermatophores (capsules containing sperm) into the water; the females collect these in their cloaca. Females usually lay eggs. The larvae live in water. Some species have a tendency towards neoteny (the larvae re-

producing sexually). Most species live in the temperate climatic zone. They are absent from Africa and Australia.

The Apoda are the most specialized group of amphibians. They have no limbs or the middle ear, the skin appears to be segmented (thus resembling earthworms) and the eyes are covered with skin. They live in humid places, mainly in the soil, and the larvae develop in water. The females are either viviparous or lay eggs which they often protect with their own body until hatching.

Reptiles (Reptilia) are already fully adapted to life on land. The body is covered with skin in which small shields or scales are embedded. The skin is dry and almost without glands. They are the first vertebrates with a neck region clearly separating the head and trunk. They are also the first animals whose embryos develop in membranous embryonic sacs. They lay leathery-shelled eggs or eggs in calcareous shells, always on land, and they never incubate them. Some species are ovoviviparous, while others are viviparous. Paired mating organs are developed in the males.

The skeleton of reptiles is bony and in the course of evolution the cranial bones of the skull have become typically reduced. The teeth (if developed) are not adapted to chewing and biting but to holding the prey; sometimes fangs connected with poisonous glands inject poison into the wound. The senses of eyesight and smell are well developed. Reptiles live all over the world except for the cold regions and occupy all habitats except the air. Though cold blooded (poikilothermic), they are, to a certain extent, able to maintain a body temperature higher than that of the environment.

Turtles, tortoises and terrapins (Chelonia) are an ancient group of reptiles, which have not changed much since the Permian. The body is covered by a carapace which is made of bone and covered with horny plates. Teeth are absent and their function is performed by the sharp horny edges of the jaws. The limbs of the turtles are strong, adapted to digging or swimming. Chelonians breathe atmospheric oxygen through lungs. Marine species have developed auxiliary anal sacs through the walls of which oxygen is absorbed. Turtles are never viviparous. They always lay eggs on land, the eggs often hatching after a very long time (even more than a year).

Lizards and snakes (Squamata) are mostly terrestrial reptiles. The skin is covered by scales, plates, etc. They regularly shed the top skin layer either in pieces (lizards) or whole (snakes). The cranial bones are often linked by joints and are thus mobile.

Lizards (Sauria) usually have well developed limbs. If the feet are undeveloped the remains of the pectoral girdle on the skeleton persist. The two halves of the lower jaw are fused together in front. Eyes are usually developed and have mobile lids, sometimes the vestiges of the pineal eye are apparent. Some species when in danger are able to discard the tail which later partly regenerates. This is called autotomy.

Snakes (Ophidia) are legless and even the vestiges of the pelvic and pectoral bones are nearly always absent, only in boas are traces of the pelvis found. The bones of the skull are rod-shaped and extremely mobile. The branches of the lower jaw are joined in front by a flexible ligament; alternating movements of the two branches against each other help to swallow large prey. The tongue is long and forked; it picks up smells and transmits them to the sensitive Jacobson's organ. The middle ear is reduced; snakes are almost deaf. The fangs are pointed, usually curved backwards, and sometimes connected to openings of poison glands. Snakes swallow their prey (which is sometimes very large) either alive, or they strangle it in the loops of the body, or kill it by injecting venom. They move by crawling, which is made possible using the ribs and powerful muscles.

Birds (Aves) were primarily adapted to active flight, although some species move only on the ground (for example, ostriches) or in water (penguins). The body is covered by dry skin, the only gland being a preen gland on the rump. The unique and typical body covering of birds are the feathers. The jaws are transformed into a bill and the front limbs into wings. On solid ground birds move exclusively on their hind limbs. The skeleton is bony and the bones are generally lightened (the long bones are connected to the air sacs). The lungs are small, slightly distensible and extended to form a system of air sacs. The air sacs are a reservoir of air and reduce the density of the body; they also decrease inter-muscular friction, assist thermoregulation, sometimes function as resonators and, for example in gannets and boobies, they can absorb some of the shock from landing on the water. The muscles of birds are powerful, particularly those used in flying. Eyesight is eminently well-developed, though the other senses are also highly advanced. The eyes of birds are the most efficient among vertebrates. Fertilization in birds is always internal. The cloacas of a mating pair are placed against each other and then the sperm is injected into the sexual ducts of the female; the males of only a few species possess a penis, for example ostriches and ducks. In connection with reproduction, birds developed many complicated courting rites, so-called courtship displays. The females lay eggs with a calcareous shell. Birds usually take an active part in the process of hatching, that is they sit on their eggs and, after the eggs have hatched, the parents care for the young. The young of some groups of birds, for example perching birds, are completely dependent on the care of their parents — after hatching they are bare or covered with soft down, blind, often deaf, with limited powers of thermoregulation and locomotion. These are called nidicolous birds. The young of other groups are feathered when they hatch, well able to move around and with developed senses. These are known as nidifugous young. The young of gallinaceous birds and ducks for example, are immediately able to fend for themselves; the parents only take them around, warm and protect them. In gulls and grebes, the parents also feed their young. Birds are the first vertebrates with efficient thermoregulation. Their basic body temperature is maintained at around 40 °C. They feed on a variety of food and their metabolic rate is the highest among vertebrates. Birds are distributed all over the world, they have invaded all the accessible terrestrial habitats regardless of climatic conditions (owing to their thermoregulation).

Grebes (Podicipediformes) are good swimmers with legs set far back and to the sides of the body. Their feet are partially webbed. The feathers on the belly are remarkably thick and fine. The young are nidifugous but are fed by the parents. The parents can be seen carrying the young on their backs.

The Pelecaniformes are large water birds with legs adapted for rowing. They all feed on fish, have a powerful bill and often also a pouch which hangs from the lower bill. They hunt for fish under water (cormorants — Phalacrocoracidae), by plummeting after it from a height (gannets and boobies — Sulidae), or they collectively herd the fish to shallow water (pelicans — Pelecanidae). They nest in colonies either on the ground or in trees. The young are nidicolous.

Members of the Ciconiiformes are generally large birds with a long neck and bill and with long legs adapted to wading. In flight their legs are trailed behind, the neck either stretched out (storks — Ciconiidae) or bent in an S-shape (herons — Ardeidae). They have broad wings which are usually adapted for gliding. They live close to fresh water and nest in reed beds, in trees or on chimneys, etc. The young are nidicolous.

Members of the Anseriformes usually have a short bill, often with horny lamellae on the sides of the jaw (for sieving food out of the water), short legs and a crop; the males possess a penis. The preen gland is well developed. They live close to water, fly and swim well, some species are good divers. They mostly nest on the ground; the young are nidifugous.

Birds of prey (Falconiformes) typically have a short, strongly hooked bill with sharp edges, and strong legs equipped with claws. Most are excellent fliers and skilful hunters; some species (vultures, etc.) live on carrion. They are diurnal birds with perfect eyesight. They usually nest in high trees, on rocks, etc. The large species (for example eagles) lay only one or two eggs. The young are nidicolous, and hatch several days apart.

Fowl-like birds (Galliformes) have legs adapted for digging and scratching, they have a short bill and a crop. Males and females often differ from each other in appearance. They usually stay on the land, and do not bathe or swim. They lay large numbers of eggs; the young are nidifugous.

Most members of the Gruiformes have mostly a slender pointed bill; they have no crop and live close to water or in the steppes. They nest on the ground; the young are nidifugous and some species are fed by the parents.

Waders (Charadriiformes) are mostly water birds, often excellent fliers, distributed all over the world including the polar regions. They live on animal food. They nest on the ground (rocks, banks) often in colonies, and lay one to four eggs; the young can be either nidicolous or nidifugous.

Pigeons and doves (Columbiformes) typically have a short bill, a swollen cere and feet adapted for walking. The sacral gland and down feathers are absent. They feed on seeds and fruits. They usually lay two eggs, the young are nidicolous and the parents feed them at first with regurgitated food of a cheesy consistency. When drinking they suck up water through the bill, while other bird species need to raise their heads for it to run down into the throat.

Owls (Strigiformes) are nocturnal birds with large eyes, a hook-shaped bill and strong feet with long claws. They blink with their upper lids (while the other species move the lower lids). Their feathers are soft, which accounts for their silent flight. Owls nest in cavities, in abandoned nests of other birds and even on or under the ground. The young are nidicolous.

Kingfishers and their allies (Coraciiformes) have their toes usually fused at the base, the bill is large and the feathers are colourful and stiff. They always nest in cavities in trees or steep banks; their young are nidicolous.

The feet of all woodpeckers and their allies (Piciformes) are adapted for climbing. Their feathers are strong, and true woodpeckers (Picidae) use the tail as a support in climbing. They live in trees, and nest in cavities or excavated holes. The young are nidicolous.

Perching birds (Passeriformes) are the most numerous and evolutionarily the most advanced

Chordates (Chordata:  a — *Doliolum denticulatum,*  b — *Branchiostoma lanceolatum,*  c — Nile crocodile (*Crocodylus niloticus*), d — African elephant (*Loxodonta africana*)

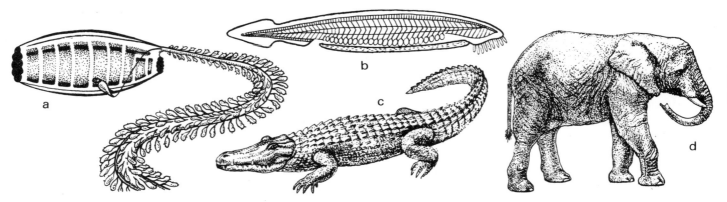

bird order. Their forms vary widely as do their ways of life. All, however, possess feet with all four toes set at the same level and of about the same length, they have a smaller number of neck vertebrae and a syrinx in the throat. Members of this order always build a nest; the young are nidicolous. They beg for their food with their bills, which are usually vividly coloured at the corners and inside.

Mammals (Mammalia) are primarily adapted to terrestrial life. Evolutionarily they are the most advanced group of vertebrates. They are warm-blooded (homoiothermic), the body temperature of most species fluctuating between 36 and 39 °C. In nidicolous offspring, marsupials, monotremes and edentates, the temperature may be variable and lower. The body temperature of mammals which spend unfavourable periods of the year in a dormant state drops considerably, often to the level of the temperature of the environment. The skin of mammals contains numerous glands of different types; through the transformation of sweat glands, mammals have developed the typical mammary glands, while through the modification of sweat and sebaceous glands they have developed scent glands. Fur is a characteristic skin formation, composed of variously formed hairs. In some groups hairs have been modified to form spines (hedgehogs and porcupines), or replaced by scales (pangolins) or plates (armadillos).

The lower jaw of mammals is formed from a single bone. Mammals are the only vertebrates with three small bones in the cavity of the middle ear — the malleus, incus and stapes (hammer, anvil and stirrup). The neck part of the spine usually consists of seven vertebrae. The teeth of mammals are usually differentiated into incisors, canines, premolars and molars. The original dentition of adult placental mammals contains three incisors, one canine, four premolars and three molars in each half. As an acquired feature the number of teeth becomes reduced (for example in ruminants) or increased (dolphins have up to 250 teeth); the originally differentiated teeth may become simplified (for example in dolphins).

Limbs are primarily designed for locomotion on land but in a number of species they have become adapted for climbing, swimming or digging, etc. Mammals either step on the whole area of the foot (bears, insectivores), on parts of the toes (for example, cats) or on the tip or tips of the toes (Artiodactyla, Perissodactyla).

The heart is completely divided into two atria and two ventricles which prevent the oxygenated and deoxygenated blood from mixing. Features peculiar to mammals are the diaphragm, the epiglottis and, in most species, well developed facial musculature responsible for expressions.

Mammals have occupied all terrestrial habitats. Cetaceans and sirenians are specialized for life in water and the only ones which can fly actively are the bats.

Mammals reproduce in three different ways which correspond to the organization of the female sexual organs. The egg-bearing mammals (Prototheria) lay eggs and incubate them on their bellies (duck-billed platypus), or in a marsupium (echidna). The hatched young feed on their mother's milk which they lick from small milk patches (nipples are not developed). The female sexual organs resemble those of reptiles — there are paired oviducts leading into the cloaca.

Female marsupials (Metatheria) have the oviducts differentiated into a pair of Fallopian tubes, two uteri and two vaginae (in some species the uteri are linked up). The embryos have a yolk placenta developed and the mother and offspring are connected by capillaries of the yolk sac of the embryo. The young of marsupials are very underdeveloped at delivery and small; even large kangaroo species produce offspring only about 2cm long. They develop further in the ventral pouch (marsupium) on the mother's belly. While the period of pregnancy in marsupials lasts only days, the period of postnatal development in the pouch sometimes takes many months.

In the females of placental mammals (Eutheria or Placentalia) the lower parts of the oviducts merge to form a single vagina; the uterus varies in form from the markedly doubled one to a single one. The placenta is a specific organ for embryonic development of placental mammals which allows for prolongation of the intra-uterine period of embryonic development. It also aids nutrition, respiration and excretion. The period of pregnancy corresponds with the size of the species and may range from two or three weeks (in rodents) to 22 months (in elephants). Some species of mammals have developed so-called latent pregnancy; the development of an embryo ceases for a certain time between mating and birth. The young are born either bare, blind, with little power of locomotion (nidicolous) and are reared in nests or shelters, or they are covered with fur, and are mobile, with well functioning senses (nidifugous) — these are able to follow their mother soon after birth.

Insectivores (Insectivora) are generally small mammals with complete dentition and an elongate skull with the orbit open behind. The brain has well developed olfactory lobes. Insectivores usually move on the ground and feed on insects. Their young are nidicolous.

Bats (Chiroptera) are the second most numerous mammalian order. All species fly actively, they are active at night and orientate themselves mainly by echolocation (the echo of ultrasonic waves). The front pair of limbs is developed into wings and the hind pair is adapted for suspension. In some species latent pregnancy may be observed (the sperm of the males survive in the sex organs of the females often for several months before the egg ripens and only then do they fertilize it). The females generally produce a single nidicolous offspring. However, they never build nests. They are mostly insectivorous although some species live on fruits, nectar, pollen and also blood or fish.

Carnivores (Carnivora) are flesh-eating or omnivorous mammals with a complete dentition, including large canines and often specially adapted shearing teeth (the last upper premolar and first lower molar on either side of the jaws). The skull is usually massive and the chewing muscles powerful. Carnivores are mostly active at night or at dusk. They live on the ground, often in trees and in water. Usually they produce several (two to six) nidicolous offspring.

Primates (Primates) are the most advanced group of mammals. They have become adapted to active diurnal life and many live in trees. Their limbs, especially the front pair, are very mobile and the thumb is set in opposition to the other fingers enhancing manual dexterity.

The brain cavity and the brain itself is increased in primates; the facial part of the skull has become shortened in many species. The number of teeth is reduced to two incisors, one canine, two premolars and three molars in each half of the jaw. In most species the females possess a pair of mammary nipples on the chest; males have their testes in the scrotum and a pendulous penis.

Rodents (Rodentia) are the most numerous mammalian order (some 2,000 species) and they are also a biologically successful group which is still developing. They are mostly small and herbivo-rous. In the upper and lower jaw they have a pair of gnawing incisors with enamel only on the front, so that the tooth is ground off only at the back and maintains the shape of a chisel. The canines (and sometimes also the premolars) are absent. The chewing muscles are powerful. Rodents reproduce rapidly and produce a large number of nidicolous offspring. They live all over the world with the exception of the polar regions.

The rabbits, hares and pikas (Lagomorpha) were until recently classified as rodents. Modern physiological, serological and ethological research has revealed, however, that they are more closely related to artiodactyls. Hares and rodents are similar to each other, mainly in their way of life. Hares also have four gnawing incisors. Unlike rodents, however, they have another pair of smaller incisors in the upper jaw. Hares are plantigrade and the pads of their feet are covered with hairs. The males are the only placental mammals with the scrotum set in front of the penis. The young are either nidicolous (rabbits) or nidifugous (hares).

Even-toed ungulates (Artiodactyla) are usually large mammals. The axis of each limb lies between the third and fourth toes which are equally developed and each covered with a hoof. The second and fifth toes may be present and also covered by hooves. The stomach of artiodactyls often consists of several parts (not only in ruminants but also in some non-ruminants such as peccaries and hippopotamuses), and their dentition is sometimes reduced. The females of some species have two to four nipples in the inguinal region and produce one to four very independent offspring (for example, the deer family). Females of other species have more nipples on the ventral side in two rows between the front and hind limbs and produce up to 14 young (for example, the pig family).

The Artiodactyla comprise ruminants (Ruminantia) and non-ruminants (Suina). The canines of non-ruminants are sometimes extended to form tusks; the stomach may not be partitioned or may have up to three divisions even though they do not ruminate. Included in this group are members of the pig family and the hippopotamus family. The dentition of ruminants is usually incomplete (the upper incisors, and very often the canines, are absent), and the stomach is divided into four parts. They are herbivorous. While resting they regurgitate food (the cud) and chew it further. Sexual dimorphism is often conspicuous.

# Zoological Terminology

Every branch of science, including zoology, has its own terminology. The need to create a system of specialized nomenclature is one of the conditions of successful development of every branch of science. Specialized terminology allows scientists and laymen of different nationalities to be precise in a given scientific discipline because each unit then has an exact name. Let us, however, stay in the sphere of natural sciences. The original popular regional names of animals and plants were coined spontaneously and gave scientists no possibility of understanding one another. It was necessary to find a common language, to unify the names and give them international validity. In the Middle Ages scientists spoke to each other in Latin, the language which is still, albeit to a much lesser extent, a unifying tongue.

The first names in Latin were created randomly, in the same way as the popular names were previously; they were often sophisticated and descriptive. The first scientist who started to use scientific names for the different species of animals and plants in a consistent manner was Linnaeus. He first used them in the above-mentioned treatise "Systema naturae". After the first edition in 1735, Linnaeus revised the work several times. In 1758 the tenth edition was published and this was a landmark in the development of the system. Scientists have agreed that only names included in this publication could have scientific validity whereas the other, older names were to be considered invalid. Up to the time of the French Revolution scientists adopted the names coined by Linnaeus and other leading scientists without reservations. Rules for the formation of new names were nonexistent, the only valid rule was that of priority (the older name had priority over the newer one). After the French Revolution, however, the international exchange of information was curtailed to a certain extent so new species were given different names in different countries. The effort was uncoordinated and understanding the developing terminology was very difficult. It became necessary to devise rules for the creation of new names and other terminological requirements. The first attempt to formulate the rules was the Strickland Code of 1842. This was followed by other suggestions but none was given general approval. Widely acceptable rules were not approved until 1901 at the Zoological Congress in Berlin. These rules were supplemented over the years and later revised. In 1958 the XI International Zoological Congress in London adopted a new code in French and English wording (Code International de Nomenclature Zoologique — International Code of Zoological Nomenclature) which is still obligatory today. Some difficult or disputable questions of nomenclature are authoritatively solved by the International Committee for Zoological Nomenclature (ICZN). The basis of Linnaeus's and of the new natural scientific terminology is a binomial (composed of two words) name for a species. The first word denotes the genus and always starts with a capital letter, for example, *Papilio, Felis, Anser,* the second name denotes the species and always starts with a small letter *(domesticus, silvestris)*. Trinomial names denote subspecies and represent a further refinement of the system; the denotation of the subspecies also starts with a small letter. When denoting a subspecies the geographical name of the site inhabited by the subspecies is often taken as a root; for example, *Panthera tigris altaica, Rupicapra rupicapra tatrica*. The subspecies which served as the prototype for the description of the whole species is known as the nominate subspecies and the words denoting the species and subspecies are identical *(Parnassius apollo apollo)*.

In scientific literature the name of the species or subspecies is followed by the name of the scientist who first described it and also by the year the description was published, for example *Lacerta agilis* Linnaeus, 1758 and *Panthera pardus* (Linnaeus, 1758). If the name and year are enclosed in parentheses this indicates that the given species was originally included in a different genus. For example, in 1758 Linnaeus placed the leopard into the genus *Felis* as *Felis pardus*. After some time, however, it was felt that the leopard and other large cats have so many distinctive features that it would be more suitable to include them in a separate genus Panthera — hence *Panthera pardus* (Linnaeus, 1758).

Sometimes, for convenience's sake, the names of famous authors are abridged and even the year is left out (*Lacerta agilis* L.). However, if the rules are to be strictly observed, only the name of Linnaeus can be shortened to L. and Fabricius to Fabr or F. To give the name of the author of the description and the year is not obligatory but it is desirable and important in scientific work because they are often helpful in sorting out some of the problems which can arise. For it sometimes happens, for example, that different authors describe the same species independently, each giving it a different name. According to the rule of priority only the earliest name, the one published first, is valid. The starting date for the determination of priority is 1758, the year of publication of the tenth edition of "Systema naturae". Sometimes there is a time difference between the two descriptions and the identification of the older one is then easy; at other times the descriptions may have been published in the same year and then it is necessary to find out the exact date of publication. The later names then become synonyms of the valid name. Invalid names may also be created in other ways. For example, there is a principle that in the animal kingdom no two genera can have the same name and no two species within a single genus may have identical names. If, for example, a new genus of beetles is described under a generic name already in use for another group of animals, then this new name is an invalid homonym and must be substituted by the nearest (in time) synonym (if there is one) or by a newly invented name.

Scientific names are formed according to many grammatical rules. The generic name is always a noun and the specific name can also be a noun, or an adjective or a pronounceable group of letters without specific meaning. The noun denoting the species is in the nominative or genitive case; the gender (masculine, feminine or neuter) of the adjective must correspond with that of the generic name. As a precaution against errors the zoologist should always give the etymology and the grammatical gender of the genus or subgenus.

Besides the scientific terminology there is also national terminology, which is not so consistent, is usually not binomial and derives from conventional popular names. In any event it is not exhaustive for it provides names only for species which are common, conspicuous or well-known in that country.

National terminology has thus only local validity and to avoid international confusion it is necessary to adopt the scientific terminology as well as the local vernaculars.

# The Distribution of Animals

Every country has its typical landscape of mountains, rivers, lowlands etc., each with a characteristic assemblage of plants and animals. In the 19th century biologists discovered that the distribution of the fauna and flora over our planet is not random but that the various forms are distributed in typical communities over large areas. Some forms are found in all communities but every community has its own specific and typical forms. The biogeographical regions roughly correspond with the continents; they have different geological structures, topographies and climates, and consequently also different floras and faunas. This fact was first documented by Alfred Russel Wallace, a collaborator of Charles Darwin, whose division of the world into biogeographical regions is, after some revisions, used even today.

The various animal species are distributed over certain geographically delimited spaces (areas). The areas may reach over the boundaries of biogeographical regions and they may also be limited to a single island or mountain. Within an area each species inhabits sites with a particular climate and a typical plant cover, and becomes integrated into a characteristic community or biome. Within a biome animals seek sites with certain conditions to which they are adapted and which are essential for their life. The nature of the sites and biomes is determined by various external factors, the most important being the climate (temperature, humidity, light and so on) and the substrate (composition of soil and its character). These conditions have a direct effect on the structure of the flora and, indirectly through the flora,

on the composition of the fauna. The existence of plants is a prerequisite for the existence of animals; a certain type of plant community attracts a certain type of animal community. Living organisms and their physical (abiotic) environment are inseparably bound together and influence each other. The faunas of the different geographical regions result from a long and complex development. A whole set of factors have participated in this development; for example, the centres of origin of different groups of animals, their adaptability and migratory abilities. The movement of continents and changes in their topography are of prime importance because of their connection with the creation and effect of natural barriers (mountain ranges, deserts, seas, rivers). These barriers often had a permanent effect in forming the limits of an animal's distribution, and their influence remained even after the actual barrier ceased to exist; the fauna of the Neotropical (South America) is a good example. One of the oldest and most effective barriers is the Lombok straits in the Malay archipelago through which the so-called Wallace's line runs, marking the eastern limit of the Oriental region. Islands to the east of the Lombok straits represent a transitional zone where the Oriental region, with a diverse vertebrate fauna, meets the Australian region, which is much less diverse. In the eastern direction there are progressively fewer animals from the Oriental region and in the western direction progressively fewer Australian animals.

Land on the Earth is usually divided into several units of unequal size — three realms, five regions and seven sub-regions. This results from an effort to emphasize the separation of different faunas in terms of time and to reveal the different relationships between the regions. The realm Arctogaea (Megagaea) is the largest and includes the Holarctic, Oriental and Ethiopian regions. Neogaea comprises the Neotropical region (South America) and Notogaea (the smallest realm) the Australian region. On maps the boundaries between the regions are sharp; in reality, however, transitional zones exist between them where the corresponding plants and animals of the adjacent regions meet.

The largest zoogeographical region of the world is the Holarctic region. It extends over much of the temperate northern hemisphere and includes a great part of Eurasia, Africa north of the Sahara and North America. The fauna and flora of the Holarctic region has been profoundly affected by recent glaciations and therefore it is not so varied as the fauna and flora of the warm regions. Glaciation took place in several stages, it lasted about 500,000 yars and ended some 10,000 years ago. In this period the severe sub-arctic climate affected mainly Europe and many warmth-loving species died out or withdrew to warmer areas. On the other hand with advancing glaciation various sub-arctic and high mountain alpine species migrated to Europe. After the recession of glaciers these species returned north or survived in high mountains and became a permanent component of the European fauna. Species common to European mountain ranges and the northern regions are known as boreo-alpine; species surviving only in European mountains are alpine; and species found only in the north are known as boreal.

The Holarctic is sometimes divided into two sub-regions, the Nearctic sub-region, comprising North America, and the Palearctic sub-region, which covers the rest. The relief of the Holarctic region is exceptionally rugged and its plant cover is varied. The pole is covered with sea, ice and snow but further south, the land bears tundra and taiga in both sub-regions. Beyond the tundra and taiga in each sub-region there appear various biomes — deciduous (broadleaf) forests, coniferous (hard-leaf) forests, temperate grasslands or steppes, semi-deserts and deserts. The Holarctic region is inhabited mainly by small and medium-sized animals; typical inhabitants are members of the deer family, squirrels, beavers, hedgehogs, moles, and buzzards. In both sub-regions there are many pairs of similar and closely related species.

The most similar species are found in the tundra and taiga of both sub-regions, where the animals could spread accross the Bering Strait and inhabit the whole region around the pole. Species thus distributed are the reindeer and caribou, European elk or moose, polar bear, lemmings, wolf, snowy owl, etc. Towards the south there are progressively fewer widely distributed species. Each sub-region has its endemic species which do not live elsewhere. For example, the Nearctic sub-region is inhabited by the pronghorn, bison, prairie-dogs, skunk, wild turkey, and rattlesnakes, etc. The Palearctic sub-region is inhabited by the European bison, wild cat, Old World rats and mice, Old World jerboas, and camels.

Closely connected with the fauna of the Holarctic region are those of the Ethiopian and Oriental regions. There are no unsurpassable barriers between these regions and so the fauna of all three has many groups in common. The basic difference is in the tropical climate of the Oriental and Ethiopian regions resulting in a very rich and varied fauna.

The Oriental region covers India, south of the Himalayas, the southern part of China, and the Malay archipelago including the Philippines. The tropical forest is predominant there. The fauna of the Oriental region resembles that of the Ethiopian region in many respects. It is inhabited by some typical groups and species of higher primates, for example gibbons, the orang-utans, macaque monkeys, tarsiers, tree shrews, tiger, Indian elephant and flying lemurs.

The Ethiopian (sometimes referred to as the Afro-tropical) region includes the whole of Africa south of the Sahara desert, the southern part of the Arabian peninsula and the island of Madagascar. Although the relief of the Ethiopian region is heterogeneous, it includes tropical forests, steppes, and deserts, but the most striking fauna is that of the African savannas. On them the unique and imposing communities of odd-toed and even-toed ungulates — zebras, giraffes, antelopes, and large carnivores (lions, leopards and hyaenas) evolved. The Ethiopian region is inhabited by many endemic species and groups; for example, elephant shrews, the hippopotamus, the pigmy hippopotamus and okapi. Other typically African species such as rhinoceroses, apes, pangolins and elephants are found also in the Oriental region although these belong to different genera or

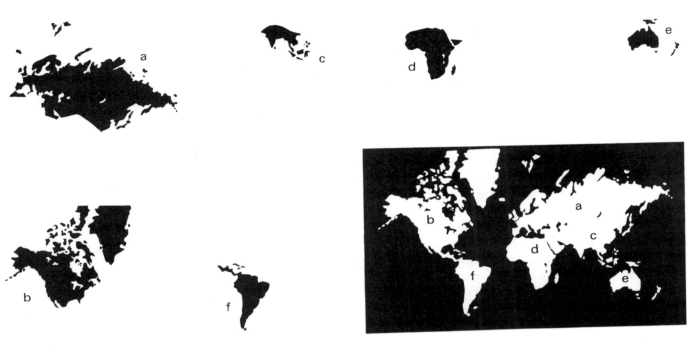

a – Palearctic subregion
b – Nearctic subregion
c – Oriental region
d – Ethiopian region
e – Australian region
f – Neotropical region

species. Both regions are rich in insects. The relationship between the two faunas thus indicates a similar development of both regions.

A sub-region of the Ethiopian region is the island of Madagascar. It is inhabited by strange animals which are not found elsewhere on the continent of Africa. Many primitive animal forms can be found there, for example, tenrecs, various strange and primitive primates such as the aye-aye, endemic reptile species (for example the Madagascar boa *Sanzinia madagascariensis*), geckos, numerous insects and so on. Madagascar is unusual in not being inhabited by ungulates (except for one species of pig), higher primates or large carnivores. Madagascar became separated from the African mainland during the early Tertiary, before the Eurasian fauna started moving into the African continent accross the Sinai region.

The Australian region is inhabited by the most curious fauna in the world. Various forms of marsupials are predominant and even several monotremes have survived. Indigenous to the Australian region are, for example, the lungfish, the platypus and the echidnas or spiny anteaters. These ancient forms of animals survived and developed in isola-

tion from the competition of more advanced mammals because the Australian region had separated from the rest of the world's land masses at a very early period. Placental mammals are represented on the island by bats which, due to their ability to fly, could reach the land without difficulty, the Old World rats and mice, which penetrated the region gradually from the surrounding islands, and the dingo, which most probably came with the first human occupants. The Australian region is inhabited by a large number of reptiles, especially agamids and various species of venomous and other snakes.

The Australian region includes Australia, Tasmania, New Guinea and associated islands. Lowlands with savanna, semidesert and desert plant formations are predominant; tropical forests occur locally in the north.

The Neotropical region covers southern and central America, the tropical part of Mexico and the islands in the Caribbean. The vegetation in this region is varied and mainly tropical. The fauna bears conspicuous signs of long-term isolation of the South American continent throughout the Tertiary. The original inhabitants of South America – primitive edentates, ungulates and marsupials – settled in the region at the time when the North and South America were still connected. Over the millions of years of isolation of South America, an island-specific animal and plant community devel-

35

oped. After the appearance of the terrestrial bridge between South and North America, some 3 million years ago, the faunas of the two regions started to mix. The south was penetrated by the more advanced forms of animals, for example, lamas, tapirs and carnivores, which became adapted and began to displace the original inhabitants. About half the species of the South American mammals come originally from North America. Most of the species that did penetrate the north were unable to withstand the competition of local species and gradually died out; among those that did successfully colonise the north are, for example, the opossums *(Didelphis)* and porcupines *(Erethizon)*.

Typical inhabitants of the Neotropical region are the armadillos, sloths and anteaters, lamas, marmosets and tamarins, capuchin monkeys, American vampires, South American lungfish, anaconda and hummingbirds. The region is inhabited by a huge number of insect species of different forms and sizes (for example the world's largest capricorn beetle, *Titanus giganteus,* lives here).

Not even the current distribution of animals is final. In keeping with changes of the environment, considerably promoted by the activity of Man, their distribution pattern changes too. Men often affect nature very considerably yet not always carefully. Man destroys the original plant covers and transforms them into cultivated steppes, he uses herbicides and insecticides and, instead of growing indigenous plants, he imports and acclimatizes others. As a result, some species and even whole families of animals die out, while others become rare. On the other hand, however, many species spread far and wide as a consequence of human activity, and some even spread all over the world.

# The Adaptability of Animals

Animals live in permanent contact with the environment. They are affected by various abiotic factors — humidity and temperature — and influences from living things — food and mutual relationships with other living organisms. The immediate environment of an individual or a group is its niche. Only within the niche do the mutual interrelationships of all factors stand out clearly: factors such as climate, food and cohabitation of organisms. All these factors produce a permanent pressure on the animals to which they must be capable of responding if they are to survive. This means adapting to the conditions of a given niche so that each animal can obtain as much food (that is, energy) as possible from the niche resources, to build up effective protection against enemies and the climate, and to be able to reproduce. The adjustments which enable the individuals or species to do this are known as adaptation.

Adaptation allows many individuals of various species to live socially in one niche, for specialized animals draw on the energy of the same niche in different ways and therefore need not compete. They are also better able to assert themselves in a stable environment than more generalized species. Different adaptations allowed them to invade all sorts of environments and to utilize new resources. The process of development through which these adaptations were made is known as adaptive radiation. An example of adaptive radiation is provided by Darwin's finches. When Charles Darwin investigated finches from the Galapagos he found their striking likenesses in plumage and body build very noticeable. Only their bills were different. The physical likeness of the different species indicated a common ancestor: probably a species of finches that arrived on the island and reproduced as long as a certain type of food was available in sufficient quantity. When there ceased to be enough food natural selection started to work in favour of the more adaptable types. As each island was able to support only a limited number of birds living on a given type of food, the other birds were forced to adapt themselves to other types of diet. Hence specialized forms that live on all available kinds of food developed on the Galapagos Islands; some, for example, catch insects on the wing, others on the ground or under bark; some crack fruit or suck nectar, and so on. The shapes of their bills became adapted accordingly. One of the most remarkable adaptations is shown by an insectivorous finch, *Camarhynchus pallidus*, which exploits a food source normally only available to woodpeckers. Though it is not equipped with the harpoon-shaped tongue of a woodpecker it has developed an ingenious alternative way of extracting insects from tree-bark: with its bill it enlarges a small hole in the bark which it then probes with a thorn until the insect creeps out; the finch then puts down the thorn and picks up its prey. Many individuals even make stores of thorns. Another example is the adaptive radiation of marsupials in Australia. The few original forms developed into many species which, owing to adaptations, came to live on various kinds of food and inhabited every suitable habitat. They live on the ground, under ground, in the branches of trees, in water and some are even able to glide.

Yet another example is shown by the Anseriformes (waterfowl). They developed from a single ancestor into a number of forms, which hunt various types of food in different ways. They may therefore live together in a limited area (around one lake) without competing with one another (Gause's principle).

The cost which specialized animals must pay for their success is high. They are not so flexible as the more generalized animals and therefore are not able to respond to further changes in the environment. The more specialized the animal the less adaptable it is. Thus it can be said that in a stable niche the specialized organism is at an advantage whereas in an unstable niche the generalized organism is better off.

The various adaptations of different species probably occurred as a result of random genetical deviations which favoured the affected individuals, thus enabling them to pass the sieve of natural selection. There are countless different adaptations but all have ensued from the ability of animals to respond to changes in their environment. In general a distinction is made between adaptations of external organs and body form (structural), and physiological adaptations (resulting from the adaptation of physiological functions of internal body organs, for example, for the digestion of a special kind of food) and finally behavioural (ethological) adaptations. The suggested division, however, does not indicate the reason for the appearance of a given adaptation. Therefore, it is more expedient to divide adaptations according to the purpose they are supposed to serve, for example, adaptations to locomotion, hunting food, orientation or toilet.

Many animals confined to forests adapted themselves excellently to movement within the tree canopy, for example, sloths (Bradypodidae). Sloths spend most of their time suspended upside down in the branches of trees. Consequently, they have long, remarkably strong limbs with powerful hooked claws on which they hang. The direction of hair growth on the body of sloths is from the belly towards the back (in the other mammals it is the other way round); rain water can thus run down without soaking the creatures. Sloths climb down to the ground only when they want to move to a different tree or when they want to defaecate. On the ground, however, they are very awkward and almost defenceless. As a result they have developed an interesting adaptation: they have a very distendable urinary bladder and rectum, enabling them to retain waste products for as long as 30 days. In this way they avoid having to go down to the ground very often. This adaptation is also associated with water conservation within the sloth's kidneys and other organs.

Some tree monkeys such as capuchin monkeys and spider monkeys have a long prehensile tail which they use as a fifth limb. Spider monkeys have on the underside of the tail a bald spot for grasping, which is covered by dermal ridges (humans also have dermal ridges on the pads of their fingers). Many tree animals became adapted to gliding flight or what could be described as parachute falls. Flying lemurs and flying squirrels have an extendable skin membrane around most of the circumference of their body. Flying lemurs have the largest skin membrane of all animals. These allow them to cover distances of up to 60 metres, covering a height difference of 12 metres. They are also able to transport their young on such glides. Some reptiles have also become adapted for gliding. The flying lizard (Draco) has five or six pairs of ribs which straighten out on the sides of the body and support a skin fold — the flying membrane. Geckos of the genus Ptychozoon have their body and tail rimmed by a thin membrane which also joins their toes. When flying through the air the "flying snake", Chrysopelea ornata, straightens out and stiffens its body, the ventral side of which appears to sink in, and the ribs become extended to the sides, creating a lifting force under the body.

The scalytails (Anomalurus), which, incidentally, are also gliders, have developed scales with sharp edges on the underside of their tails to assist them when climbing trees. When the animal presses itself against a tree the scale penetrates the bark and helps to maintain the position.

Many adaptations have been developed for movement on ground too. The gerenuk (Litocranius walleri), for example, has sharp triangular hooves which allow it to stand on its hind legs when reaching for acacia branches. The klipspringer (Oreotragus oreotragus) has stubby hooves which assist it in climbing rocks. This animal, when jumping, is able to land on a very small platform. The chamois (Rupicapra rupicapra) has sharp outer edges to its narrow hooves which allow the animal to move over rocky and slippery terrain. The sitatunga (Tragelaphus spekei) lives on marshy ground; its hooves are elongated, thus preventing it from sinking into the mud. The reindeer *(Rangifer tarandus)* has broad hooves which help it to walk over snow.

Members of the genus *Physalia* live on the surface of oceans. They move on the water surface with the aid of a large gas-filled pouch which contains a high proportion of nitrogen and carbon dioxide. The pouch floats on the water surface and from it sting filaments up to 30 metres long are suspended in the water. The pouch (pneumatophore) is asymmetrical with a comb about 30 cm high which has the function of a sail. Because of the comb's oblique position and its indented shape, the animal is not simply blown about haphazardly but moves at a sharp angle to the direction of the wind and is therefore never driven onto the shore. In this way *Physalia* floats obliquely and from time to time it changes direction by turning round. As it approaches the coast the long filaments touch the bottom and the animal turns round and floats slowly back to sea.

Rattlesnakes (Crotalidae) have on both sides of their head, between the eye and nostril, a pit furnished with sensory cells which are highly sensitive to heat. The pits are wave guides for infra-red radiation. The sensory cells are able to detect the body heat temperature of prey even if its temperature deviates by only tenths of a degree from the temperature of the environment. Similar equipment in the form of a whole system of pits which line the upper jaw is found, for example, in the snake *Epicrates angulifer*. Heat receptors allow these snakes to hunt even by night (anacondas live in caves and hunt bats) and also to locate inactive prey. For this reason they do not depend on their sight when hunting.

Some fish species are equipped with an electric organ. The most powerful example is that found in the electric eel *(Electrophorus electricus)* which lives in fresh water in South America. The organ takes up some three-quarters of the whole length of the fish. The front and middle parts of the body contain the main component which is able to produce discharges of 550 to 800 volts. These discharges have both a protective and offensive purpose (for hunting food). The rear part of the body contains the so-called Sachs' organ which produces

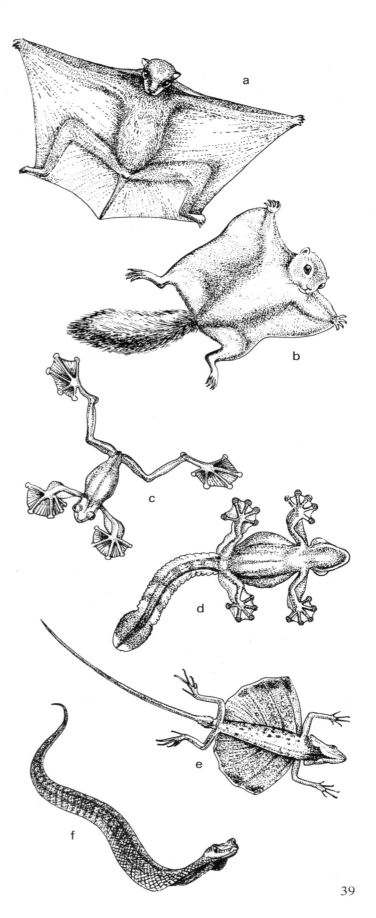

The adaptation of some arboreal animals to passive flight by which they may cover large distances. a — *Cynocephalus*, b — *Pteromys volans*, c — *Rhacophorus*, d — *Ptychozoon kuhli*, e — *Draco volans*, f — *Chrysopelea ornata*

only weak discharges. These are used mainly for orientation purposes. The electric eel lives in turbid waters which makes orientation by sight difficult. Therefore in seeking the numbed prey and for moving in general this electric "radar" is of great importance to it.

The neck of the anhingas *(Anhinga)* resembles a perfect harpoon. These birds are able to use the weapon effectively due to the special design of their ninth neck vertebra which is conspicously long and is joined with the eight vertebra almost at a right angle. The abrupt contraction of the appropriate muscles straightens out the angle and the bill shoots forward.

The tropical archer fish *(Toxotes)* hunt mainly terrestrial insects which move in vegetation along the banks of streams. The fish act like small water pistols when shooting down the insects with drops of water. The water is squirted out by abrupt contractions of the gill covers (opercula) and the pipe-shaped mouth with the assistance of the tongue and grooved palate. The accuracy of the hits is remarkable, especially when one considers that in aiming the fish must compensate for the refraction of light. Some individuals shoot as far as up to three metres.

Chameleons *(Chameleo)* approach their prey with slow swinging movements copying the movements of twigs in the wind. They capture the prey by a very rapid extension of their tongue. The tongue of the chameleon is longer than its body and its tip is broad and sticky.

It was thought at one time that insects obtain water only from their food or by drinking. It has been found, however, that silverfish, cockroaches, locusts and other arthropods can obtain water from the air, through the cuticle of the body surface. The

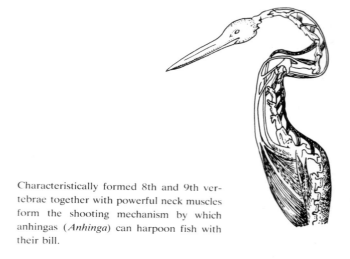

Characteristically formed 8th and 9th vertebrae together with powerful neck muscles form the shooting mechanism by which anhingas *(Anhinga)* can harpoon fish with their bill.

silverfish *(Thermobia domestica)* was found to be highly efficient in this respect, being capable of absorbing water from air with a humidity of 45 percent and over. Scientists believe that insects possess a "cuticular water pump" which is based on active suction of water through the pores in the body cuticle. Only in this way do the desert species of insects obtain sufficient water to enable them to survive the arid conditions.

Lamas *(Lama)* which live in the high mountains of the Andes have haemoglobin in their blood which has the power to bind more oxygen than that of lowland mammals. That is why lamas are able to move quickly in thin air with a low oxygen content unlike unadapted humans.

An important adaptation of cetaceans for life in water is their system of breathing. Sperm whales dive to depths of more than 1,000 metres and are able to stay there for up to two hours, while dolphins dive to depths of 250 metres for five to ten minutes at a time. This is possible owing to the

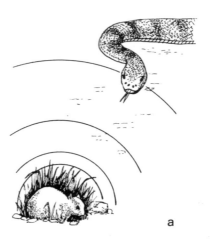

a

The indentations between the eyes and nostrils are directional heat receptors used by rattle snakes (Crotalidae) for a — hunting, and b — for orientation in space

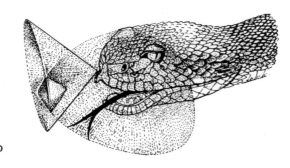

b

property of their haemoglobin (blood pigment) which binds much more oxygen than in other animal species. Moreover, oxygen is also bound to a muscle pigment, myoglobin. Cetaceans have a large quantity of blood and are not sensitive to high concentrations of carbon dioxide in the blood. They also breathe very slowly (a dolphin inhales one to three times a minute compared with man who inhales sixteen times). Consequently air exchange in their lungs is more effective — with one breath cetaceans can replace up to 90 percent of their air.

The larvae of cixiids *(Cixiidae)* in the insect order Homoptera are protected from enemies and against the effect of rain water by a thick covering of wax. The wax-producing cells are dispersed over the body of the larvae and produce wax fibres which are often very long, variously coiled and therefore flexible. The family of tropical splendour beetles, for example *Julodis ornatipennis,* also uses wax for protection — in this case against extreme heat and desiccation.

One of the species of tapir, *Tapirus indicus,* has different mimetic colouring in its youth and maturity. The young animal is dark brown with longitudinal whitish spots and stripes. Such a pattern corresponds with the play of light and shade on the ground of the jungle, thus rendering the creature almost invisible. In contrast, the adult tapir is black and white. At night, when tapirs are active, the black head, shoulders and legs are hidden by darkness, while the white parts break up the outline, thus obscuring the shape of the animals. In this way the appearance as a whole disintegrates. This type of body colouring is one kind of camouflage. The second type of protective colouring is designed to deter. Animals that are conspicuously coloured usually possess some effective weapon which turns them into unpleasant prey. For example, the salamander *Salamandra salamandra,* which is known for its poisonous secretion, is yellow and black in colour. This is called aposematic colouration.

Some defenceless animals protect themselves by copying the appearance of other better protected animals; for example, some hover-flies copy the appearance of wasps and hornets. Other animals try to resemble various objects from their environment. Leaf insects *(Phyllium)* not only mimic the shape and colour of leaves but also quiver like them, thus creating an almost perfect illusion.

Some moths in industrialized regions acquire dark colouring to be less conspicuous in an environment partly transformed by industrial pollution. For example, the dark (melanic) form of the birch beauty or peppered moth *(Biston betularia)* is hard to see on tree trunks which, because of pollution, are lacking in lichen cover. In this way the moth is protected against insectivorous birds. The common form, with light patches, is clearly visible, even at a distance, on such trees.

Sea slugs *(Nudibranchia)* which have a soft and vividly coloured body without a shell, have developed a particular method of protecting themselves. After hatching, the young slugs live on stinging hydrozoan polyps, and when feeding they swallow some of their host's sting cells. The unripe cells of the polyps pass through the digestive tract of the slug and settle in the liver. There they ripen, move into the skin of the slug and function in the same way as in their original owner. The stinging thread, when not in use, is coiled in a capsule inside the cell. After the stimulation of a special process projecting externally from the cell, a lid flies open and the stinging thread shoots out of the cell. Moreover, the cell also releases a poisonous substance which painfully burns the damaged skin of the offender.

When in danger some animals take on the appearance of being dead, for example the opossum *(Didelphis),* the true water snakes *(Natrix),* the barn owl *(Tyto alba)* and many insect species.

Crabs of the species *Dotilla myctiroides* feed on organic substances which they sieve from the mud. They make little balls from the refuse and with these they build protective bunkers against tidal waves. They dig holes in the sand which they bridge over with these balls. In this way air-filled chambers are created. The crabs reinforce the chambers from the inside with the excavated sand and there they survive the period of high tide.

Some cobras, for example, *Naja nigricollis* or *Hemachatus hemachatus,* have developed a unique method of using their venom at a distance. The cobras spit, or more exactly squirt, the venom to distances of up to 3 metres. The venom is ejected by the contraction of a special muscle from the venom gland into the duct of the fang. The venom is under considerable pressure and therefore flows through the duct at great speed; in addition the fang is moved to describe a circle so that on ejection the venom is dispersed by centrifugal force. Cobras can see well and aim their weapon very accurately, usually at the face of their victim. The farther away the intruder is from the cobra, the larger is the area affected by the discharged venom which can blind the aggressor.

An important part of the daily routine of animals is care of their body covering (fur, feathers, skin). Therefore many species have developed adaptations which faciliate this activity. Prosimians comb

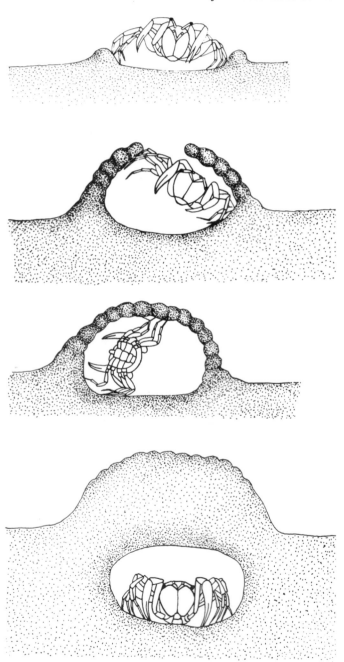

The crab *Dotilla myctiroides* builds a bunker as shelter against high tide.

their fur with specially adapted lower incisors which form a kind of comb. On the first toe of their hind leg hyraxes have a special hollow claw which they use for combing the fur. Similar claws are found on the second toe of the hind feet of beavers and on the second and third toes of kangaroos.

Some sea fish, such as members of the genus Crenilabrus have become specialized as cleaners. They bite parasites off the skin surface and out of the inside of the mouth and gill cavities of other fish. These cleaners are typically coloured to be easily distinguished by the other fish. A special ritual for communication purposes has developed between the cleaners and their clients.

Many adaptations have evolved in connection with reproduction and upbringing of the young. Cuckoos *(Cuculus canorus)* lay their eggs into the nests of other birds and do not take care of their young. To make sure that the strange egg is not thrown out of the nest, the size and colour of the cuckoo's egg has to match those of the host. Because of the immense variety of bird eggs each cuckoo has one particular favourite host species. Cuckoos which have grown up in the nest of, say, a robin place their eggs only into the nests of other robins and in colour and size the eggs resemble those of robins.

The male of the pipa frog *(Pipa americana)* helps to place the eggs on the female's back during mating. After a few hours the skin on the female's back swells and creates pockets around the eggs. In these the tadpoles develop until metamorphosis.

The female of the Australian frog *(Rheobatrachus silus)* swallows the fertilized eggs which she has laid and keeps them in her throat until hatching. The hatched tadpoles then move into their mother's stomach. The presence of the tadpoles stops the digestive processes and the creation of digestive juices. If the female is forced to disgorge the tadpoles they die, for they are not able to live in water before metamorphosis.

Young kangaroos (Macropodidae) are very underdeveloped at birth and complete their development in the ventral pouch of their mother — the marsupium. A few days after delivery the female mates again. The fertilized egg undergoes cleavage and after some time ceases to develop. The embryo is at rest in the womb of the mother while the young kangaroo continues to grow in the pouch. If the offspring in the pouch dies the embryo immediately resumes its development. Otherwise the waiting embryo does not start developing until the young grows up and leaves its mother's pouch.

In different places of the Earth there are regions with approximately the same ecological conditions. It is not surprising that we encounter in such places similar plants and animals. These species are not related but have acquired similar characteristics and appearances due to similar living conditions. The phenomenon is known as convergence. Convergent evolution leads to the formation of identical features in unrelated animal species. A classic example of such convergence can be seen in dolphins and sharks. Both groups are adapted to life in water and therefore have developed the same body shape. Similar but not identical body shapes have been acquired by cetaceans, pinnipeds and sirenians as well as many fish.

Pinnipeds, cetaceans and penguins have developed, independently of each other, a tough layer of fat under the skin as a protection against the cold of the polar seas.

Many animal species curl up into a ball when threatened by an enemy, for example armadillos, hedgehogs and pangolins among the mammals, and millipedes and pill bugs in the arthropods. Even trilobites used to curl up into balls.

Mammals which live on ants and termites, for example, anteaters, pangolins and echidnas have typically formed rod-shaped jaws, a cylindrical sticky tongue, similarly structured stomachs and feet adapted to digging and scratching.

When hippopotamuses, alligators and frogs of the genus Rana are resting in water, their eyes and nostrils protrude above the water line, while the rest of the body is concealed below. Eyes set as close as possible to the upper contour of the head is a feature typical of many water mammals.

Convergent adaptations are particularly conspicuous in environments which place special requirements upon their inhabitants. Animals living in fast running water (worms, leeches, slugs and some fish) have a streamlined body shape, their skin, as far as possible, is without appendages and they possess sucking equipment by which they can anchor themselves to the substrate.

It would be possible to find many more examples of convergence. Scientists have drawn some generalizations which can be applied to warm-blooded vertebrates. They are mostly formulated in connection with a given species, but their significance is broader. According to Bergmann's rule animals gradually increase in size towards colder regions. The colder regions should be understood not only latitudinally, that is towards the poles, but also vertically from lower altitudes to the mountains. The larger the animal the smaller its body surface in relation to its volume. Hence it expends less heat and needs less energy to maintain its constant body temperature. An example of Bergmann's rule is the size of brown bears (*Ursus arctos*). The smallest form (*U.a. arctos*), which weighs about 60 kg, lives in western Europe, while the largest forms — kodiak bear (*U.a. middendorffi*) and the Alaska bear (*U.a. gyas*) live in Alaska and associated islands and weigh 780 to 1,200kg.

Bergmann's rule is usually associated with Allen's rule. According to the latter the legs and other parts of the body (ears, tail) are shorter in colder regions in order to reduce body heat losses. According to another Allen's rule birds are found to

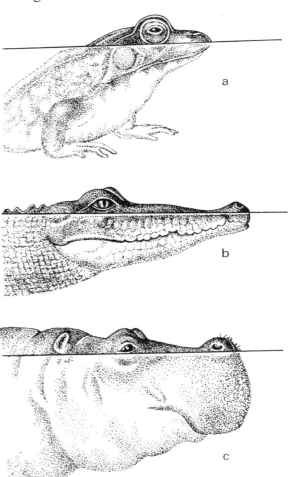

The location of eyes and nostrils in some aquatic animals
a — frog.  b — crocodile,  c — hippopotamus.

lay more eggs as one nears the colder parts of the world. Von Lehmann's rule says that individuals living on the edge of the range of a given species are smaller than those living closer to the centre of the range. Gloger's rule generalizes the fact that in more humid and warmer areas the animals are of darker colour than in arid and cold areas. According to Waterhouse's rule, aquatic forms are the largest within a certain group of related animals; for example, in the weasel family (Mustelidae) river otters (Lutrinae) and sea otters (Enhydrinae) are the largest.

# Communication among Animals

Although the ability to communicate is closely associated with the evolution of man, many other animals communicate in various ways. Other animals do not possess a language in the human sense of the word, but they have developed a great variety of non-verbal signals which they use when responding to certain situations. The communication systems have different levels and may often be very complicated. Every act of an organism which stimulates a reaction in another organism may be considered a manifestation of communication. The simplest forms of communication are connected with the direct perception of the surrounding environment and with picking up general (unspecific) stimuli which originate from this environment. Flagellate protozoans respond to the products of metabolism excreted into the water by other unicellular organisms. In different animals the nervous system is tuned to receiving non-specific stimuli from the environment; for example, fish respond to vibrations caused by the movement of other fish, snakes register earth tremors caused by a man walking etc. Some animal species have developed receptors which register non-specific stimuli from the environment (for example the lateral line in fish and larval amphibians).

Far more versatile, advanced and impressive forms of communication have evolved on the basis of specific signals. For their relaying and receiving, special organs of communication have been developed (receivers and transmitters).

The means of expression which serve to communicate within a species or between different species depend largely on the development of anatomical and physiological features such as facial musculature, skin covering of fur or feathers and on the environment in which they live. In some groups the development of means of expression is limited. Reptiles and some amphibians, for example, do not have a varied repertoire of signals for communication, be it vocal or by body movements. Such groups use simple forms of movement, for example moving the head, stamping the feet etc., and ascribe to them a different meaning; that is they ritualize them. In other groups, for example in birds and mammals, the repertoire of means of expression is much wider.

It is remarkable to note that in different groups of vertebrates there appear similar forms of expression (though their meaning may differ). The threat of a wide opened mouth or bill is probably a very old expression; it may be observed in some frogs, in almost all species of reptiles, and in mammals and birds. Movements of the tail are used by various species of lizards, anoles, geckos and many species of mammals. Stooping and arching of the body is common in salamanders, frogs and various carnivorous mammals. It is used either as a threat or to make an impression. Nodding of the head is a ritualized expression of threat in anoles and rodents, especially sciuromorphs and gerbils. In primates, threat is expressed by swaying the whole body. Sticking out the tongue as a threat may be observed among woodpeckers, insectivores and some primates, as well as among monitor lizards, lizards and other reptiles. Limb shaking, sometimes connected with foot stamping, is a manifestation used widely in many animal groups to express subordination. Danger or possible attack may also be communicated in this way (examples are kangaroos and even-toed ungulates).

The frequency with which these signals are used depends, as had been noted, on the physical structure of the environment. For instance, in a thick forest sounds do not carry very far and therefore to be effective they have to have a certain timbre. In a dark cave or at great depths communication by postures is of no use for it cannot be seen. Species living in caves or in the abyss must employ acoustic or light signals.

The ways of communication employed by different species or groups of animals vary remarkably. They are essentially based on three relatively universal types of signal and occur in a great variety of animals. Closest to human communication are sound signals (though they are not widespread in the animal kingdom) and visual signals.

Visual signals are very common among animals. They are conspicuous and therefore attract the attention of many animals, even those to which they are not directed. Visual signals are thus easily understandable. Moreover, forms of communication exist which are appropriate to the abilities of expression and understanding of the lower animals. The significance of visual signals is as a rule specific within the individual species or groups of animals; that is, various species, or even individuals within the same species may interpret the same signal in completely different ways. For example a special step used by the female deer means a warning while the same step used by the male means a threat. When the corners of the mouth in a chimpanzee are drawn back and the teeth revealed, it expresses insecurity and fear; in tigers the same expression means a threat, and in man, a smile.

Visual signs are used in a variety of ways. Many animal species bear colour signs on their bodies. The signs are either permanently visible, for example, the vivid patterns on coral fish, the coloured patches on the rump and cheeks of the mandrill, the markings on the head of the blackbuck, or they are concealed and the animal reveals them only under certain conditions. For example, some butterflies show the conspicuous "eyes" on the hind pair of wings, while males of the Diana monkey show the rust-coloured insides of their thighs. Visual signals also include changes in size, posture and the shape of the body or of its parts. Animals lower or erect their fur, feathers, ears or tail, extend their

The springbok (*Antidorcas marsupialis*)

fins, inflate their body etc. The white fur surrounding the anus of stags and deer is normally not very conspicuous, but, in moments of danger, the tail and the hairs in this part are raised, making a vivid white flash. The spring-buck has long hairs hidden in a skin fold along the spine; if the animal is disturbed the fold opens out and the hairs are erected to form a wide stripe which is visible at a great distance. The mane of lions can be erected to appear bigger, anoles bend down their tongue to show the coloured throat, cobras extend the ribs in the neck section which form a "hood", bitterns draw their feathers to the body to look slimmer, while owls on the other hand puff their feathers out and extend their wings.

The most advanced form of visual communication is by facial expression. Animals with well-developed facial muscles (for example, lion, wolf and primates) are able to express a whole range of emotions and show their intentions in this way. Effective visual signals can also be by various movements and particular body postures, for example, movements of the tail in canines, prancing steps in the deer family and stooping or arching of the back in the cat family. Very complex signals for communication are used by bees which inform other bees about the location, distance and quality of food by performing complicated dances.

The least common form of communication is by the production of light signals. This is used by some insects such as glow-worms, tropical fireflies — for example *Pyrophorus noctilucus,* lantern flies, deep-sea fishes — for example *Bathysidus pentagrammus,* cephalopods — for example *Vampyroteuthis infernalis,* and so on. The radiated light varies in intensity and rhythm.

Visual signals are used mainly by vertebrates, insects and crustaceans, regardless of whether eyesight is their main sense organ. The same applies also to acoustic signals which are used among many groups of insects as well as in vertebrates. Arthropods produce sounds almost exclusively by rubbing parts of the body against each other. Crickets and locusts, for example, have a stridulatory apparatus close to the base of the wings, together with strengthened and adapted veins in the wings which when rubbed against each other produce the chirrup sound. Short-horned grasshoppers rub the stridulatory apparatus on their thighs against the wings. The receptors which detect the sounds are situated on the tibia of the legs or on the abdominal segments. Vertebrates commonly produce sounds by forcing air through a system of membranes in the respiratory system. For example, perching birds possess a special singing organ (syrinx) in the shape of a drum which is located at the point where the trachea divides. The sounds produced are often amplified through various resonators, for example, in cranes the resonator consists of a coiled trachea which rests on the breast bone. Some reptiles exhale sharply and hiss (snakes) or bellow (crocodiles). Fishes produce sounds with the aid of the swim bladder. Other vertebrates, however, produce sounds in different ways; rattlesnakes rattle the specially adapted segments at the end of the tail, other snakes rub the keels on the scales against each other, storks clap their bills, gorillas beat their chests, ungulates stamp their hooves, etc. The complexity of sounds produced by vertebrates and arthropods differs. It is generally said that the most complicated sounds produced by arthropods are never more complicated than those produced by vertebrates. This interesting point probably ensues from the fact that arthropods only change the intervals between the different sounds, whereas the sound signals of vertebrates differ in intensity, frequency, intervals and modulation or timbre.

In using sound and visual signals the animals usually determine the time and duration themselves but when chemical signals (olfactory or taste signals) are used, this cannot be done very easily. Chemical signals usually have a long-term effect and they are used only occasionally for direct communication. Olfactory signals are commonly used by insects. Information is transmitted through special substances collectively known as pheromones. The most thoroughly investigated pheromones are the attractants which are used, for example, by female insects to attract the males. A sitting female releases from special scent glands a minute quantity of an attractant into the air and sometimes helps to disperse it by flapping her wings. She then takes up the courting position. The male picks up the smell with his antennae, often at a great distance. The antennae of the males are often specially adapted for this purpose. Complex chemical systems of communication have developed in social insects such as bees, wasps, ants and termites. Ants especially have a remarkably well-developed system of glands for secreting substances outside their body. Ants communicate almost exclusively by means of pheromones. These insects produce trail marking, alarm, crowding and conciliatory substances and also substances for soliciting food or other services. The effect of pheromones persists even in dead ants and only when it evaporates are the corpses cleared away by other ants. Pheromones are also used among mammals. Males of ungulates responds to the odour of urine of a female on heat, dogs reliably determine a female on heat, etc. The olfactory signals are released either from the secretions of scent glands, or from faeces, urine etc., and mammals use them mainly in marking the boundaries of their territory.

Communication systems affect the life of animals in a great variety of ways. First of all they assist in orientating the animal. This is particularly important in nocturnal animals such as bats, in animals living in caves such as oilbirds and some salamanders, and in some aquatic mammals, for example, dolphins. In these groups therefore, a special technique (sonar) has been developed which functions on the principle of reflected sound waves. With their nose or mouth animals produce high-frequency sounds and orientate themselves according to the echo. Such systems are mainly for communication among individuals of the same species (intra-specific communication), or between members of different species (inter-specific communication). Intra-specific communication allows the identification of not only an individual with a species, but also membres of its family, group or herd. In addition, suitable signals can communicate its status (dominant or submissive) or its sexual state among members of a flock, herd or family.

Within a given population, each member has its own specific smell, shade of colour, voice intensity etc. which, though still characteristic of the species, make it possible to recognize it as an individual.

Many elements of intra-specific communication occur also in inter-specific communication. These are mainly threatening displays, expressions causing surprise in the attacker, warning or protective colouring. All serve to distract or deceive the attacker. Outstanding is the significance of warning signals which again may vary widely. Some animal species give warnings against some unspecified dangers (for example the barking of dogs), but many species produce signals in connection with very specific kinds of danger, for example the ground squirrel *Citellus beechei* produces a characteristically modulated whistle when it sees a snake, a different one when it spots a carnivorous animal and yet another one if the danger comes from a bird of prey.

Through the linking of the various components of intra-specific and inter-specific communication within groups — herds, packs, flocks — typical forms of behaviour, which are of outstanding importance for all members of the group, have evolved. They consolidate the cohesiveness of the group, family or pair, help to establish a pair, and identify the rank of each member within the group etc. Such gestures are, for example, greeting, expressions of subordination and superiority, cleaning of the fur, and so on.

Gestures of social communication often ensue from some activities of everyday life, for example the cleaning of fur, scratching, licking, stretching of limbs. These are in fact linked with hygiene and body comfort and are aptly called comfort gestures. The animal performs them only when in good humour, when feeling safe and when in good physical form. Comfort gestures are phylogenetically very old. They have become ritualized and form part of the ceremonials, which are outstandingly important in the life of animals. One of the commonly practiced ceremonies is greeting, as seen, for example, in birds. The Galapagos cormorant *Nannopterum harrisi,* which cannot fly, takes turns on the nest with its partner. The relieving bird must first find a tuft of algae or a starfish before it approaches the nest. The sitting partner accepts the present, places it on the ground and only then walks off. The black-crowned night heron (*Nycticorax nycticorax)* must first bow in a certain way otherwise the young and the female will not let him into the nest. Storks, when greeting, clap their bills. All these gestures show precisely that the newcomer has good intentions, and subdue the possible agression between the partners. The duels of males at mating time, the courting itself, soothing etc. are usually of a ritualistic nature. Rites are performed by every species according to a strict set of rules which are accurately observed by the animals. Rituals are also regularly used by man in non-verbal communication.

# Animal Habitats

When referring to the habitat or home of an animal we are inclined to imagine an excavated hole or a nest. But the concept of habitat is much broader, for it includes the whole area within which the animal lives as well as its hiding-place.

Hiding places are certain permanent refuges where animals regularly seek shelter. They may take various forms, depending on which animal builds them and the purpose it is to serve.

Many animals, for instance fishes, frogs and most reptiles, do not build shelters. Other species, such as ungulates, use their knowledge of the terrain and seek suitable sites which are protected mainly against wind. They do not of course improve such natural shelters but, by their presence, they often change them. Apes have no permanently built hiding-places but build a new nest every day, usually at a different place.

In contrast with these animals are those which build permanent shelters. They build them underground, on the ground, on the water surface, amidst tree branches and in cavities, etc. The constructions vary in complexity. Imposing underground labyrinths of passages and caves, in which the animals rest and store food, are excavated by moles, mole rats, marmots; impressive constructions on the water surface with sophisticated interiors are built by beavers; cleverly knit nests suspended from tree branches are made by penduline tits, while plovers use only a shallow depression in the ground.

Some animals have only one shelter while others may have several. Every shelter has a definite place in the territory inhabited by the animal. Each individual, pair or group of animals is relatively restricted in space. They move in an exactly delimited area, the boundaries of which, under normal conditions, they do not cross. This territorial unit, known as the home range, includes a still smaller space, the territory.

The territory is an area with which the animal or group of animals is perfectly familiar. It knows its way about, knows where to find the best food, and knows where water and shelters are to be found. It marks and defends the territory against other members of its species. Within the territorial range it produces and brings up its young, eats, rests and mates. The size of the territory depends not only on the size of the animal but also on its food requirements since the main purpose of establishing the territory is to ensure sufficient food for its inhabitants. For example, large herbivorous mammals must occupy a territory which will provide enough food and at the same time will allow enough time for the vegetation to regenerate after being grazed. Carnivorous animals must have a territory of such a size that the stock of prey is not significantly reduced through hunting. Perhaps the largest territory is occupied by the Siberian tiger — up to 1,000 square kilometres. The size of the territory is not always constant, even for individuals of the same species. It depends, among other things, on the topography and capacity to provide food, on the number of competitors for food and on the season of the year. Females and young males usually occupy smaller territories than old males. Some parts of the territory are preferred by its inhabitants, while others are used only occasionally.

For the animals, obtaining and maintaining a territory is a question of life and death, therefore they mark out the boundaries very carefully and fiercely defend them against intruders. The boundaries are usually recognized by other animals. If they trespass they try to avoid getting into conflict with the owner, who attacks them immediately. If the meeting cannot be avoided the intruder leaves the area without fighting or after no more than a symbolic brawl. The most violent fights take place when a new territory is fought for. The merciless defence of the territory is not without purpose since it leads to a balanced distribution of pairs over the region. The accumulation of a larger number of members of the same species on a small area would result in mutual competition for food and the animals would be unable to sustain their young or themselves. The use of territories is mainly a feature of vertebrates: fishes (perhaps even sharks), amphibians, birds and mammals. The existence of home ranges, however, has been observed even among some groups of insects and crustaceans, for example crabs, but we do not deal with those in this chapter.

Many animals occupy a territory all the year round, while some species do so only occasionally, for example, during the breeding season. Some species such as the great tit create winter territories which serve to protect their food resources. Some species do not live within the borders of a territory but lead a nomadic life.

The internal structure of the territories corresponds with the way of life of the different animal species. There is one point, however, in which all the territories are alike: they all have a place where the animal drinks, where it eats and feels safe (that is, a shelter), places where it cleans itself and spots where it marks the territorial boundaries. These places are connected by a network of paths which the animals use when going for food, for escape and for moving around the territory. This, though, does not mean that the animals walk only along these paths. When hunting or grazing they move away from them.

The places within the territory to which the activities of each individual are linked are most varied. For example the place where the animal attends to its toilet habits may be a muddy puddle in which reindeer or pigs may wallow, or a termite mound used by zebras to scratch against, or just a depression filled with warmed dust in which pheasants dust themselves. Some animal species always eat in the same place; for example, water voles and muskrats typically build small food platforms in reeds, while birds of prey tear their captures on favoured plucking posts. Some species, for example carnivores, hyraxes, rhinoceroses and hares, defaecate only in specially selected places.

For a territory to be recognized by the other members of the same species it must be distinctively marked. The ways of marking involve the use of visual, acoustic and olfactory signals. Combinations of these give various signs which specifically inform the other animals that the space is occupied.

A large number of species mark their home range by using their voice. A classic example is the singing of birds. The birds usually sit in an elevated position inside the territory and by singing they convey the message that the territory is occupied. Besides birds, for which sound signals are typical, there are also some mammals which use their voice for marking, for example reindeer and monkeys. The males of orangutans, gibbons, and howler monkeys possess special resonators so that their voice can be clearly heard in the jungle.

Another way of marking out the territorial boundaries is with visual signs. In this case the animals usually show off vividly coloured or unusually formed parts of their body. Anoles alternately bend the tongue and stretch out and relax the vividly coloured throat; males of cercopithecine monkeys show their conspicuously coloured sexual organs or thighs. Some animals do the marking with the whole body, for example coralfish with their patterned body and colobus monkeys with the white hairs on the black background of their fur.

The male blackbuck (*Antilope cervicapra*) marks the borders of his territory by spreading the secretion of the sub-orbital olfactory glands onto twigs.

While the visual and acoustic markings are often apparent only for a limited time, chemical markings are more permanent. Olfactory signals are employed mainly by mammals, in which the sense of smell is developed best of all. For marking purposes they have developed special glands which produce a powerfully smelling secretion. The glands may be situated in different places on the body of different species. For instance, deer have their scent glands between the hooves and do the marking while they walk; some antelopes and reindeer have special glands below the eyes and spread their secretion onto twigs; chamois have their scent glands behind their horns, rabbits under the chin, badgers and martens under the base of their tail. The scent glands of hares are in the mouth on the inside of their cheeks; when a hare licks its paws the secretion adheres to them and from them it goes onto the ground.

Mammals which lack special scent glands use faeces and urine for marking. Canines and some members of the cat family mark important places on the border of their territories with small doses of strongly smelling urine, while prosimians catch their urine in their hands and spread it over the branches of trees. Rhinoceroses defaecating at the entrance to their territories always use the same place so that the faeces eventually build conspicuous mounds, marking the boundary. Similar boundary marks are built from the faeces of the house mouse. The hippopotamus and pygmy hippopotamus disperse their excreta on bushes, in a circle reaching several metres in diameter, by rotating their tails during defaecation and urination. Olfactory marking may also be used by aquatic mammals.

The boundaries of home ranges may overlap in some species. In this common (action) space the animals from neighbouring territories meet. Rhinoceroses, for example, graze or bathe together in the action space. At other times life in the action space is adjusted to the time schedule of the different animals. For instance several cats may hunt in the same range without having to meet each other, because each one visits any point in the range at a different time.

Many animal species lead a nomadic way of life and, for various reasons, often undertake long journeys. A number of birds species regularly migrate — they move to their winter sites to feed and return again to nest — but this is not so common among mammals. Among the mammals, reindeer, zebras, antelopes and cetaceans regularly migrate in search of food. Bats of the temperate climatic zone migrate to warm winter sites. In connection with reproduction long journeys are made by seals, some cetaceans, marine turtles and some fish species (salmon and eels). Migrations which are smaller in extent are usually undertaken by territorially living species in inclement weather, or when food conditions deteriorate; for example, mice and shrews may move into people's houses.

# The Social Life of Animals

Many animals live a solitary life and contact with others of the same species is limited to the time of reproduction. Such a union does not last long as a rule. However, a number of vertebrates do try to form longer lasting unions with others of the same species, and thus form a society. The societies need not be permanent, for example, chamois live together for only part of the year and then their herds disintegrate, forming maternal groups (comprising mothers with offspring) and herds of young males; old males usually lead a solitary life. Migratory birds, too, flock for only limited periods. Other communities are more permanent: herds of wild horses, antelopes, buffalo, bison, prides of lions, packs of dogs, hyenas and so on.

Several advantages result from the social way of life. The community gives its members a degree of safety against potential danger. It is not only the fact that more eyes see more, and that they can see the enemy more easily, but a moving mass of animals usually frustrates the offender even if it does not deter it altogether. Unless the attacker succeeds in separating an individual from the group he loses the chance of hunting it down. Forming groups can also be of value in obtaining food. Large groups of monkeys, for instance, are able to win and defend larger and more productive territories than could be held by smaller groups. Some animal species have developed hunting methods which depend on others participating. The classic example is the hunting pack of wolves. A remarkable relationship has developed among herds of zebras, gnus and Thomson's gazelles. Each species lives on a different variety of plants which grow together in the same region. The herds enter these regions in succession, first the zebras, followed by the gnus and finally the gazelles. It has been found that if the numbers of one species decrease, the numbers in the other two groups are also affected, usually aversely.

The formation of societies is important also for reproduction. It is easier for the partners to meet in a group and young are more efficiently protected against potential danger. In dolphins and elephants the herd provides protection for the females about to give birth. The females of some rodents even help each other during delivery. Living in a large group stimulates the start of reproduction and tunes the different pairs to the right reproductive condition much earlier than if they were living alone. This is very advantageous for animals living in the cold north or in deserts, where suitable climatic conditions last for only a short time.

A further advantage of living together is in the possibility of division of labour. With a pair it is quite simple, the parents either alternate in the duties or one is always the feeder while the other keeps guard. In groups this is more complex; for example, in group hunting each member has his well defined role. The division of labour among social insects is very complex. There the individuals are even morphologically distinguished into fertile females (queens) and males and females with undeveloped sex organs (workers and/or soldiers). Different workers again have different duties.

In societies of animals with better developed brains one learns from the other and the whole society benefits from the acquired knowledge.

Postures of superiority (left) and subordination (right) among dogs.

The most primitive form of society is the passively formed accumulation of individuals, for example, whirligig beetles (Gyrinidae) or aquatic larvae of various insects. These obviously do not form societies actively but are brought together by wind or the movement of water. Nevertheless, the members of even passively formed groups are better protected against danger.

Animals of the same species often live in unorganized communities the social structure of which is insignificant. They form an open social group the members of which do not know each other and are not bound to each other in any particular way. They may leave this union at any time and return to it again or join a different one. Such communities are found among fish, frogs and migratory birds.

For the group to be more than a mere assemblage of anonymous individuals it has to have an internal structure and the members must have exactly defined duties. This requires the formation of more or less organized groups. A simpler social formation is a closed anonymous group which is often created after an unusual multiplication of a smaller group. The brown rat and the black rat create large so-called families through rapid and repeated reproduction of the parental pair and their offspring. Their numbers can become so large that the individuals do not know each other "personally" and membership of the group is recognized only by the typical smell. This closed group may not be joined by any other individuals. If it happens that a member of this large family is forced to leave and returns after some time it is attacked as an intruder, having lost the typical smell of the group. Closed anonymous groups are also formed by social insects. These units are among the best organized units in existence.

The most advanced societies are based on the individual relationships of animals which know each other well. The smallest unit based on the individual cohabitation of animals well known to each other is the partnership of male and female. This union is permanent if the partners live together all their lives. Such a union is not based merely on the reproductive instinct, because the period of reproduction is usually limited to a certain part of the year. Other factors are involved such as various ceremonials which considerably strengthen the bonds. The permanent unions of mated pairs are very strong and loyal and they usually persist until the death of one of the partners. Many species of animals live in such unions, for example wild geese, pigeons, and ravens. Other species of animals such as perching birds or wild ducks live together throughout the breeding season and then they part.

More numerous societies based on individual contacts of one with the others are packs, herds, flocks or families. Within them each individual knows its own place and rank. The cohabitation of the different members of the family, herd or pack is based on a certain inborn social code according to which the rules of mutual behaviour are exactly defined. This discipline is important because all animals possess a certain degree of aggression, or offensive behaviour, but the amount of conflict is controlled by each animal knowing its position within the group.

The relationships based on rank are based on the recognition and acceptance of degrees of dominance between individuals. Some animals within the group possess greater initiative, they are stronger and more aggressive than the rest and fight among each other to establish dominance. The strongest and most experienced becomes the leader, to which all the other animals are subordinate. The leader of the herd guards, protects and leads it to food sources, chooses shelters for the night, mates with the females and maintains order. An experienced leader is very valuable to the group; all respect him and protect him at the same time. The other animals in the group form a kind of social ladder where each step consists of one of the members. Each member of the ladder is then dominant to all that stand below him and subordinate to all standing above him. This basic pattern has different variations in different species. Initially, the place in the social hierarchy must be won by each subject and then defended; only young off-spring are excluded from these rank-determining fights. Such confrontations take place not only among males but also among females and even among older offspring. The group may thus consist of several overlapping "sub-ladders". The male leader is superior to all the other males, who maintain a hierarchy of rank among each other and are superior to all the females and the young. Though the highest ranking female is subordinate to the males she is superior to all the other females and the young animals. The older young have a similar rank ladder.

The order in the hierarchy may constantly change. It varies according to victories and losses in the fights and is also related to the physiological condition of the animals. If the highest ranking red deer sheds its antlers it loses its leading position, for it may then be defeated by a weaker subordinate which still bears its antlers. Pregnant deer or females in heat among monkeys, for example, immediately rise in rank.

Every member of a group communicates its rank position to the others on meeting or when feeding or drinking together. Dominance and subordination are expressed by the animals using many different postures, movements, facial expressions etc. These expressions are characteristic of the species and the individuals strictly observe and obey them.

Expressions of subordination are an effective means of protecting the weaker individuals from the stronger members of the same species for it subdues their aggressiveness. Every animal of lower rank shows its subordination whenever it meets a more dominant individual. The simplest way of expressing subordination is the greeting ritual. This is used very frequently and strengthens good relations within the group. A subordinate individual may copy the behaviour of a young animal towards its mother and this reliably calms the potential attacker as the gesture is accepted as conciliatory. Positions of absolute subordination (when the animal reveals or puts forward the most vulnerable part of its body) can end fights without bloodshed. The defeated individual shows his subordination and may leave without being punished. Gestures of submission which are expressed in good time may even prevent clashes altogether.

The word fight is frequent in this chapter. Is fighting really such an important part in the life of animals? Aggressive behaviour, that is, threatening

Giraffe males (*Giraffa camelopardalis*) fighting

and fighting, is of outstanding importance in the life of an individual. It should be remembered that this is always fighting among members of the same species, and not the struggles which take place between hunter and prey. Aggressive behaviour is primarily important in choosing and defending a territory. It provides for sufficient living space for the individual or group, prevents the animals from overcrowding in a small territory and serves to disperse them regularly over the whole area of a suitable habitat. It is essential for the determination of rank within the group. Fighting for rank eliminates weaker animals and those with less experience and gives priority to strong and experienced ones. Fighting is important also in connection with reproduction, for the weaker individuals do not usually get the chance to mate.

The object of fights within a species is certainly not the destruction of the opponent but to chase him away. Indeed, to keep to this principle, fights are subject to certain rules which are observed by both rivals. One rule is that the animals do not use the weapons which they employ to defend themselves against enemies. For example male giraffes do not kick but push each other with their necks and use their small horns. The fight is in reality a kind of ritual or trial of strength which may be ended without any damage being inflicted on the weaker contestant. The opportunity of ending the fight by displaying submission also prevents dangerous wounds being inflicted or being killed, and instead allows the preservation of aggressive behaviour on a full scale for defending the territory and rank.

# Plates

# Hedgehog

*Erinaceus europaeus*

Hedgehogs are well-known and very popular mammals. Most interesting is their peculiar coat consisting of several thousands of tough prickly spines, which are in fact modified hair. This unusual body cover and the ability to curl up instantly into an invulnerable spiny ball provide the hedgehog with an ingenious protection against all enemies. It leaves its shelter after dusk in search for food, being easily identified on its hunting expeditions by its noisy stamping, accompanied by loud snuffling. It consumes large amounts of food, mainly insects, worms, molluscs and small vertebrates. Its diet also includes venomous snakes which exhaust themselves against the hedgehog's spines. It is not, however, completely immune from snake venom. Hedgehogs are also very fond of birds' eggs and young and therefore are not very welcome visitors to pheasantries. In spite of this, they are generally considered useful as they destroy large amounts of harmful insects. In most European countries hedgehogs are protected by law, but many of them die every year under the wheels of cars and many others are poisoned by various chemicals used in pest control. The hedgehog spends the winter sleeping in a burrow thickly lined with dry plant material. It leads a solitary life and confines its activities to a relatively small home range. It can be found over much of Europe and Asia; in Europe it occurs almost everywhere from the lowlands up to the tree line, with the exception of the northernmost parts and some islands. There are two distinct colour forms of hedgehog in Europe, a western brown-bellied form and an eastern white-bellied form.

Body length:
200—290 mm.
Tail length:
20—45 mm.
Weight:
700—1,200 g.
Litter:
3—10 young once or twice a year.
Life span:
8—10 years.

Strong skin muscles allow the hedgehog to curl up into a ball

The head of the Eastern white-bellied form.

# Common Shrew

*Sorex araneus*

Of all the European shrews, the common shrew is the most abundant. It can be found everywhere in regions with enough dampness and some undergrowth for it to hide in, from the lowlands high up into the mountains, and is most abundant in woods, shrub growths and meadows with dense, tall grass. It is a tiny, active animal with a pointed snout and a coat which is at first brownish but later turns blackish-brown. It feeds on insects, spiders, small molluscs and worms and can be met with during the day as well as at night, both in summer and in winter. It is a very voracious creature, consuming daily its own body weight of food, which it chews quickly with its 32 sharp teeth with brown-red tips. The reason for its voracity is quite simply explained: it needs lots of energy for its constant activity and, being a small animal, it has a relatively large surface area over which to lose body heat. Shrews only rarely dig their own burrows, usually making use of those of other small mammals, but sometimes they build nests of dry leaves in tree stumps or between roots, under stones or in long grass. The female gives birth to the young from April to September. They are born blind and hairless but grow very quickly, attaining their parents' size and appearance within some three weeks. The common shrew inhabits all of Europe, with the exception of Ireland and the northernmost regions. In Asia it is widespread north of the steppe belt as far as Japan. In America, members of the genus *Sorex* are widespread, and are generally called long-tailed shrews. In some years their numbers increase considerably.

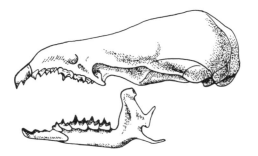

Body length:
65—85 mm.
Tail length:
32—47 mm.
Weight:
5—13 g.
Litter:
5—7(10) young, three or four times a year.
Life span:
approx. 16—18 months.

# Pygmy Shrew
*Sorex minutus*

## *Sorex minutissimus*

The pygmy shrew is one of the smallest mammals in the world. It differs from its closest relatives, particularly the common shrew, by its smaller dimensions, by its brownish coat which does not change colour in adult animals, but mainly by its relatively long, bushier tail which seems slightly depressed at the base. Its habitats are similar to those of the common shrew, but it is found in even denser vegetation. In spite of its small size, it seems to be more resistant to cold and dampness than the common shrew and can therefore be found even on moorlands at higher altitudes. The habitats of these two related species often overlap without any apparent enmity between the animals, and if they meet they never attack one another. The pygmy shrew is one of the most widespread and abundant mammals in Europe, even though it is five to ten times less abundant than the common shrew. Like all other shrews, it is very vulnerable to starvation and will die quickly if its food supply runs out. For this reason it is very difficult to keep in a terrarium. Very little is known about its way of life, but it seems to differ only very slightly from that of its relatives. Its area of distribution is roughly the same as that of the common shrew, except that it has penetrated to Ireland and some northern European islands. In southern Europe, however, its occurrence is limited almost exclusively to hilly and mountainous regions. In the damp coniferous forests of Finland and in the north of USSR, one may come across its close relative, *Sorex minutissimus* which is even smaller.

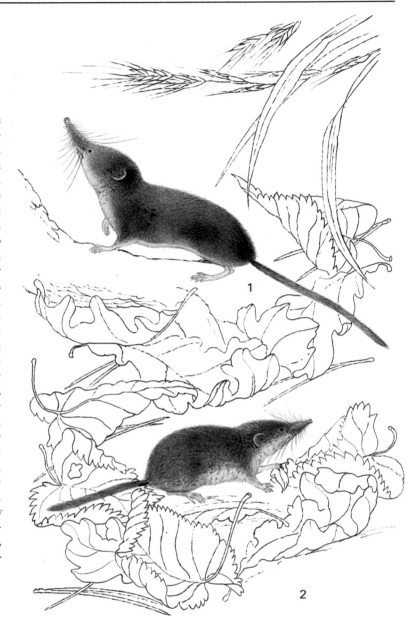

1 — *Sorex minutus*:
Body length:
45—60 mm.
Tail length:
32—46 mm.
Weight:
3—5 g.
Litter:
5—8 young once or twice a year.
Life span:
16—18 months.

2 — *Sorex minutissimus*:
Body length:
39—53 mm.
Tail length:
23—29 mm.
Weight:
2—4g.

a

b

Hairs on the tail of shrews:
(a) *Sorex*
(b) *Crocidura genera*

# Alpine Shrew
*Sorex alpinus*

This shrew is only found in the mountainous regions of central and southern Europe, from the Pyrenees as far as the Carpathians and the Balkans. In the past, however, it was quite abundant throughout the whole of Europe, including lowland areas. It occurs most frequently in the dense weed growths near mountain streams, on mountain meadows and in scree fields, where it always seeks the dampest and most shaded spots. Along streams and torrents, it descends in certain places even to the foothills, down to altitudes of 300—400 metres, but it is most at home between the altitudes of 700—2,000 metres. The Alpine shrew can be very easily identified: its coat is greyish-black and its tail is strikingly long and white on the underside. It is, however, sometimes mistaken for the water shrew, from which it differs only in its hairless, light paws, which are flesh red in living animals. Its way of life is the least known of all the European shrews. It probably feeds mainly on mountain molluscs, but certainly also on other invertebrates. The breeding season is from April to mid-September. As in all other shrews, the young of the Alpine shrew grow very quickly and are probably sexually mature in the first year of their life.

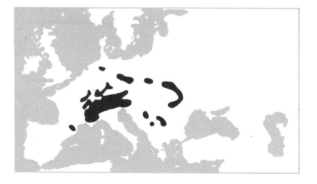

Body length:
62—77 mm.
Tail length:
54—75 mm.
Weight:
6—10 g.
Litter:
5—7 young twice to three times a year.
Life span:
16—18 months.

# Water Shrew

*Neomys fodiens*

Of all the European shrews, only the water shrew is a good swimmer. It is also a skilled diver and can even run underwater. Surprisingly, its anatomy is only slightly adapted for this unusual way of life: the coat is thick and waterproof, the wide hind paws are bordered with a rim of lengthened tough bristles which act like a web, and the underside of its tail is equipped with a keel-like ridge of stiff hairs. It is a marvellous experience to watch this animal hunting in water. It is active both day and night and, when diving, it resembles a moving silver ball, the silver sheen being due to the reflection of light on the air bubbles which remain attached to its fur. It moves swiftly on the water surface as well, with its snout projecting upwards, and it can run without difficulty on the river bed. It is equally agile out of water, on dry land. The greater part of the water shrew's diet (mainly aquatic insects and their larvae, freshwater shrimps, aquatic molluscs and fish fry) is found in the water. Sometimes it does considerable damage to fish fry, and is therefore not very popular with fishermen. It is particularly fond of streams with densely overgrown banks, which provide ample hiding places among roots and stones, and sometimes inhabits the overgrown parts of still waters. Its range comprises the forest belt of Asia as far as the Far East and the whole of Europe, except Ireland and the Mediterranean region. Its relative, the Mediterranean water shrew *(Neomys anomalus),* which is not so closely associated with water, also occurs in Europe.

Body length:
70—96 mm.
Tail length:
47—77 mm.
Weight:
10—20 g.
Litter:
3—18(11) young two to four times a year.
Life span:
about 1—2 years.

# Lesser White-toothed Shrew or Scilly Shrew

*Crocidura suaveolens*

Unlike the other European and American shrews, white-toothed shrews have completely white teeth, without the characteristic red tips. Their tails are also different — besides the normal hairy cover, they are thinly interspersed with long hairs. White-toothed shrews were originally inhabitants of grasslands, and consequently they are found in dryer places than other shrews. In central Europe they now inhabit mostly open spaces. During the winter they usually move into haystacks, stony walls and even houses. Due to their great adaptability and resilience, they have even penetrated forest and high-mountain regions. The most abundant in central Europe is the lesser white-toothed shrew, which can be readily identified by its smaller size and by the gradual transition of the greyish coloration of its sides into a lighter shade on the underside. It is more abundant in the warmer European regions as far north as central Germany and central France, also occurring in Asia and north Africa. In Britain, it is found only on Scilly and Jersey. The female leads her half-grown young in Indian file: the young walk in line one behind the other after their mother, each holding with its teeth the hairs at the base of the tail of the preceding animal. Europe is also the home of the common European white-toothed shrew *(Crocidura russula),* which is larger and darker in colour, and the bicolour white-toothed shrew *(Crocidura leucodon),* whose grey-coloured sides are distinctly separated from the nearly white belly. Neither of these species is found in Britain, but the common white-toothed shrew occurs on Guernsey.

Body length:
53—83 mm.
Tail length:
25—44 mm.
Weight:
3—7 g.
Litter:
2—6 young twice to four times a year.
Life span:
1—2 years.

1 — *Crocidura suaveolens*
2 — *Crocidura leucodon*
3 — *Crocidura russula*

# Mole

*Talpa europaea*

The mole is excellently adapted for its underground existence. It has a cylindrical body covered with a short, thick coat and powerful spade-shaped forelimbs with back-turned palms. There are no external ears, but the openings are protected by a narrow ridge of skin. The eyes are small and are sometimes completely covered with soft skin. The mole spends nearly all its life in its complex network of underground burrows and passages, only rarely emerging to the surface. Although classed with the insectivores, its diet consists not only of insects and their larvae, but also of earthworms and sometimes even small vertebrates, particularly frogs. It gathers its food during the continual expeditions along its underground passageways, where it sometimes makes 'stores' of earthworms, first paralysing them by biting into the head end. The importance and usefulness of the mole is still a subject of dispute. It kills large numbers of harmful insects but at the same time it is itself harmful as it kills earthworms and undermines plant roots, not forgetting the unwelcome mole-hills it leaves in meadows and gardens. It can be found both in the lowlands and high up in the mountains, usually in meadows, pastures, and also in deciduous forests. It is widespread throughout Europe, with the exception of the northernmost parts, extending eastwards as far as the Urals. Several similar species occur in eastern Asia and in the Mediterranean region, and their relatives are also found in North America. The most peculiar among them is the star-nosed mole *(Condylura cristata)*, which has a rosette of 22 hairless fleshy outgrowths arranged round its nostrils.

Body length:
115—160 mm.
Tail length:
23—28 mm.
Weight:
65—120 g.
Litter:
4—5 young once a year.
Life span:
3—4 years.

Skeleton of the front leg

# Pyrenean Desman
*Galemys pyrenaicus*

The Pyrenean desman, an insectivorous relative of the mole, is well adapted for life in water. It has a glossy, close-packed waterproof coat, the toes of its large hind paws are connected by a short web and the long, sparsely haired tail is compressed from side to side so that it will serve as a kind of rudder. Worth noting is also its snout, which is extended into a long, hairless, mobile trunk, with which the animal can easily seek and examine its food. The musk gland, located at the base of the tail, produces an offensive-smelling secretion. It lives in the Pyrenees and in the mountains of northern Spain and Portugal, usually in areas around rapid-flowing, clean and well-aerated mountain streams or in marshy meadows at the altitudes of 300—1,200 metres above sea level. It digs burrows in soft banks and, like the water shrew, it gathers its food — mainly worms, molluscs, insects and small invertebrates — in the water. Its sexual activity starts as early as the end of winter, usually in January, and the young are born from March to July. In eastern Europe, particularly the Don and Volga river valleys, there is a larger relative, the Russian desman *(Desmana moschata),* which has been successfully introduced to some other regions of the USSR. The fur of this species is being commercially exploited. The present-day populations of these two species are no more than remnants of the great numbers of desmans which inhabited Europe in the not-so-distant past.

1 — *Galemys pyrenaicus:*
Body length:
110—135 mm.
Tail length:
130—155 mm.
Weight:
50—80 g.
Litter:
about 4 young once a year.
Life span:
2—3 years (?).

2 — *Desmana moschata:*
Body length:
200—300 mm.
Tail length:
185—200 mm.
Weight:
350—485 g.
Litter:
1—5 young once a year.
Life span:
2—3 years.

# Lesser Horseshoe Bat

*Rhinolophus hipposideros*

The lesser horseshoe bat is the commonest European representative of the family Rhinolophidae, which differ from common bats (Vespertilionidae) by the special membranous outgrowths on the snout, by the typical pointed shape of their ears, the lack of tragus, the relatively short tail membrane and also by certain slight peculiarities in the anatomy of the skull and in the formation of their teeth. All horseshoe bats are warmth-loving mammals and are most common of the warm regions of Africa and Asia. In the temperate zone, they are most abundant in the Mediterranean. The lesser horseshoe bat is widespread throughout nearly all of Europe and as far north as central England, western Ireland, central Germany, Poland and southern Russia. It is also found in north Africa and central Asia. It is not, however, equally abundant in all these regions, and particularly towards the northern boundary of its range it frequents only sheltered localities with enough underground hiding places for hibernation. Originally the lesser horseshoe bat was a cave-dweller; today it is found in lofts, in belfries and in old, abandoned houses. It sleeps throughout the winter in warm mining galleries, in caves and cellars. During hibernation it hangs itself head downwards from the ceiling, covering its whole body with its soft wing membranes, so that it looks like a suspended pear. It lives in large colonies both in winter and in summer. It leaves its hiding place to hunt only after dusk, and flies close to the ground catching small insects.

Body length:
37—43 mm.
Forearm length:
34—42 mm.
Wingspan:
190—225 mm.
Weight:
3.5—10 g.
Litter:
one young once a year.
Life span:
up to 18 years.

Membraneous processes on the nose of a horseshoe bat

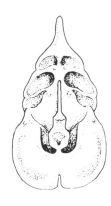

# Mouse-eared Bat or **Brown Bat**

*Myotis myotis*

The mouse-eared bat is one of the largest and also one of the commonest bats of Continental Europe. Like all other members of this genus, it has translucent membranous ears which are pointed at the ends. Its mouth is equipped with 38 small teeth. A warmth-loving, originally cave-dwelling species, it is most abundant in southern and central Europe, and, apart from a single colony, is completely absent in the British Isles and in Scandinavia. It occurs also in north Africa, in the Caucasus, Asia Minor and western Asia. Further east, in tropical Asia, the very similar lesser mouse-eared bat occurs, which is also widespread in southern Europe. In its central European habitats, the mouse-eared bat usually spends the summer hidden in the loft of an old house, where the females and their young form large colonies of 50 to 500 individuals. It hibernates in various caves, mining galleries and large cellars, either singly or in groups. It can cover relatively long distances (as much as 260 km) flying from its summer habitats to the wintering grounds. As a rule, it remains faithful for all its life to a single summer roost and a single winter roost. The hairless and blind young are born from the end of May to the beginning of June in the summer habitats. After a month, when they have reached the size of their parents, they are already able to fly independently. The mouse-eared bat starts hunting only after dusk, when it visits housing estates, parks, gardens, avenues of trees and the margins of woods. Its diet consists mostly of larger insects, particularly moths, and also large beetles.

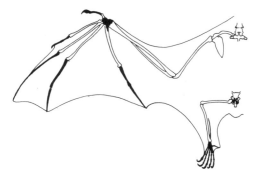

Body length:
60—80 mm.
Forearm length:
55—68 mm.
Wingspan:
350—430 mm.
Weight:
20—40 g.
Litter:
one young once a year.
Life span:
up to 15 years.

# Long-eared Bat
*Plecotus auritus*

# Barbastelle
*Barbastella barbastellus*

The long-eared bat, as its name suggests, has extremely long ears, in fact the longest of all European species. Surprisingly enough, it has only recently emerged that two very similar species exist in the Eurasian region. These two species are very difficult to distinguish from each other. The long-eared bat is the hardier species and is therefore also more common towards the north (as far as 63° N).

Both these species share the same habitats in Europe and Asia as far as China and Japan. In summer they live in colonies in lofts, birds' nestboxes and tree cavities. From October to the end of March they hibernate individually in caves, mining galleries and cellars, but also in various buildings, where they usually hide in crevices. When they are hibernating, their long ears are hidden under the flying membranes, so that only the narrow tragus is visible, like a miniature ear. They start hunting at dusk, flying slowly and skilfully round the crowns of trees.

The North American big-eared bats *(Plecotus rafinesquei* and *Plecotus macrotis)* are found over much of the United States and Mexico, and are similar in habits.

The barbastelle is a small bat with a short, slightly flattened snout. Its blackish-brown coat is a lighter shade on the back. It spends the summer in lofts or wall crevices and hibernates in galleries and caves, sometimes forming large colonies comprising hundreds of individuals. It is, however, rare in Britain.

1♂

2♂

1 — *Plecotus auritus:*
Body length:
42—51 mm.
Forearm length:
35—42 mm.
Wingspan:
220—265 mm.
Weight:
4—8 g.
Litter:
one young once a year.
Life span:
12—15 years.

2 — *Barbastella barbastellus:*
Body length:
40—52 mm.
Forearm length:
36—42 mm.
Wingspan:
250—280 mm.
Weight:
6—13 g.
Litter:
one young once a year.
Life span:
15 (max. 20) years.

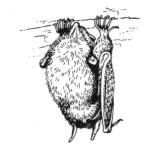

During hibernation the long-eared bat tucks its ears under its wings

♂

# Noctule Bat
*Nyctalus noctula*

# Pipistrelle or Common Bat
*Pipistrellus pipistrellus*

The noctule bat is a representative of the so-called tree bats, i. e. those which spend the summer period almost exclusively in the cavities of old trees. The noctule is moderately common over a wide area comprising Eurasia, except the northernmost parts, and north-western Africa. Its favoured habitats — deciduous and mixed forests, parks and avenues of trees are usually found in the lowlands and plateaux. During the summer, the females form colonies of some 20 to 60 individuals in tree cavities, whereas the males lead a solitary life. In winter, both males and females hibernate in large groups consisting of several hundreds or thousands of bats. Their most common hibernating sites are tree cavities. Noctule bats set about their hunting expeditions soon after sunset, at first hunting at a moderate height in a zig-zag flight and only later, with the growing darkness, descending closer to the earth.

The pipistrelle is the smallest European bat. Its range comprises nearly the whole of Europe as far north as 60° N, the greater part of Asia and north Africa, and it is very common in all these areas. During its autumm migration flight it often visits buildings in large numbers. In summer it hides behind window shutters, in wall and tree crevices and in birds' nest-boxes. It spends the winter hidden deep in the crevices of cave walls, in mining galleries, in cellars and often also behind the frames of pictures in old houses. It never starts hunting before dusk. Bats similar to the Eurasian pipistrelles occur over much of the United States.

The pipistrelle

Skull of the noctule bat

*Nyctalus noctula:*
Body length:
60—80 mm.
Forearm length:
47—56 mm.
Wingspan:
300—400 mm.
Weight:
15—40 g.
Litter:
2 young once a year.
Life span:
up to 8 years.

*Pipistrellus pipistrellus:*
Body length:
33—45 mm.
Forearm length:
27—34 mm.
Wingspan:
180—210 mm.
Weight:
3.5—8 g.
Litter:
2 young once a year.
Life span:
up to 8 years.

# Pine Marten
*Martes martes*

# Beech Marten
# or European Marten
*Martes foina*

Martens are some of the best-known representatives of the mustelid family, which are slender, short-legged, small beasts of prey. They are very cautious, wary animals which set out for their hunting expeditions only towards the evening or at dawn. Their excellent sight and hearing is well known. Both species are widespread over nearly the whole of temperate Eurasia, but only the pine marten occurs in Britain.

The pine marten, which is a strict tree-dweller, is an adept climber. It can even jump skilfully from tree to tree. It makes its nest in tree cavities and abandoned squirrels' nests. Trees are also its favourite hunting grounds, as it preys mainly on squirrels which it pursues along the branches. It also feeds on small rodents and birds, sometimes supplementing its diet with eggs and fruit. Its hunting grounds are marked out by secretions from the stink glands which are located at the base of its tail. The pine marten's reproduction is also of interest, particularly the so-called latent pregnancy.

The beech marten is mostly found in the vicinity of Man — sometimes even in large cities. It hides in rock and wall crevices, in lofts, etc., and usually hunts its prey on the ground. Its diet mostly consists of rats, but sometimes the beech marten takes poultry.

The American marten *(Martes americana)* and the fisher *(Martes pennanti)* of the northern American forests are similar in habits and appearance.

1 — *Martes martes:*
Body length:
480—530 mm.
Tail length:
230—280 mm.
Weight:
1.2—1.6 kg.
Litter:
3—5 young once a year.
Life span:
8—10 years.

2 — *Martes foina:*
Body length:
450—500 mm.
Tail length:
250—270 mm.
Weight:
1.7—2.1 kg.
Litter:
2—6 young once a year.
Life span:
up to 15 years.

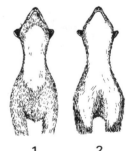

# Weasel
*Mustela nivalis*

# Stoat or Ermine
*Mustela erminea*

The weasel and the stoat, close relatives, are also, with their small, slender bodies, typical representatives of the family Mustelidae. They differ from each other in size and particularly in the colour of the tail tip, which in the stoat is always black both in summer and winter. Furthermore, stoats develop a white winter coat, whereas this only happens in weasels in the most northerly populations. The weasel, the smallest of all European mustelids, inhabits open country with fields and meadows, also forest margins and uncultivated shrubbery, and is moderately abundant in all these habitats. It feeds mainly on small rodents, which, thanks to its small dimensions, it is even able to pursue into their own burrows. Damage caused by the weasel to game is generally quite negligible. There are well-marked size differences between the sexes in both the weasel and the stoat, the females being noticeably smaller. In addition, however, there are also individuals which are so much smaller than the rest of the population that they were until recently regarded as a different species. The weasel's range of occurrence includes the whole of Europe except Spain, Ireland, Corsica and Iceland. It also lives in north Africa and all the temperate belt of Asia as far as Japan. The stoat's European area of distribution is limited in the south by the Pyrenees and the Alps, and it also occurs in Ireland and Greenland, the whole of Siberia and North America (where it is known as the short-tail weasel). The phenomenon of latent pregnancy has also been observed in the stoat.

The ermine or stoat in winter fur

1 — *Mustela nivalis:*
Body length:
130—240 mm.
Tail length:
50—70 mm.
Weight:
75—130 g.
Litter:
5—7 young once (twice) a year.
Life span:
approx. 1—2, max. 5—8 years.

2 — *Mustela erminea:*
Body length:
240—290 mm.
Tail length:
80—90 mm.
Weight:
150—260 g.
Litter:
4—9 young once a year.
Life span:
approx. 2, max. 7—10 years.

# European Polecat
*Putorius putorius*

# Asiatic Polecat
*Putorius eversmanni*

Polecats have a stink gland located below the base of their tails, the secretion from which they use both to mark out their territory and also to scare off potential enemies. The native European polecat occurs in lowland as well as mountain areas, and in various types of country — fields, shrubland, gardens and even built-up areas. Being a good swimmer and diver, it is particularly fond of water habitats, where it catches frogs and fishes. Its main diet, however, consists of small rodents, birds and their eggs, insects, worms and molluscs. It will also attack rabbits, muskrats and pheasants. It is particularly hated by farmers because of its raids on hen-houses. The polecat's hiding place is usually a well-sheltered corner in a barn or stable, or a pile of stones, and it will also construct its own underground burrow. It hunts mainly after dusk. Although rare in England, the polecat is common in parts of Wales and Scotland.

The Asiatic polecat's area of distribution reaches as far west as eastern Austria, Czechoslovakia and Poland. It inhabits steppes, pastures and fields, where it digs its own burrows. Its diet consists mainly of field rodents, but it also hunts reptiles, amphibians and birds. The ferret, which is used by trappers to drive wild rabbits out of their burrows, is probably a domesticated form of one of these polecats. The American black-footed ferret *(Mustela nigripes)*, though not closely related, is similar in many respects to these polecats.

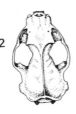

1 — *Putorius putorius:*
Body length:
400—440 mm.
Tail length:
130—190 mm.
Weight:
500 g — 1.5 kg.
Litter:
4—5 young once a year.
Life span:
5—6 years, in captivity up to 8—10 years.

2 — *Putorius eversmanni:*
Body length:
320—560 mm.
Tail length:
70—180 mm.
Weight:
500 g — 1.3 kg.
Litter:
3—7 young once a year.
Life span:
unknown.

Distribution of the European polecat

# Badger
## or **European Badger**

*Meles meles*

Although the badger also belongs to the mustelids, it is much larger than martens and polecats, has a stout body and is plantigrade, i. e. it treads on the whole of its sole when walking. Its coat is also characteristic, being greyish on the body and white on the head, with one wide black band running across the eye on either side. Its feet are equipped with strong claws which the animal uses adeptly when digging its complicated, deep underground passages. These lead into a set, which provides both a shelter for the day and a place for hibernation. The badger does not normally leave its set until it is completely dark and even then it is usually extremely cautious. Its winter sleep is not very deep, its body temperature does not drop and it wakes up several times during the winter, sometimes even leaving the set. Of all the mustelids, the badger shows the greatest tendency to omnivorousness. It feeds on small rodents, insects, earthworms, slugs, but also on carrion, birds' eggs, seeds, berries, plant roots and mushrooms. In spite of this, it has been quite unjustly persecuted and its sets destroyed. Today, however, it is legally protected in most countries. The badger is widespread over nearly the whole of Europe and the temperate part of Asia as far as China and Japan. It is particularly fond of country with scattered copses and can be found at any altitude from lowland to high-mountain elevations. The American badger, *Taxidea taxus,* is similar in many respects, but is generally found in treeless country, especially the prairies.

Body length:
700—850 mm.
Tail length:
110—180 mm.
Weight:
7.5—15 (20) kg.
Litter:
1—5 (usually 2) young once a year.
Life span:
up to 15 years.

# Otter or Common Otter

*Lutra lutra*

The otter differs considerably from the common mustelid type by its perfect adaptation to an amphibious way of life. It has a longish, agile body and a wide, flat-topped head with long tactile whiskers and short ears. The tail is long and strongly thickened at the base, and the toes are connected by a short web. The otter's coat, short and thick, is very much prized as fur. In the past it was quite abundant near waters throughout Europe, occurring also in north Africa and in Asia as far as Java and Sumatra, a similar species being found in North America. As a result of many years of severe persecution, when it was hunted both for its fur and as a threat to fisheries, it has completely disappeared from many areas and is very rare in others. It frequents both flowing and still waters, mostly in localities with inaccessible, overgrown banks in the upper reaches of rivers. Its present situation is uncertain, as otters are shy, wandering animals and change their habitats very quickly. In the water they move nearly as skilfully as fishes, which form, together with crayfish, frogs and dryland vertebrates, the main part of the otter's diet. Its holt, or den, is dug in high river banks, with the entrance often located under the water surface.

Body length:
650—800 mm.
Tail length:
350—500 mm.
Weight:
5.5—10 kg.
Litter:
2—4 young once a year.
Life span:
15—18 years.

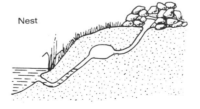

Nest

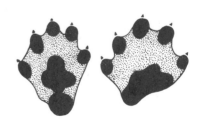

Imprint of the front (left) and hind (right) foot

# Wolverine or Glutton

*Gulo gulo*

The wolverine is a peculiar beast of prey with a robust body and a long-haired, dense coat, rather like a bear. It is the largest of all mustelids, attaining a weight of 20, sometimes even 30 kg. It inhabits the extensive taiga and tundra regions of Eurasia and North America, but its European distribution is today limited to Scandinavia, northern Finland and the north of the USSR; its American range comprises most of Canada. It is nowhere very abundant, and in many places and particularly in Europe it is threatened with extinction. Except during the breeding season, the wolverine leads a solitary life. The individual animals have permanent hunting grounds, which for some males may measure as much as 1,000 sq km. Wolverines hunt during the day as well as at night in these large areas. Their role in the natural food chain is quite a positive one, as they mostly feed on carrion and usually only attack weak or crippled animals. They are not, however, very popular with trappers, because of their habit of stealing game from traps and provisions from trappers' cabins. Generally, the wolverine's diet is very varied, consisting in summer of birds and their eggs, insects and insect larvae, small rodents (particularly lemmings), berries and oil-rich seeds, and in winter of larger mammals, ungulates, carrion and various chance titbits. Its method of hunting is mostly by trailing, but it will also often ambush its prey. It is also fond of stealing prey from other animals. The wolverine's mating season begins towards the end of summer and the young are born after a period of latent pregnancy at the end of winter or the first half of spring.

Body length:
700—830 mm.
Tail length:
160—250 mm.
Weight:
10—20 kg.
Litter:
2—4 (5) young once in two years.
Life span:
15—18 years.

# Brown Bear

*Ursus arctos*

The brown bear is a native inhabitant of the once-impenetrable forests of Europe, temperate Asia and North America. In this extensive area there are a number of subspecies which differ from each other in colour and size so considerably that they were formerly considered as completely separate species. Worth noting, for instance, is the large Siberian bear *(Ursus arctos beringianus)* and the North American grizzly bear *(Ursus arctos horribilis)* of Alaska and the Rockies. The largest of all brown bears is the Kodiak bear *(Ursus arctos middendorffi),* which inhabits Kodiak Island off the coast of Alaska. Originally, the brown bear was distributed throughout the whole of Europe, including the British Isles; today it occurs in significant numbers in Europe only in the Carpathians, Scandinavia and in the remnants of the original mountain forests of the Pyrenees, Italy and the Balkans. The diet of this large mammal is extremely varied: in spring and in the autumn it predominantly consumes vegetable food but it is also fond of carcasses, its favourite delicacy being honeycombs full of honey and young bees. It supplements this food with smaller vertebrates and insects. When the salmon migrate, brown bears descend to the rivers to fish. A few individuals specialize in hunting larger prey, particularly farm cattle and game. The brown bear spends the winter hidden in its den, but its sleep is not very deep one; it often wakes up and its body temperature does not drop. The female even gives birth and rears her young during the winter months.

Body length:
1700—2500 mm.
Tail length:
60—140 mm.
Weight:
70—350 kg.
Litter:
2—3 young once a year.
Life span:
30—35 years.

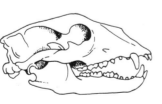

Comparison of the sizes of the Kodiak bear (behind) and brown bear (front)

The brown bear marks his territory by tearing bark off trees

# Wolf

*Canis lupus*

The wolf is the largest native canine beast of prey in Eurasia and North America. Like all other canine beasts of prey, it is a relentless runner and catches its prey by hunting it down. Its senses of smell and hearing are extremely well developed, but its vision is rather poor. Wolves remain in families or packs the whole year round. In winter, the packs are fairly large (10 to 15 individuals) and the animals hunt together. There are numerous exaggerated stories which describe the wolf as an extraordinarily astute, bloodthirsty and dangerous animal. However, it is not, and probably never has been, really dangerous to Man, usually preferring to avoid him in the wild. It is nevertheless a tireless hunter and is able to kill even the larger ungulates such as sheep and goats, and particularly domestic dogs. There are also known cases of wolves attacking a bear in its den and cannibalism has also been recorded among these animals. The largest part of the wolf's diet is formed by small rodents, birds, carcasses and various fruits. Originally, it inhabited the extensive area stretching from Europe as far east as India and Japan, and also North America down to Mexico, occurring mainly in tundras, forests and grasslands and along the margins of deserts. Today it occurs in reduced numbers only in the mountainous regions of Spain, Italy, Scandinavia and the Balkans. It is still moderately abundant in eastern Europe, particularly in Carpathians. In North America its range covers most of Canada and Alaska. According to the latest research, the wolf seems to be the sole ancestor of all modern breeds of domestic dog.

Body length:
1000—1600 mm.
Tail length:
350—500 mm.
Weight:
30—50 (75) kg.
Litter:
3—8 young once (twice) a year.
Life span:
15—16 years.

# Fox or Red Fox

*Vulpes vulpes*

Although the fox is quite popular with many people, it is heavily persecuted by hunters and gamekeepers and is killed by all possible methods. The fact that it is still relatively abundant in Europe serves to demonstrate its extraordinary hardiness, its cautiousness and a certain degree of intelligence. It is a very retiring animal which hunts mostly at night. During the day it usually remains hidden in dense thickets or in its burrow, which is built in dry out-of-the-way places, often in rocks, overgrown ravines or bushes. It mates in January or February, and the young are usually born in March or the end of April. They are reared in burrows, called earths, which are dug in the ground, accessible through several entrances and lined with soft hair. The earths are complicated structures, which are continually enlarged and repaired and may be used for several years. Foxes usually remain in the same hunting area all their life, and they are not very keen to make long expeditions. They live either singly or in permanent pairs. During their nocturnal hunting they capture small rodents, birds or larger invertebrates, and they will even attack a small hare, a young roe deer or some domestic animal. However, they probably eat a certain amount of vegetable food as well, particularly berries and fruit. Larger prey is taken into the burrow and stored for leaner days. The fox occurs, with a number of subspecies, over the whole of Europe, in North Africa, central and northern Asia and also in North America. The tundras of Eurasia and America are the home of the Arctic fox *(Alopex lagopus)*, which has very short ears and a white coat in winter.

2 – *Vulpes vulpes:*
Body length:
640–760 mm.
Tail length:
350–440 mm.
Weight:
5–8.5 kg.
Litter:
3–8 young once a year.
Life span:
10–12 years.

3 – *Alopex lagopus:*
Body length:
500–750mm.
Tail length:
250–420 mm.
Weight:
4.5–8 kg.
Litter:
2–10 young once a year.
Life span:
6–10 years.

1

2

3

The enormous ears of the fennec (1) help to dissipate excessive heat by radiation. In related species, living toward the polar regions, the ears and tails are reduced in size.

# Jackal

*Canis aureus*

The Asiatic jackal resembles a small wolf in appearance and is actually its close relative. However, its haunts are found in warmer regions than those of the wolf; it occurs in the area stretching from the Balkans and southern Russia across Asia Minor and Central Asia as far as India and east Africa. It mostly keeps to regions covered with dense shrubland, but it is equally abundant in marshy river lowlands and reed-beds. A relatively shy animal, it does not go hunting before dark. Its presence is usually revealed by its characteristic howling, which can be heard from a great distance. The jackal's diet is very varied; it captures small rodents, ground-nesting birds, insects and reptiles, and will not reject a carcass or the rubbish found in the vicinity of human habitation. When hunting in packs, it will sometimes tackle larger prey as well — game, sheep and goats. It is therefore not very welcome in place where it is abundant. Some valuable information about this animal has only recently come to light in studies of the east African form. It spends the day hidden in a burrow which it digs in the shelter of shrubs. Sometimes it will also make use of a natural rock crevice or even the abandoned den of another mammal. There the female gives birth to the hairless and blind young, usually at the end of March. Within some 3—4 months the young are already capable of an independent existence, and are sexually mature after the first year of their life. The North American coyote, though not too closely related, is similar to the jackal, although it is more widely distributed.

Body length:
850—1,050 mm.
Tail length:
200—240 mm.
Weight:
7—13 kg.
Litter:
4—6 young once a year.
Life span:
12—14 years.

# Raccoon-like Dog

*Nyctereutes procyonoides*

The raccoon-like dog is at home in the Amuro-Ussurian region, in eastern China and in Japan. Because of its economically valuable fur, it has been repeatedly introduced into the Caucasus, Ukraine and Byelorussia since the 1930s, and today it is an established member of the fauna of the western USSR. It has also spread into Scandinavia, Romania, Poland, Czechoslovakia and Germany, and is still colonizing new areas. The raccoon-like dog can hardly be considered a welcome addition to the European mammalian fauna, however; it destroys many small mammals and also large numbers of useful birds and game birds. It also feeds on amphibians, reptiles, various invertebrates and carrion. As yet very little is known about its way of life in its new home. It is a secretive animal hiding in damp forests, overgrown riverbanks and even in reedbeds, and it is active only after dusk and at night. It digs its own burrow or uses the deserted burrow of some other mammal. During the winter its activity is considerably reduced and it may even sometimes fall into a winter sleep, similar to that of the badger.

The raccoon-like dog may sometimes be mistaken for the raccoon *(Procyon lotor)* which, however, belongs to a completely different family of beasts of prey. It is slightly smaller than the raccoon-like dog and weighs about 5—6 kg. It comes from North America, where it can be found over Mexico and most of the USA. It has established itself in Europe by escaping from fur farms, and there are now resident colonies in some places, particularly in Hesse (German Federal Republic).

*Nyctereutes procyonoides:*
Body length:
400—600 mm.
Tail length:
150—250 mm.
Weight:
4—10 kg.
Litter:
5—7 young once a year.
Life span:
7—11 years.

*Procyon lotor:*
Body length:
400—600 mm.
Tail length:
Weight:
5—16 kg, usually 7—8 kg.
Litter:
2—8 young once a year.
Life span:
6—8 years.

The raccoon

# European Wild Cat

*Felis silvestris*

The European wild cat and the lynxes are the only two representatives of the cat family living in Europe. A number of geographical forms of the wild cat inhabit Eurasia and Africa. The European form is widespread from the Caucasus and Asia Minor across southern and central Europe to western Europe, and as far north as Scotland and the coasts of the North and Baltic Seas. In the course of the last century, however, it was completely wiped out from many parts of central Europe, and today it is only abundant in the Carpathians. Due to its recent status as a protected species, its numbers have increased to a certain extent and it has even penetrated some new areas. Like the lynx, the wild cat was originally a forest-dweller but today it prefers warmer, dry places or coppices in open country. It hunts in the evening and at night, capturing mainly small rodents, birds, reptiles and fish. Only exceptionally, when it is feeding its young, does it catch larger prey. Wild cats mate from February to March, and the kittens are born in May in tree cavities, rock crevices or the abandoned burrows of other mammals. Except when they are rearing the young, the adults lead a solitary life, hunting in an area as large as 2 sq km. The wild cat is sometimes mistaken for stray domestic cats, but it can be distinguished by its thick, bushy, crosswise-striped tail, the end of which looks as if it has been lopped off.

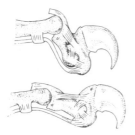

The mechanism for withdrawing cat claws

Body length:
790—970 mm.
Tail length:
290—350 mm.
Weight:
2.5—6.5 kg.
Litter:
2—6 young once or twice a year.
Life span:
10—15 years.

# Lynx or European Lynx

*Lynx lynx*

The lynx was originally widespread over the whole forest belt of Eurasia, from England and France to Siberia, Alaska and Canada. Its present limited distribution, particularly in Europe, is the result of human pressures, mainly the clearing of forests and large-scale hunting. It is only found today in significant numbers in certain parts of the USSR, the Carpathians, eastern Poland, Scandinavia and some areas of the Balkans. A smaller form, the pardellynx, is found in Spain. Even there, however, it remains well hidden and is seen very rarely. It mostly keeps to woodlands, particularly mountain forests and larger shrub growths. The lynx hunts in the evening and again at the dawn, usually resting during the day and at night. Its hunting methods are either to attack its prey by jumping at it from an ambush or to prowl after it, relying on its keen sense of hearing and perfect vision. It has to defend its relatively large hunting area, which may sometimes cover several square kilometres; only rarely does it undertake journeys farther afield. The lair is usually built on the ground surface in a tree cavity, rock fissure or under a fallen tree; sometimes it will occupy an abandoned burrow. Its diet consists mainly of small mammals, birds and hares, but it may also attack a weak roe or red deer and some individuals are bold enough to attack a wild boar. Damage caused to game is quite negligible, however, even in areas where the lynx is fairly common.

Body length:
900−1300 mm.
Tail length:
150−200 mm.
Weight:
13−38 kg.
Litter:
2−4 young once a year.
Life span:
15−17 years.

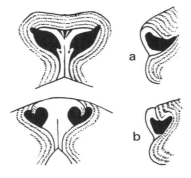
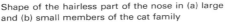

Shape of the hairless part of the nose in (a) large and (b) small members of the cat family

# The Barbary or **Gibraltar Ape**

*Macaca sylvanus*

Besides Man the barbary or Gibraltar ape is the only primate living in Europe. Its original habitat is North Africa, particularly the mountains of Algeria and Morocco. From there it spread to southern Spain and Gibraltar where its numbers are maintained through occasional imports of these animals from Africa. In 1969, in Vosges, France, a reserve, La Montagne des Singes was established, where barbary apes from the Atlas Mountains in Morocco were transferred and now live.

Barbary apes live in rocky places covered by low vegetation. They skilfully climb about on rocks. As the temperature in parts of their original home often fluctuates considerably, and sometimes even drops below freezing point, they can tolerate cold weather well.

Barbary apes are active in daytime. They live on fruit and seeds, roots and shoots of plants as well as larger insects and small vertebrates.

The apes live in groups comprising females with young of various ages. Each herd is headed by an old and experienced male to whom all other members of the herd are subordinate. The old males are very intolerant of each other and quarrelsome. Their behaviour forces the young males to leave their native herd and establish a new one.

The females are pregnant 145—180 days and the young are born hairy and with eyes open. Immediately after delivery they cling firmly to the fur of their mothers who carry them everywhere they go. They mature sexually at the age of three to four and a half years.

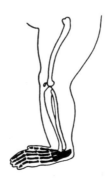

Body length:
600—710 mm.
Tail:
missing.
Weight:
5—10 kg.
Litter:
1 young a year.
Life span:
over 20 years.

# Red Squirrel
*Sciurus vulgaris*

# Grey Squirrel
*Sciurus carolinensis*

The red squirrel is a tree-dwelling rodent. When it is climbing a tree, it holds very fast to the bark with the help of its sharp claws. It can often be seen jumping from tree to tree or to the ground, moderating the fall by its widely spread limbs and by its long, bushy tail. Most of its time it spends moving swiftly along the branches of trees, in quest of its favourite food — the seeds of coniferous and deciduous trees. It will also eat various fruits and mushrooms, and complements its diet from time to time with insects or even birds' eggs and young. This occasional theft from a bird's nest, together with the bad habit of nibbling young spruce shoots, are the only sins of this beautiful, agile animal. Its spherical nest, called a drey and made of twigs and leaves, is built in trees. The red squirrel inhabits the woods and parks of Europe, with the exception of Iceland, the islands of the Mediterranean and the treeless regions of southern Ukraine. It is equally abundant throughout the forest belt of Asia up to Japan. The populations inhabiting this vast area differ considerably from each other in colour and size. In some places squirrels are hunted and killed in large numbers for their fur.

The grey squirrel is equally popular in North America. Its original home was in the eastern USA, but in the years between 1876 and 1930 it was introduced into England, where it has multiplied to such an extent that its numbers have to be severely reduced by shooting.

1 — *Sciurus vulgaris:*
Body length:
200—236 mm.
Tail length:
165—200 mm.
Weight:
250—400 g.
Litter:
3—8 young twice a year.
Life span:
8—10 (in captivity even 18) years.

2 — *Sciurus carolinensis:*
Body length:
240—300 mm.
Tail length:
200—250 mm.
Weight:
340—750 g.
Litter:
1—6 young twice a year.
Life span:
approx. 6, sometimes up to 12 years.

Typical traces of squirrel feeding activity

# Ground Squirrel
# or **European Souslik**
*Citellus citellus*

The souslik, although closely related to true squirrels, differs from them considerably. It lives in underground burrows and its body lacks all the typical squirrel features, such as the tufted ears and the long, bushy tail. Numerous related species inhabit the grasslands and lightly wooded regions of Eurasia and North America. The souslik is widespread from Asia Minor, southern Ukraine and the Balkans westwards to southern Poland and Czechoslovakia, and it is the only representative of this genus which penetrates from its eastern habitats as far west as central Europe. The sousliks' native home was the steppes and consequently they have colonized uncultivated land, dry pastures, etc., where they form large colonies in a fairly deep (up to 2 metres) and complex network of underground burrows. The animal can often be seen running swiftly around the entrances to the burrows or sitting up in a 'begging' position. If danger threatens, it utters a warning whistle and disappears instantly underground. It is active during the day and feeds mostly on various seeds and the green parts of plants. The souslik starts its winter sleep relatively early, towards the end of summer, and does not wake up before the end of March or even April. During this time it lives solely on the fat reserves under its skin. In some years sousliks may overmultiply to such an extent that they cause considerable damage to field crops. They have, however, quite a number of natural enemies, mostly small mustelids and various birds of prey which, together with Man, are able to control their numbers.

Body length:
195—220 mm.
Tail length:
60—70 mm.
Weight:
240—340 g.
Litter:
6—8 young once a year.
Life span:
4—5, max. 8—10 years.

# Alpine Marmot or Marmot

*Marmota marmota*

This very popular inhabitant of the European mountains is native only to the Alps, the High Tatras and the Pyrenees, but it has been introduced to other mountain regions, such as the Low Tatras and the Black Forest. In the Balkans, on the other hand, it has been completely exterminated. Related species inhabit the mountains of Central Asia and also Siberia and North America. A relative of squirrels, it resembles a large ground squirrel. Its colonies are usually situated on the grassy and stony slopes in the dwarf pine zone, at altitudes of 1,300—2,750 metres. It is active in the daytime, but is fairly cautious. When danger approaches, it emits the characteristic warning whistle and quickly hides in the dense underground system of its burrows and passages. These are sometimes as much as 10 metres long and may go down to a depth of some 3 metres. Only those individuals living near tourist chalets in the Alps seem to be bolder and not afraid of Man. Its worst enemy is the imperial eagle. Marmots live in very extreme climatic conditions, and it is therefore not surprising that their winter sleep lasts from end of September late into the spring — to the end of April or even to May. They hibernate in their burrows, which are thickly lined with dry grass and hidden deep under the snow cover, living only on the fat reserves stored under their skin. During the summer they feed on green vegetation near their burrows. The young are born towards the end of May or in June. They are blind and hairless at birth and are suckled for the first month of their life. The marmot is legally protected in all areas of its distribution.

Body length:
530—730 mm.
Tail length:
130—160 mm.
Weight:
5—6 kg.
Litter:
2—6 young once a year.
Life span:
15—18 years.

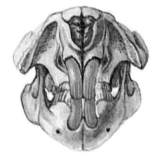

Skull with pigmented gnawing teeth

# Flying Squirrel or **European Flying Squirrel**

*Pteromys volans*

Flying squirrels belong to the same family of rodents as true squirrels, and they resemble them both in appearance and in their way of life. Their fore and hind limbs, however, are connected by a fold of skin covered with soft hair. When this is pulled taut between the limbs it makes it possible for the animal to lengthen its leaps in a kind of gliding flight to a distance of some 35 m. The flying squirrel inhabits the mixed and coniferous woods of northern Europe and the whole of Siberia as far as the Far East. It hides in rock crevices and tree cavities, often using abandoned woodpeckers' nests. It feeds on the buds and seeds of trees, birch leaves and bark and on mushrooms and berries. Although it does not hibernate, it often remains hidden in its nest on frosty days, living on the food stored during the warmer parts of the year. It leads a secluded life and Man is often not aware of its presence, even when it occurs very close to his dwellings. The flying squirrel is well-concealed by its shyness and its nocturnal way of life, as well as by its inconspicuous coloration, which enables it to merge with the bark of trees, particularly birch. Nowadays the flying squirrel has become fairly rare in many places, the main reason being that it needs mature forest for its existence and that it is very sensitive to Man's presence and to changes in the environment caused by his activities. Similar habitats in North America are the home of related species, the southern and northern flying squirrels *(Glaucomys volans* and *G. sabrinus).*

Body length:
135—205 mm.
Tail length:
90—140 mm.
Weight:
110—170 g.
Litter:
2—4 young once a year.
Life span:
6—8 years.

# European Beaver
*Castor fiber*

The beaver is the largest rodent of Europe and North America. It inhabits banks of still and slow-flowing waters with dense vegetation. It was once widely distributed; but today it is abundant only in a few areas of the USSR and Canada. In Europe, the last small populations live around the mouth of the river Rhône, in Scandinavia, the German Democratic Republic (about 400 animals), in Poland and the USSR. In the rest of Europe, the beaver has been exterminated by Man who hunted it for its valuable fur, tasty meat (in the Middle Ages it was regarded as a fasting meal) and for the anal scent gland to which a healing power was ascribed. Beavers are perfectly adapted to an amphibious mode of life and can swim and dive well. They have a thick, waterproof coat, closeable nostrils, broad, webbed hind feet and a strikingly broadened, flat tail covered with epidermal scales. With their strong, sharp rodent teeth, they gnaw round the whole circumference of small tree trunks and fell them. In this way they obtain food — leaves and bark — as well as building material for their lodges and dams. Beavers' lodges are huge structures built over the water and made of branches and turf, with a chamber in the centre. Sometimes they also dig burrows in banks, with underwater exits. Beavers are active at night and are very agile the whole year round. The North American form is sometimes classified as a separate species, *Castor canadensis*.

Body length:
800—1,000 mm.
Tail length:
300—350 mm.
Weight:
21—30 kg.
Litter:
2—4 young once a year.
Life span:
max. 17 years.

Female carrying an offspring in her front feet

A tree gnawed around its whole circumference falls at the force of even a slight wind

# British Dormouse or **Hazelmouse**

*Muscardinus avellanarius*

This species is the smallest of all European dormice. It is the size of a small house mouse but its large dark eyes and the long, thickly haired tail distinguish it as a separate species. The hazelmouse is distributed over the whole of Europe with the exception of Spain, the Mediterranean islands, Denmark and northern Scandinavia; it extends east as far as the Volga River and Asia Minor. It is the only dormouse that is native to England. It inhabits mainly deciduous woods but, being hardier than other dormice, it occurs everywhere from lowlands high up to the mountains and even in the dwarf pine belt. It is most abundant in forests with dense undergrowth and overgrown clearings. The hazelmouse builds a spherical nest 6—12 cm in diameter, made of leaves and moss and located in bushes near, or even on, the ground. It also often makes use of tree cavities and birds' nesting boxes. Its favourite place for hibernating is a den under a layer of leaves. It starts its winter sleep in September or October, having eaten its fill during the summer, and wakes in April or May. It feeds on buds and flowers, berries, seeds and insects. It can easily be kept in captivity for, unlike its relatives, it is not irritable and does not bite. Like all dormice, it is a nocturnal animal and spends the daytime sleeping in its burrow. It can climb well and is quite at home in the branches of trees.

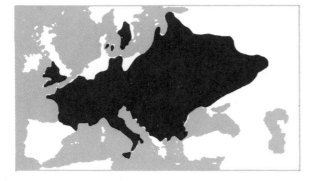

Body length:
75—86 mm.
Tail length:
55—77 mm.
Weight:
15—25 g, in autumn up to 40 g.
Litter:
3—4 young once (occasionally twice) a year.
Life span:
3—5 years.

# **Edible** or **Fat Dormouse**

*Glis glis*

The edible dormouse is the best-known Continental representative of the dormouse family whose distribution is limited to Europe, Africa and Asia. It resembles a small grey-coloured squirrel with its long, bushy tail and ability of climbing trees. The edible dormouse, with its large, dark eyes, leads a secretive, nocturnal life. Like all other members of the dormouse family, the edible dormouse once inhabited open, warm deciduous woods. Now it can also be found in gardens, orchards and overgrown parks. Its area of distribution ranges from Spain across southern and central Europe to the Caucasus, Asia Minor and Northern Iran. It has been successfully introduced into England. The edible dormouse is the most abundant of all European dormice and its way of life has been studied relatively thoroughly. It builds a nest, made of leaves and twigs, in the forks of branches, sometimes several metres above the ground; it also hides in tree cavities, rock crevices and even in attics of houses. When winter approaches, the edible dormouse looks for a protected shelter, usually in the roots or trees, in walls and rock fissures, where it spends up to 7 months (October—May) hibernating. It feeds on seeds, fruits, buds, leaves and insects, and occasionally even on young birds and birds' eggs. Being rather ill-natured, it is not easily bred in captivity. Like all dormice, it is legally protected.

Body length:
130—180 mm.
Tail length:
100—150 mm.
Weight:
70—120 g.
Litter:
4—7 young once a year.
Life span:
approx. 3, max. 8—9 years.

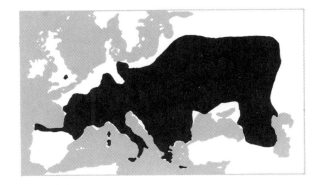

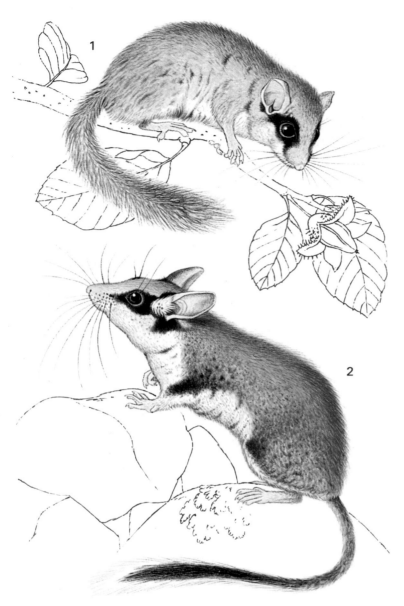

# Forest Dormouse
*Dryomys nitedula*

# Garden Dormouse
*Eliomys quercinus*

These two species of European dormice are less common and less well-known than the preceding species. They are both more brightly coloured, and the conspicuous colouring of their faces and tails makes them two of the most attractive mammals. The garden dormouse is larger in size and has a bicoloured tail, broadened at the tip. Being a warmth-loving animal, it is most abundant on the European as well as African Mediterranean coasts, whence it extends as far as central Asia. Its distribution in central Europe is only local, to the north up to the Baltic coast and central Finland, to the east as far as the Urals. In the south it inhabits thickets, and in central Europe it occurs in both deciduous and coniferous woods, parks, vineyards and near human habitation. Its way of life does not differ very much from that of related species, except that it spends more time on the ground and eats more insects.

The smaller forest dormouse's area of distribution extends from the mountains of central Asia and Caucasus across central Russia, the Carpathian region and the Balkans to Italy and through a narrow belt to the Swiss Alps. In central Europe it is most often found in deciduous and mixed woods, and in the south it also occurs in the Alpine mountain belt. Its nest is built of leaves and located in trees fairly high above the ground, and it also makes use of natural hollows and birds' nesting boxes.

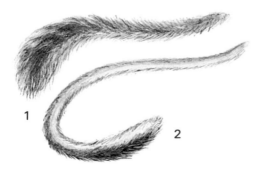

1 — *Dryomys nitedula*:
Body length:
80—115 mm.
Tail length:
70—100 mm.
Weight:
23—41 g.
Litter:
2—6 young once or twice a year.
Life span:
approx. 2, max. 6 years.

2 — *Eliomys quercinus*:
Body length:
105—147 mm.
Tail length:
80—135 mm.
Weight:
60—140 g.
Litter:
2—8 young (average 4) once, occasionally twice a year.
Life span:
up to 8 years.

# Common Hamster

*Cricetus cricetus*

The common hamster, a medium-sized, brightly coloured rodent, is native to the steppes of eastern Europe and western Asia. The extension of cultivated grassland brought it farther west, so that today it makes its home in the whole of central Europe as far as Belgium. However, its abundance fluctuates from one area to another. It occurs only in lowlands and hills up to about 500—600 metres above sea level, in places where there is a fairly deep layer of rich soil. It lives mostly in fields, on pastures and in scrubland. It digs a relatively complex and deep network of underground passages, with a nesting chamber and several storerooms and exits. For the winter, the storeroom is filled with up to 15 kg of food which consists of grain, potatoes and sugar beet, which the hamster carries in its facial pouches. These stocks serve to feed the animal during its interrupted winter sleep. In summer it feeds on crops and weeds, as well as invertebrates and small vertebrates. It is active mainly at dusk and at night but, when the population is particularly abundant, often during the whole day. The hamster is an irritable animal, when in danger it adopts an imposing posture on its hind legs, and defends itself by snapping its teeth, snuffling and biting. Hamsters live in their burrows, usually solitarily, but the female stays with the young for a certain time. They are very prolific animals; in times of overpopulation they may even become a dangerous pest to crops. The related golden hamster (*Mesocricetus auratus*), originally of western Asia, is often kept in laboratories and as a pet.

Body length:
200—340 mm.
Tail length:
25—65 mm.
Weight:
250—600 g.
Litter:
4—12 young twice or three times a year.
Life span:
6, in captivity up to 10 years.

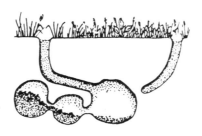

A sectioned burrow of the common hamster

The golden hamster

# Norwegian
## or **Norway Lemming**
*Lemmus lemmus*

# Wood Lemming
*Myopus schisticolor*

Lemmings, which are related to voles, inhabit the northern regions — Scandinavia, Siberia and North America. They are well known for their periods of overpopulation which occur at almost regular intervals. During these periods, lemmings throw themselves *en masse* into streams and sea bays where they die. This extraordinary behaviour, however, applies only to some species. In appearance, the wood lemming greatly resembles a vole. It lives in the woods and peat bogs of northern Scandinavia and northern Russia; in Siberia it inhabits the taiga belt as far as Mongolia and the Far East. Its network of burrows spreads under a layer of soil or moss not far below the surface of the ground. It is not as prone as its relatives to overpopulation.

The larger and more brightly coloured Norwegian lemming inhabits the mountains and tundras of Scandinavia and the Kola Peninsula. It is a very agile and fearless animal with an immense reproductive capacity. The periods of overpopulation come at intervals of 3—4 years. During these periods, the scarcity of food causes long migrations which always end in the almost complete extermination of the over-multiplied population. In the north, lemmings form an important part of the diet of beasts of prey, mainly wolverines and foxes, and owls and other birds of prey. Several related species, the best known of which is the brown lemming *(Lemmus trimucronatus),* live in Alaska, Canada and northern parts of the USA.

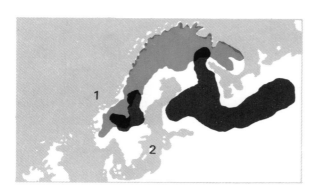

1 — *Lemmus lemmus:*
Body length:
130—150 mm.
Tail length:
15—19 mm.
Weight:
40—112 g.
Litter:
4—10 young three times a year.
Life span:
1.5—2 (3) years.

2 — *Myopus schisticolor:*
Body length:
85—95 mm.
Tail length:
15—19 mm.
Weight:
20—32 g.
Litter:
3—7 young twice a year.
Life span:
1.5—2 (occasionally 3) years.

# Water Vole

*Arvicola terrestris*

The water vole lives chiefly near water — brooks, rivers, ponds, lakes, pools and marshes — but it is often also found in fields, meadows and gardens. The immense area of its distribution embraces the northern parts of Eurasia from the tundra to the forest-steppe belt, from western Europe to central Siberia, covering lowlands as well as high mountains. It is found in various forms over almost all of Europe, being absent only in Ireland, the peninsula of Italy and in the southern Balkans. The form found in parts of France and in the Iberian peninsula is sometimes recognized as a separate species, *Arvicola sapidus*. Although the water vole's body shows no special adaptation to life in water, it swims and dives with great skill. It digs a network of burrows and a nesting chamber in banks, not far below the ground surface. Occasionally, especially near still water, it builds its nest in a tuft of sedges or other aquatic vegetation. Like all voles, it is active both during the daytime and at night. In favourable conditions it can overmultiply considerably. Its staple diet consists of the green parts of plants, supplemented by roots in winter. It is a serious pest of young fruit trees, gnawing their roots so that they wither. It is difficult to protect the trees against this harmful rodent because it pursues its underground activity unnoticed. It is often captured in mole traps.

Body length:
120—211 mm.
Tail length:
60—130 mm.
Weight:
80—200 g.
Litter:
4—5 young three to five times a year.
Life span:
2—4 years.

# Muskrat

*Ondatra zibethicus*

The muskrat is a native of North America, where there are a number of forms from Alaska to Louisiana. Its occurrence in Europe dates from 1905 when it was introduced into central Bohemia, whence it spread in a short time over the whole of central Europe. Later the muskrat was also brought to western Europe, Scandinavia and the USSR. Today it is one of the most familiar and well-adapted mammals of this area. The muskrat, and especially its nests, can be found near still as well as running water. At the time of its initial spread, it was regarded as a pest because it dug in ponds and dykes, and also because it was erroneously believed to catch fish, but nowadays it is highly prized for its valuable fur. Today we know that the muskrat is essentially herbivorous; it eats various parts of aquatic plants and sometimes also aquatic crops, now and then adding to its diet mussels, crayfish and only occasionally some fish (in most cases dead ones). Its lair can be of two types: either it digs burrows with underwater entrances in river banks, or it builds lodges, large structures made of the roots and stems of aquatic plants, situated in reedbeds. Muskrats swim and dive well, using their large hind feet and long, laterally flattened, almost bare tail.

Hind foot

Body length:
300—400 mm.
Tail length:
190—250 mm.
Weight:
800—1,600 g.
Litter:
7—8 young three to four times a year.
Life span:
3—5 years.

# Common Vole
# or Continental Field Vole
*Microtus arvalis*

# Short-tailed Vole
# or Field Vole
*Microtus agrestis*

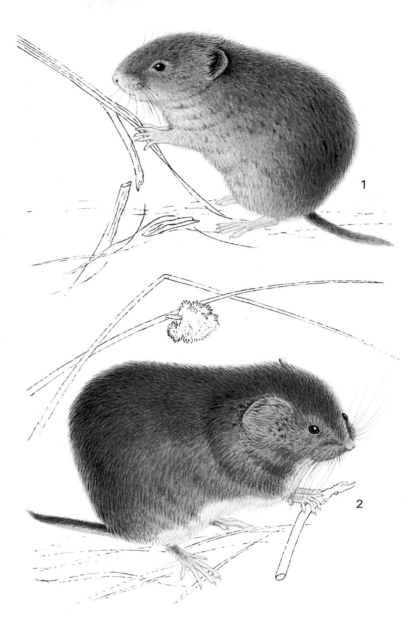

The Continental field vole is mostly found in culti-vated grasslands. It apparently reached Europe with the development of agriculture and, thanks to its adaptability, colonized all suitable habitats from the lowlands up to the mountains. In years of overpopu-lation, it spreads along paths and railroads to closed forest areas and persists even in wet places and in some alpine meadows. Today it lives over the whole of Europe, except the British Isles, Scandinavia and part of the Mediterranean, but including Orkney and Guernsey. In favourable conditions, it rapidly in-creases in numbers, causing enormous damage in fields. It digs its burrows just below the surface of the ground, so that in years of overpopulation the fields, meadows and field boundaries are literally riddled with millions of passages and covered with a thick network of paths. Like all other voles, the Continen-tal field vole mainly eats the green parts of plants, a small amount of seeds and only occasionally insects. It is active during the daytime as well as at night.

The similar short-tailed vole inhabits wetter and cooler habitats, such as the edges of water, damp meadows, marshes, peat bogs, the margins of moun-tain streams and forests with undergrowth. It is therefore more likely to be found at higher elevations (up to 1,800 m). It is the common species of northern Europe and England, where it replaces the Continen-tal field vole. The related meadow vole *(Microtus pennsylvanicus)* of northern North America occurs in similar habitats.

1 − *Microtus arvalis:*
Body length:
90−120 mm.
Tail length:
35−40 mm.
Weight:
18−40 g.
Litter:
4−10 young three to seven times a year.
Life span:
approx. 1−1.5 year.

2 − *Microtus agrestis:*
Body length:
95−130 mm.
Tail length:
30−47 mm.
Weight:
25−55 g.
Litter:
3−6 young three to four times a year.
Life span:
approx. 14 months.

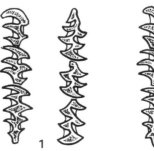

The top (left) and bottom (right) line of molar teeth in the continental field vole (1) and the British field vole (2)

# Lesser Mole Rat

*Spalax leucodon*

This rodent is perhaps the most peculiar of all European mammals, being perfectly adapted to an underground way of life. Its cylindrical body is covered with very short, thick, glossy fur, its eyes are completely overgrown with haired skin and external ears are altogether absent. Its strange large, flat head, with protruding huge incisors, is ornamented with a row of hard, light-coloured whiskers on the cheeks. With the help of its powerful incisors, the mole rat gouges, rather than digs, its underground passages, using its forelimbs with their large claws to remove the excavated soil. The passages run not far below the surface of the ground, and only the winter burrows are located at greater depths (up to 2 m). This peculiar rodent inhabits the Balkans, with Hungary as the northernmost limit, south-eastern Europe (especially Ukraine), Asia Minor and Transcaucasia. It occurs from the lowlands high up into the mountains (2,400 m) and is to be found in fields, meadows, steppes and on mountain slopes. The lesser mole rat rarely abandons its burrow, feeding mainly on the subterranean parts of plants and occasionally also various invertebrates. For the winter it lays in underground stocks of food, which may sometimes consist of up to 15 kg of sugar beet, potatoes and roots. It does not sleep in winter but its activity is much reduced.

The North American pocket gophers (family Geomyidae), although quite unrelated, are very similar to the mole rat in appearance and habits.

Body length:
150—240 mm.
Tail:
reduced.
Weight:
140—220 g.
Litter:
1—4 young once a year.
Life span:
unknown.

# Harvest Mouse or **European Harvest Mouse**

*Micromys minutus*

In general, mice are not among Man's favourite animals. However, anyone who had the opportunity of watching it closely, could not fail to like the harvest mouse. It is a minute animal, the smallest of all European rodents, and has a rusty yellow coat, pure white underside and large, black eyes. It is active all the time, running quickly about and skilfully climbing blades of grass and plant stems with the help of the prehensile tip of its long tail. The harvest mouse is neither common nor continuous in distribution. Originally it was an inhabitant of densely overgrown marshes and reedbeds, but today it can be found in damp meadows, vegetation by pond margins and wet places in cornfields. For the winter it retires to undisturbed vegetation, haystacks and often also to buildings. Unlike other mice, it builds a neat spherical nest woven of grass, which it hangs among reeds, the stalks of cereals or among other plants, 20 to 80 cm above the ground. In this way it adapts itself to living in places which may often be flooded. The harvest mouse's area of distribution covers the whole of Europe, with the exception of Spain, Ireland, Scandinavia and the southernmost regions of Italy and the Balkans; it also inhabits the whole of Asia as far as Japan and North Vietnam. However, its incidence in this area is confined to limited places where there are suitable conditions. In Britain it is locally abundant, but most often escapes Man's attention in the dense tangle of grasses.

Body length:
50—70 mm.
Tail length:
45—65 mm.
Weight:
5—9 g.
Litter:
3—7 young two or three times a year.
Life span:
1.5 years in the wild, up to 4 years in captivity.

# Yellow-necked Mouse
*Apodemus flavicollis*

# Woodmouse or Long-tailed Field Mouse
*Apodemus sylvaticus*

These woodmice are widely distributed and very abundant in Europe. They both have large dark eyes and prominent ears, and are grey-brown to golden-brown above and buff underneath. The yellow-necked mouse differs from the woodmouse in being considerably larger with brighter colours. The brown of its back is in sharp contrast to its pale belly (unlike the woodmouse) and it has a distinct collar of yellow-brown fur which gives it its name. These are both essentially woodland mice. They inhabit both coniferous and deciduous woodland, where they feed predominantly on the seeds of the forest trees but also consume fair amounts of insects and other invertebrates. Their nests are underground, the burrows being dug in the soft forest soil. Both species are strictly nocturnal and have surprisingly large home ranges. Woodmice are extremely agile, running and jumping rapidly and climbing with great skill. In the more eastern parts of their range, the two species become more difficult to tell apart and present problems even to the specialist. The distribution of the woodmouse in Europe is virtually complete, and it is only absent from northern Scandinavia. The yellow-necked mouse is absent from Ireland, Scotland, the Iberian Peninsula, most of France, the Benelux countries and Italy.

The North American deermice (genus *Peromyscus*) are unrelated, but are exceedingly similar to these mice in appearance and habits.

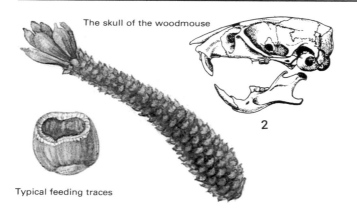

The skull of the woodmouse

Typical feeding traces

1 – *Apodemus flavicollis:*
Body length:
98–116 mm.
Tail length:
90–127 mm.
Weight:
18–25 g.
Litter:
3–8 young two to four times a year.
Life span:
in the wild 1.5–2 years.

2 – *Apodemus sylvaticus:*
Body length:
82–100 mm.
Tail length:
70–100 mm.
Weight:
18–25 g.
Litter:
2–8 young three to five times a year.
Life span:
in the wild 1.2–2 years.

# Striped Field Mouse

*Apodemus agrarius*

In coloration, the striped field mouse resembles both the yellow-necked mouse and the long-tailed field mouse. However, it can easily be distinguished by the conspicuous black stripe running down the middle of its back. Among other small European mammals, only birch mice possess this stripe but they are smaller in size and have a strikingly long tail. The striped field mouse is supposed to have come originally from the East. Its present area of distribution extends from Japan and Korea across Central Asia to southern and central Europe, Rhineland being the western limit of the range. Its distribution throughout this area is only local, and it shows preference for wood margins, bushy places alongside streams, parks and gardens. It is usually found in lowland areas or at moderate altitudes, but it will spread along roads as high as 1,800 metres. Its nest is located underground in a maze of burrows which it digs itself. As distinct from other field mice, it is not expert at climbing and jumping. It is active during the daytime as well as at night and lives mainly on vegetable matter. It is a very prolific animal: in some years it overpopulates and invades fields and other places where it is normally completely absent. Its way of life does not otherwise differ from that of other related species of field mice.

Body length:
80—115 mm.
Tail length:
65—92 mm.
Weight:
16—35 g.
Litter:
5—7 young three to four times a year.
Life span:
1.5—2 years, in captivity up to 4 years.

## Black or Ship Rat
*Rattus rattus*

## Brown or Norwegian Rat
*Rattus norvegicus*

The brown rat and the black rat are two of the most notorious enemies of Man who, however, has contributed to their spread all over the world. The brown rat is larger than the black rat and has shorter ears and a shorter tail. It is also more common, at least in Europe, and therefore causes the greater part of the damage ascribed to rats in general. It was originally a native of the marshy areas of north-eastern Asia, whence it has spread to the west both spontaneously and by the help of Man's activities. Its invasion of Europe, which dates back to the seventeenth and eighteenth centuries, was apparently assisted by rail and sea transport. Today it is mainly found in human habitations, especially in the sewers of large towns, slaughterhouses, farms, stables, storehouses and cellars. It is an omnivorous animal and in times when food is scarce it will not hesitate to attack even larger animals than itself. It lives gregariously in families, with a strict social structure. It causes great damage in food stores, and transmits various infectious diseases (for example Weil's disease).

The black rat is smaller in size, more slender, and is coloured grey, fawn or black. Originally a native of the tropical regions of the Old World, it has spread all over the world on board ships. It inhabits warm places, attics, wooden buildings and granaries. It has an erratic area of distribution, being found especially round sea ports and water-courses.

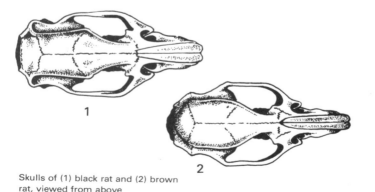

Skulls of (1) black rat and (2) brown rat, viewed from above

1 — *Rattus rattus:*
Body length:
160—235 mm.
Tail length:
190—240 mm.
Weight:
150—250 g.
Litter:
5—10 young three to six times a year.
Life span:
2—4, max. 7 years.

2 — *Rattus norvegicus:*
Body length:
190—270 mm.
Tail length:
130—230 mm.
Weight:
275—500 g.
Litter:
4—12 (sometimes up to 22) young two to three (occasionally four) times a year.
Life span:
2—4 years.

# House Mouse

*Mus musculus*

The original home of the house mouse was in the Asiatic and east European steppes, where it lived mainly on the seeds of grasses. With the beginnings of early agriculture, the house mouse became a companion of Man (this kind of association is called commensalism). With the spread of cultivated grassland, it has colonized the whole of Asia and Europe and has also been introduced to other continents. Thanks to Man's activities, its present distribution is completely worldwide. The house mouse is harmful to people living in its immediate vicinity, feeding on their food stores and emitting a disagreeable odour; it can also transmit various infectious diseases. It is hardly possible to count all the kinds of damage it can cause. Today a number of forms of the house mouse are known, differing in appearance and way of life. In western Europe it is represented by a long-tailed, dark form (2), which lives for the whole year close to human habitations and their immediate vicinity. Central and northern Europe is the home of a related, more lightly coloured form (1), which often spends the summer season away from inhabited buildings, usually in fields. The original wild form of the house mouse, which lives in the open throughout the whole year, is still to be found in eastern Austria, Hungary, Ukraine and in the Balkans. Commensal populations of the house mouse usually reproduce the whole year round and their fertility is enormous. They are also immensely adaptable and omnivorous, and they can live and reproduce even in mines and cooling plants.

Body length:
73—102 mm.
Tail length:
67—95 mm.
Weight:
15—28 g.
Litter:
4—8 young five to seven times a year.
Life span:
max. 2 years in the wild, up to 5 years in captivity.

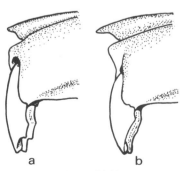

Incisors of (a) house mouse and (b) woodmouse

# Northern Birch Mouse

*Sicista betulina*

In appearance, the northern birch mouse looks like a small house mouse, but zoologically it belongs to a different rodent family which includes the American jumping mice *(Zapus)* and is also related to the well-known jerboas of the deserts. Its closest relatives inhabit the temperate zone of Asia and North America. The black stripe running down the centre of its head and back and its extremely long tail distinguishes it from all other European rodents. As distinct from true mice, it has four cheek teeth in the upper jaw (true mice have only three). This strange rodent is distributed in the forests, swamps and meadows of northern and north-eastern Europe, in the temperate regions of Asia, and sporadically also at higher altitudes (700—1,850 metres) in central Europe. Its occurrence in mountainous regions is obviously a relic of its wide distribution in the past. The northern birch mouse is predominantly a nocturnal mammal and is nowhere very common; thus little is known about its life. In summer it builds a nest of grass and moss, locating it above the ground in dense growths of vegetation; in winter it hibernates curled up in an underground nest. But even during the summer, if the temperature drops suddenly, it will easily fall into a state of torpor. It feeds on buds, flowers, seeds, berries and insects. It can climb well with the help of the twisting tail. Another very similar species, the southern birch mouse *(Sicista subtilis),* inhabits the steppe areas of south-eastern Europe.

The dark band starts between the eyes

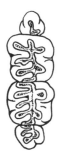
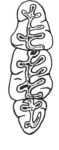

Characteristic features of the northern birch mouse are the four molars in the top jaw (left) and three molars in the bottom jaw (right)

Body length:
50—76 mm.
Tail length:
76—108 mm.
Weight:
5—13 g.
Litter:
2—7 young once a year.
Life span:
up to 3 years.

# Common or **Crested Porcupine**

*Hystrix cristata*

Porcupines are inhabitants of the warm regions of Asia and Africa; only one species, the common or crested porcupine, is found in Europe, occurring in southern Italy and Sicily. Many zoologists, however, doubt the origins of the European populations, as-suming that it was brought to this area by the Ro-mans. It is not necessary to describe this animal in detail. Everyone can recognize it by its long, black-and-white spines which form the covering of its back and flanks. When attacked the procupine erects the spines, shakes them and rattles its spiny tail. The spines are attached to the skin relatively loosely and, when provoked, the porcupine will make a sudden sideways lunge at its attacker, followed by an instant withdrawal. Since this appears instantaneous and as it usually results in several spines penetrating the at-tacker, this has led to the belief that the porcupine can shoot its spines. The common porcupine lives either solitarily or in small family groups in dry, bushy habitats, especially in foothills but also often in the vicinity of human settlements. It hides in rock crevices or digs its own burrows. It is a nocturnal animal and is guided first and foremost by the sense of hearing and smell. It feeds on vegetable matter, mainly the green parts of plants, roots, tubers and field crops, only occasionally adding to its diet some animal food. It searches for food as far as several kilometres from the burrow. The young are born with their eyes open, and are covered in soft spines.

Body length:
570—680 mm.
Tail length:
50—68 mm.
Weight:
10—15 kg.
Litter:
1—4 young once a year.
Life span:
10—15 years, in captivity up to 20 years.

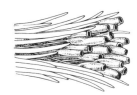

The cup-shaped rattling spines on the tail of some porcupine species

# Rabbit or **European Wild Rabbit**

*Oryctolagus cuniculus*

The rabbit is a native of the western Mediterranean (north-west Africa, Spain) and it started its spread throughout Europe about a thousand years ago. It was also introduced successfully into Australia, New Zealand and Chile. Its present area of distribution embraces a large part of Europe, including the British Isles, southern Scandinavia and Poland. Its populations, however, do not reach great numbers because of repeated epidemics of the rabbits' illness — myxomatosis. The wild rabbit shows preference for sandy places in open country, both lowlands and hills, with a dry, warm climate. It can be found on the margins of woods, on bushy, stony slopes, fallow land, pastures, along roadsides and railway embankments, and in gardens and parks on the outskirts of large towns. It seldom occurs at high altitudes (above 600 metres). During the daytime it mostly stays in its underground burrow (up to 3 metres deep) and only at dusk, and especially at night, does it come out. It keeps close to its warren and rarely leaves it for a distance farther than 600 metres. Rabbits are very prolific animals; they mate from February to July and the female, after a pregnancy of 28—31 days, produces one litter which is quickly followed by others. The naked, blind young are born and reared in special short burrows, the entrances of which are blocked by the female. Wild rabbits are popular game animals.

Newly born young

Body length:
350—450 mm.
Tail length:
40—73 mm.
Weight:
1.5—2 (occasionally 3) kg.
Litter:
4—12 young four to seven times a year.
Life span:
max. 10 years.

# Brown or European Hare

*Lepus capensis (L. europaeus)*

# Mountain Hare

*Lepus timidus*

The brown hare is a well-known animal in Europe and is an important game species. It is a native of grasslands and therefore is most abundant in open agricultural land, especially in lowland and hilly country. It is only occasionally found in woodland or in mountains. Its area of distribution comprises all of Europe, with the exception of northern Scandinavia. It is replaced by a different race in the greater part of the Iberian Peninsula and some of the Mediterranean islands. It also inhabits north Africa and western parts of Asia. The brown hare was introduced into North and South America, Siberia, Australia and New Zealand. Its original area of distribution is expanding continually, particularly in the USSR. Unlike the rabbit, it hides in a shallow open nest, a form, relying upon its camouflage coloration. With the exception of the mating period, it lives alone. The mating time lasts from January to October, and the furred young are born with their eyes open.

The mountain hare is a smaller northern species with white shorter ears and thickly furred paws; its coat turns white in winter. It is found in Iceland, Scotland and Ireland, in Scandinavia, northern Poland and northern regions of the USSR. An isolated population, obviously a relic from the Ice Age, lives in the Alps at altitudes of 1,200—3,400 metres. The American Arctic and snowshoe hares are very similar. Other American hares of the genus *Lepus* are called jack-rabbits.

*Lepus capensis:*
Body length: 550—650 mm.
Tail length: 75—100 mm.
Weight: 3.5—5 kg.
Litter: 1—5 young
three to four times a year.
Life span: 7—8 (12.5) years.

*Lepus timidus:*
Body length: 460—610 mm.
Tail length: 40—80 mm.
Weight: 2—4 kg.
Litter: 2—6 young two
to three times a year.
Life span: 8—9 years.

Skull of the European hare

The mountain hare in winter coat

Newly born young

# Wild Boar

*Sus scrofa*

Wild boar are ancient inhabitants of European woods. In the nineteenth century they were completely exterminated in many places and their numbers did not increase again until the post-war years. These large mammals are only rarely seen in the wild. They do not leave their shelters until dusk, and then move very cautiously about, guided by their excellent senses of smell and hearing. During the daytime they usually stay hidden in dense forest undergrowths or in marshy places. Females and young of various ages live in herds the whole year round. Old males live alone. They like to roll in mud and then rub off the dried mud from their skin against tree trunks, thus marking their territories. Wild boar are truly omnivorous animals, consuming anything they can find, from field crops, seeds of trees (e. g. acorns, beechnuts) and roots to insect larvae and carrion; they also hunt fish in shallow pools and root for small rodents in their burrows. Wild boar can cause great damage in fields and meadows, but on the other hand they destroy the larvae of harmful insects in the forests. Their mating time lasts from November to January. The striped young are born in March or April, usually in a shelter lined with grass and moss.

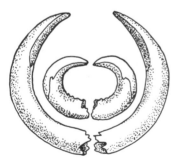

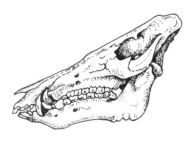

The canines of wild boars

Body length:
1100—1800 mm.
Tail length:
150—400 mm.
Weight:
50—200 kg.
Litter:
4—12 young once (occasionally twice) a year.
Life span:
10—12 years.

# Red Deer

*Cervus elaphus*

The red deer is the real king of the woods. It inhabits a vast area from the Iberian Peninsula and north Africa through the whole of temperate Eurasia to North America. Within this range there are a number of subspecies which differ in very conspicuous features and are sometimes classified as independent species. In Siberia, for instance, there is the large Altai wapiti, also called the maral *(Cervus elaphus sibiricus),* and in North America the wapiti *(Cervus elaphus canadensis).* In Europe, the red deer is abundant only in the east, especially in the Carpathians and the Alps; isolated populations also live in western Europe, as far north as Scotland and southern Norway. The red deer was originally an inhabitant of the wooded grassland belt; at present it is in most cases found in mixed mountain woods. It is also kept in enclosed parks. Red deer usually remain hidden during the daytime, coming out to graze at dusk, at midnight and at dawn. Their diet consists mainly of grass and various herbs, young shoots, leaves of trees and shrubs, beechnuts, acorns and field crops. The most interesting period of a red deer's life is the rutting time when the herds break up and the stags, which up to this time have been living a solitary life, collect groups of hinds around themselves. They announce their territory with a low trumpeting call and sometimes also fight against each other. The young are born in May or June after a pregnancy of eight and a half months and are suckled for three to four months. They become independent after a year.

Body length:
1650—2500 mm.
Tail length:
120—150 mm.
Weight:
100—350 kg.
Litter:
one young once a year.
Life span:
15—20 (max. 25) years.

The droppings of the red deer

Antlers are bony formations which grow out of the frontal bone. While growing they are covered with skin which provides them with nutrition. The skin dries up on fully grown antlers and the animals rub it off.

# Sika Deer

*Cervus nippon*

The small sika deer of eastern Asia is closely related to our native red deer. In many parts of Europe it is kept as an ornamental deer in parks and enclosed preserves and has also been introduced in the wild. Its original home is the Ussuri region of the USSR, Manchuria, China, Korea and Japan, where there are several subspecies. The sika deer can be easily distinguished from other deer. It is smaller than the fallow deer and its antlers have a maximum of eight, very occasionally ten, points. Consequently, it is not much valued as a game animal. In Europe it has been introduced into Denmark, Germany, England, France, Czechoslovakia and the USSR. It has also been introduced to New Zealand. It is not difficult to keep in captivity; it withstands the winter climate and usually completely loses its original shyness. The males shed their antlers in May or June, and the rutting season begins in the second half of October. The young are born in May or June and are tended by the hind till the end of the winter, with an interruption during the mating period. The sika deer is sometimes mistaken for the axis deer *(Axis axis)*, a native of the open woods of India and Sri Lanka. This species has been introduced into Europe from the beginning of the eighteenth century and can be found in places in Germany, England, Austria, Czechoslovakia, Yugoslavia and elsewhere.

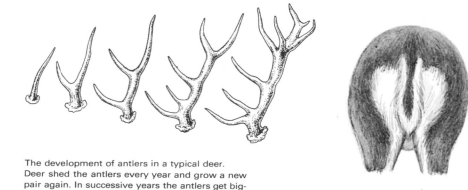

The development of antlers in a typical deer. Deer shed the antlers every year and grow a new pair again. In successive years the antlers get bigger until, at a certain age, they start diminishing in size.

Body length:
1100—1300 mm.
Tail length:
100—150 mm.
Weight:
25—110 kg.
Litter:
1—2 young once a year.
Life span:
15—20 years.

# Fallow Deer

*Dama dama*

The fallow deer is a native of the eastern Mediterranean and north Africa, but it was introduced to the whole Mediterranean region and western Europe in ancient times. By the Middle Ages it had reached central Europe, where it was originally kept as an ornament in enclosed preserves; only later was it released into the wild. These introduced herds today comprise the chief stock of wild fallow deer. The original wild populations have in the meantime been almost completely exterminated; their only remnants survive in the woods of southern Iran and adjoining Iraq and are sometimes classified as an independent species, *Dama mesopotamica*. Fallow deer are somewhat smaller than the red deer and differ from them in number of typical features, mainly their palmated antlers, spotted coloration and a black and white patch on the rump. Completely dark, unspotted individuals are often kept in enclosed preserves. In Europe the fallow deer's favourite habitats are open deciduous lowland forests or mixed, park-like woods. The rutting season falls later than in red deer, usually in October and November. The fallow buck's antlers finish growing in September and are not shed until May. The young are born after a gestation period of eight months. Fallow deer are active during the daytime as well as at night and live in herds. They do not differ markedly from red deer in their way of life, but they show less endurance in running.

Body length:
1300—1600 mm.
Tail length:
160—190 mm.
Weight:
35—100 kg.
Litter:
one young once a year.
Life span:
15—20 years.

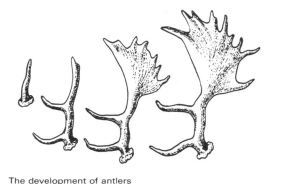

The development of antlers

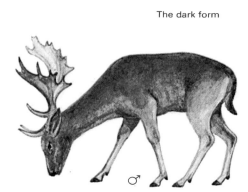

The dark form

# Reindeer

*Rangifer tarandus*

The reindeer is the characteristic deer of the north. Numerous subspecies are distributed throughout the tundra and northern taiga of Eurasia, North America, (where they are called caribou), and most of the polar islands. One of the reindeer's adaptations to life in the north is that its two main hooves are broad and outspread. The lateral hooves are also relatively large and are placed lower than in most deer. This modified foot prevents the animal from sinking into snow and muddy soil when it is running. Reindeer antlers are richly branched and have many points. They are worn by both sexes, which is exceptional in the deer family. Especially in the American continent, reindeer are known to undertake long yearly migrations from the tundra to the taiga, and *vice versa*. They are not fastidious animals, and find enough food in lichens, moss, grass, the leaves and twigs of willows, and other polar vegetation. These qualities have lead to the domestication of reindeer in polar regions, and life in the north today is hardly imaginable without these familiar animals. The wild form of reindeer, which used to be very abundant in the north, has been reduced by hunting to such an extent that some subspecies are almost extinct. In Europe small numbers of wild reindeer survive only in northern Norway, Finland and the USSR. Reindeer are expert runners and swimmers, and are active mostly during the daytime. They converge into herds consisting of females, young and young males. The rutting time falls in September and October, and the calves are born in May and June.

Footprint

Body length:
1300—2200 mm.
Tail length:
70—200 mm.
Weight:
60—315 kg.
Litter:
1—2 young once a year.
Life span:
12—15 years.

# European Elk or Moose

*Alces alces*

The elk is an ancient inhabitant of the northern forests of Eurasia and North America, where it is called the moose. In the Middle Ages it also used to live in the vast forests of central and western Europe, where it later became extinct. Thanks to the protective measures taken during the past few years, elk populations have increased and elks have again spread southwards to the boundaries of their former area and also to the northern tundra. They have already colonized immense areas of the USSR and Poland, and continue to spread into Czechoslovakia, Germany and Austria. In the summer, elks live either alone or in families. In winter, after the rutting season, they congregate in small herds numbering five to ten individuals. Except for the seasonal migrations, which are influenced by the density of population and rutting activity, elks are faithful to a restricted home range. They do not defend their territories in any way. The diet of elks consists of the leaves and twigs of trees and bushes (aspen, alder, willow, poplar), aquatic plants and the shoots of conifers. Their long legs enable them to graze on the leaves of trees; they also eat aquatic plants whilst half submerged in the water. When they are gathering food from the ground, they often bend their forefeet back and support themselves on their wrists. The rutting season lasts from September to November and the antlers are shed between the end of April and the beginning of June. Elks are guided predominantly by their sense of smell and hearing, their vision being very poor. Experiments with the domestication of elks are being carried out in the USSR.

Body length:
2500—2700 mm.
Tail length:
120—130 mm.
Weight:
250—500 kg.
Litter:
1—2 young once a year.
Life span:
20—25 years.

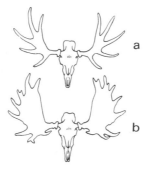

(a) rod-shaped and (b) spade-shaped types of antlers

# Roe Deer

*Capreolus capreolus*

Originally a forest-dweller, the roe deer has adapted very successfully to life in cultivated land and is now becoming an inhabitant of fields and small woods. It is very abundant in Europe and in some places is among the most popular game animals. Its distribution area, however, is not as continuous nor as extensive as that of the red deer. It ranges from western Europe across the temperate zone of Asia to China. It is absent from Iceland, Ireland, northern Scandinavia, the north of the USSR and the Mediterranean. A different, larger race, with more richly branched antlers, lives in Siberia. The roe deer is active both during the daytime and at night, but comes out to graze mainly after dusk or at dawn. Like the red deer, it feeds on grass and herbs, leaves, shoots, berries and mushrooms. During the summer, it lives either alone or in families, but it congregates into larger herds for the winter. Roe deer usually keep to their territories (measuring about 1 sq km) for the whole year round. The rutting season is in July and August but the young are not born until May or June of the following year, after a latent pregnancy. The young are born hairy and with open eyes and for the first days of their life they are kept in a shelter, the female visiting them only to suckle them. After a week they join the mother who continues to suckle and guide them for a long time.

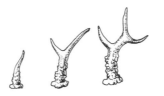

The development of antlers

Body length:
950—1350 mm.
Tail length:
20—30 mm.
Weight:
15—30 kg.
Litter:
1—2 young once a year.
Life span:
10—12 (max. 18) years.

Roebuck with deformed antlers as a result of a hormonal disturbance (for example injured testes)

# White-tailed or **Virginian Deer**

*Odocoileus virginianus*

The white-tailed deer is more closely related to the roe deer than to the red deer. Ecologically it replaces the roe deer on the American continent. In its native American home, the white-tailed deer is widely distributed from Brazil to Canada, being absent only in the westernmost parts of the USA and Canada. It was brought from these areas to Europe, and introduced successfully into south-western Finland and Czechoslovakia (central Bohemia). In its American homeland the white-tailed deer forms a number of geographical races; those of the northernmost regions reach the size of a red deer, while the southern races resemble a roe deer in size. The smallest form, a native of the Key Island off the coast of Florida, is near to complete extinction (about 30—40 animals are left). The white-tailed deer can hardly be mistaken for any other species of the deer family; its antlers are unusually bent at first outwards and than forwards. The conspicuously long tail with a white underside is raised when the deer is in danger or excited, showing a large white patch beneath the tail. This is a similar mode of communication to that of the red deer. Like the roe deer in Europe, the white-tailed deer in America has become adapted to agricultural country and, consequently, its numbers have been steadily increasing. The European populations rut in November. The males make a strange hissing sound, in contrast to the trumpet-like calls of the red deer. A related species lives in eastern North America: the mule deer *(Odocoileus hemionus)*.

Body length:
850—2050 mm.
Tail length:
100—350 mm.
Weight:
25—200 kg.
Litter:
2 young once a year.
Life span:
10, in captivity 20 years.

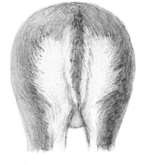

# Chamois
*Rupicapra rupicapra*

The chamois (pronounced *sham-wa*) is one of the few members of the high-mountain European mammal fauna. It inhabits the Pyrenees, the Alps, the Apennines, the Carpathians, the Balkans, Asia Minor and the Caucasus. It has also been successfully introduced into a number of other regions. Zoologically it is classified in the cattle family, as a relative of the sheep and goats. Both sexes have small, black horns, curved at the tip, which are permanent and grow continually. Chamois spend the summer in the alpine mountain belt in meadows, on steep stony slopes and amongst rocks. In winter or in inclement weather they search for the protection of woods. They climb excellently and jump from one rock to another. Chamois are active only during the daytime, slowly roaming their territories. In the morning they usually ascend to higher altitudes, coming down again in the evening. Their senses of hearing and smell are well developed, but their vision is less keen. They live in herds guided by old females; the old males live alone. In most cases chamois keep to their territories, which they mark by the secretions of their scent glands. They graze on mountain plants, and in the winter they also eat buds, moss, lichens and the needles of dwarf pine trees. The rutting season lasts from October to December, during which time the males often fight among themselves. The young are born in June and July. The Rocky Mountain goat, *Oreamnos americanus,* of North America, is closely related; although it is remarkably different in appearance, its habits are very similar.

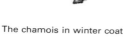
The chamois in winter coat

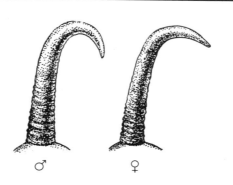

♂          ♀

Body length:
1100—1360 mm.
Tail length:
70—80 mm.
Weight:
35—40 kg.
Litter:
one young once a year.
Life span:
15—20 (25) years.

# Mouflon

*Ovis musimon*

The mouflon is the only European species of wild sheep. It is a native of the Mediterranean region, where it still lives wild in Sardinia and Corsica. Very closely related forms live in Cyprus and in the mountains of western and central Asia. In the eighteenth and nineteenth centuries, mouflons were introduced into enclosed preserves in central Europe, where they became acclimatized and escaped into the wild in places. At present, wild mouflon populations are found in Spain, southern France, Germany, Czechoslovakia and elsewhere. The total number of animals in these countries is estimated as 20,000 individuals, which many times exceeds the indigenous wild populations of Sardinia and Corsica. In their original home, mouflons inhabit rocky terrains in the mountains but in central Europe they prefer dry, stony ground. They have well-developed senses of hearing and smell and are rather shy. The females and lambs live in herds led by an old ewe for the whole year; in the rutting time, the rams also join the herd. Mouflons are not very particular animals and adapt easily to most varied habitats. They feed on plants and the twigs of trees and shrubs, and in winter they supplement their diet with various fruits, mosses and lichens. The rutting time lasts from October to the middle of December, and the lambs are born after a gestation period of five months. Huge mouflon horns are valued hunters' trophies.

The North American bighorn *(Ovis canadensis)* and Dall sheep *(Ovis dalli)* are very similar.

Body length:
1100—1300 mm.
Tail length:
50—100 mm.
Weight:
25—50 kg.
Litter:
1 (2) young once a year.
Life span:
15—20 years.

# European Bison or Wisent

*Bison bonasus*

The wisent is the largest European ungulate and is closely related to the North American bison. The wisent was originally widely distributed from western Europe as far as inner Asia, but constant persecution caused a rapid decrease in its numbers and it gradually disappeared from many areas. In the Middle Ages it was already rare in Europe and the right of hunting was granted solely to rulers and nobility. Later still, it became almost completely extinct over the whole area of its former occurrence. By the beginning of the twentieth century, all that remained was a small herd of wisents in the Białowieźa, a primeval forest in Poland, and another herd in the Caucasus. Both these remaining herds were completely exterminated during the First World War and wisents had to be newly bred from specimens surviving in zoological gardens. Careful breeding resulted in a successful increase of the wisents' total world numbers to about 1,000 animals, some of which were set free; the rest live in enclosed preserves or zoos. The American bison *(Bison bison)* has had, more recently, a similar history. As distinct from bisons, wisents are forest-dwellers and used to live mainly in deciduous or mixed woods where there were grassy clearings. The rutting time is in August and September, and the calves are born in May and June.

The wisent is sometimes wrongly considered to be the ancestor of domestic breeds of cattle. The domestic cattle's ancestral line starts with the aurochs *(Bos primigenius)*, which inhabited similar habitats to those of the wisent. This species is now extinct.

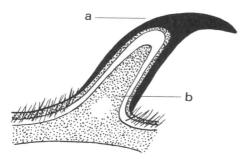

Cross section through the horn of an adult animal. The horn is a case (a) fitting on bony core (b). Horns are permanent formations.

Body length:
3100—3500 mm.
Tail length:
500—600 mm.
Weight:
up to 1,000 kg.
Litter:
1 (2) young once a year.
Life span:
25—30 years.

# Great Crested Grebe

*Podiceps cristatus*

The great crested grebe is widespread throughout most of Europe except the northern parts. The populations of northern and eastern Europe are migratory. The great crested grebe inhabits lakes or large ponds with large beds of reeds and rushes. It returns to its nesting grounds sometimes as early as February, though March or April are more usual. An interesting ceremonial courtship takes place on the water preceding nesting. The two partners, separated by a distance of several yards, greet one another by stretching their necks out above the water's surface. Then they swim towards each other, spreading their ruffs, nodding their heads and finally embracing by rubbing their necks, emitting cries throughout. Sometimes they also dive, then surface with water plants in their bills and tread water, facing each other with heads erect. The nest is built away from the bank and is made of various kinds of water plants which the grebes bring up from the depths. After it is completed the female lays three to six eggs which are white at first but then gradually acquire a brown hue. Both partners take turns incubating for a period of 25—27 days, though the female does the major share of the sitting. After they have dried, the newly hatched nestlings climb up on their parents' backs, concealing themselves under their wings and often being carried about by the adult birds even though capable of swimming and diving by themselves. The parents feed the young on small insects, molluscs etc. The diet of adult birds consists mostly of fish and insect larvae.

Voice:
A deep "kar-arr" or "er-wick", mainly during the courtship period.
Length:
48 cm. The 'horns' are absent in the winter plumage.
Size of egg:
46.5—62.7 × 33.0—39.7 mm.

One of the phases of the courtship display is carrying material from the water bottom

# Cormorant
## or **Great Cormorant**

*Phalacrocorax carbo*

The cormorant breeds throughout Asia, Europe and North America. In Europe it is found in large numbers on the seacoast but it also occurs inland on rivers and still bodies of water. It is both a dispersive and a migratory bird. When migrating it keeps close to the shoreline. It nests in colonies on rocky islands, often together with gannets, as well as in trees. Colonies may number as many as several thousand pairs of birds. Inland it is often found in heron colonies. Nests on rock ledges are only sparingly lined, nests in trees are woven of twigs and grass stems. Often the cormorant will build a new nest, but use the old foundation. Both partners take part in building the nest, and in tree colonies break off twigs with their strong beaks. The female usually lays three to five eggs between April and June, the two partners taking turns incubating them for 23—29 days. The chicks do not open their eyes until three days after hatching. They take their food from the parents' throats. After 35—56 days in the nest they form flocks and range widely together with the adult birds. The cormorant feeds mostly on fish, occasionally also on crustaceans, and above all crabs, which it sometimes catches in great numbers. It hunts in small groups, frequently of about eight birds, which chase the fish towards one another. In parts of its range, it is often found in the company of pelicans, which do not dive, whereas cormorants pursue their prey underwater. Undigested bones and scales are regurgitated.

Stance when drying feathers

Voice:
Various guttural groans like "r-rah".
Length:
91.5 cm.
The male and female have similar plumage.
Size of egg:
56.2—70.8 × 33.8—44.4 mm.

# Grey Heron

*Ardea cinerea*

The grey heron nests in western, central and eastern Europe, southern Scandinavia and with isolated populations in Spain. Western populations are resident, those of more northerly and eastern regions migrate to the Mediterranean in September/October, though one may still see flocks of herons on some ponds in central Europe as late as November or early December. When March comes they return to their nesting grounds — overgrown rivers with tree-lined banks, ponds, lakes and swamps, often also woodlands near bodies of water. Their arrival is followed by an interesting courtship display. When the male has acquired a mate the two then build a nest of twigs, sticks, reeds, and the like, usually high up in the tops of both deciduous and coniferous trees. Only rarely is the nest situated among reeds and rushes. There may be several nests on a single tree, often used by the birds several years in succession. In April or May, sometimes even in late March, the female lays 4—5 eggs which she and her mate take turns incubating for 25—28 days. The young hatch successively one after the other. At first the parents feed them by putting regurgitated food directly into their beaks, but later they regurgitate it into the nest. At the age of eight to nine weeks the young are already fully grown and capable of flight. The grey heron is a carnivorous bird which captures small fish in shallow water, and also tadpoles, frogs, small mammals, small birds, reptiles, molluscs and insects.

Voice:
Numerous croaking and retching notes.
Length:
91 cm.
The male and female have similar plumage.
Size of egg:
52.4—69.5 × 38.5—49.7 mm.

# White Stork

*Ciconia ciconia*

The white stork is one of the best known European birds, living in the close vicinity of human dwellings and availing itself of man's protection. It nests in central, northwest and southeast Europe and also makes its home in Spain. In Scandinavia it occurs only in the southernmost tip and occasionally wings its way to England and north as far as Norway and Finland. A migrant bird, it leaves its nesting territory any time from early August through September, flying southwest or southeast, depending on the population, as far as east and south Africa. In March or early April it is back again in its nesting grounds, often settling in the very heart of a village, where it builds a large nest in a tree, on a chimney, roof-top, etc. The nest, made of twigs and sticks, is often used for several years and added to every breeding season. A new nest takes about eight days to build. First to arrive at the nesting grounds is the male, the female joining him several days later. The four to five eggs are laid in April or May and both partners share the duties of incubation; however, only the female sits at night. The young usually hatch after 30—34 days, feeding themselves on food brought them by their parents and regurgitated into the nest. When they are about three weeks old the young storks begin to stand on their feet and at the age of 54—63 days they are already capable of flight. Storks are carnivorous birds, hunting their prey in shallow waters as well as in fields and meadows. They usually feed on small rodents, frogs, lizards, small fish and invertebrates.
The black stork *(Ciconia nigra)* belongs to the same genus as the white stork. It inhabits damp coniferous and mixed woods in northeastern, eastern and central Europe as well as Spain.

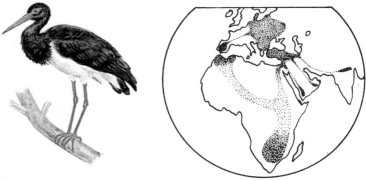

The black stork

Migration routes of the white stork to wintering regions

*Ciconia ciconia:*
Voice:
Clapping of the bill; the young make mewing sounds.
Length:
102 cm.
Size of egg:
65.0—81.5 × 46.0—57.0 mm.

*Ciconia nigra:*
Voice: Hissing sounds resembling "feeoo".
Length:
96 cm. The male and female have like plumage.
The bill and legs of the young are greyish green.
Size of egg:
60.0—74.3 × 44.0—54.7.

# Grey Lag Goose

*Anser anser*

The grey lag goose makes its home in Scotland, Iceland, and on the shores of Scandinavia as well as in parts of central and southeast Europe. The birds of Scotland are resident, those inhabiting northern and central Europe winter in western Europe and the Mediterranean, leaving their nesting grounds in September/October and returning again in March. Sites selected for their nests are large, calm expanses of water, lakes and ponds with old reed beds, above all places with extensive meadows nearby, also swampy sites, small islets by the seashore, flooded riverine woodlands, etc. Grey lag geese pair for life. On their return from their winter quarters they usually establish themselves in the same nesting territory. The nest, built by the female alone, may be located on dry ground as well as on water on piles of old bent reeds and even in the tops of small, old willows. Nests on islets may be located in quite open situations. The material of which the nest is made is gathered in the immediate vicinity. The edge is lined with a thick layer of down. As a rule the goose lays 4−9 eggs, which she incubates alone for 27−30 days while the gander keeps guard close by. Both parents care for the newly hatched goslings. The goslings are capable of flight at the age of 57 days but remain in the company of their parents, the individual families then joining to form large flocks. The diet of the grey lag goose consists mostly of the green parts of plants and various seeds. The young goslings feed themselves, nibbling fine green leaves at first.

The bean goose (*Anser fabalis*) is a little smaller than the grey lag goose. It is darker in colour, especially its wings, head and neck. The beak is conspicuously two-coloured.

*Anser anser:*
Voice: the familiar call "aahng-ung-ung".
Length:
male 82.5 cm, female 70.5 cm. The male and female have similar plumage.
Size of egg:
74.0−99.0 × 51.4−62.0 mm.

*Anser fabalis:*
Voice: sounds like "ang-ank" and "kajak" or "kaiaik".
Length: 71−89 cm.
Male and female are of the same colour.
Size of egg: 74−91 × 42−59 mm

Grey lag geese from eastern Europe have pink bills, not orange ones.

Bean goose

♂

# Mallard or Wild Duck
*Anas platyrhynchos*

The mallard is one of the commonest and most widely distributed species of duck. It nests throughout the whole of Europe, where it is either resident or dispersive, and in the northernmost areas a migrant to winter quarters in central and western Europe or in the Mediterranean. They return to their nesting grounds in pairs at the end of February or in early March, the males having selected their mates during the autumn or winter months. The mallard inhabits still waters and sometimes also rivers — even in towns. Spring is the time of courtship, when the partners swim around each other, the male lowers his bill and ruffles his feathers, twitches his tail, nods his head, then plunges his bill into the water, and so forth. The nesting site is selected by the drake but the nest is built by the duck. It is usually located on the ground, often some distance inland, but also in trees in nests abandoned by other birds as well as in holes. It is lined with leaves, plant stalks, small twigs, etc. gathered in the immediate vicinity, and subsequently covered with a layer of down. Before leaving the nest the duck carefully covers the eggs with down. There are usually 9—13 eggs, which the duck incubates alone for a period of 22—26 days. When the young ducklings' feathers have dried she takes them out to the water. Mallards forage for food after dusk. They feed on various seeds, plant shoots and grass and also collect food on the water's surface, hunt insects, worms, etc. The young ducklings' diet consists mostly of insects, crustaceans, molluscs as well as some green plant parts.

♀

Voice:
The male's note is a whistling "yeeb", the female quacks loudly.
Length:
male 57 cm, female 49 cm. Marked sexual dimorphism. The male's non-breeding plumage resembles that of the female.
Size of egg:
50.0—65.0 × 37.0—45.8 mm.

# Golden Eagle

*Aquila chrysaetos*

The golden eagle makes its home in rocky locations in Scotland, Scandinavia, Spain, the Alps and Carpathians, and sometimes also in other parts of Europe. This huge bird of prey is generally a resident species, though young individuals roam far afield at the onset of autumn, often to be found in lowland areas and even in the vicinity of large cities. At the end of March or in April the golden eagle builds its large nest, which resembles a huge basket composed of sticks and branches. It is sited, usually, on an inaccessible cliff face, very occasionally in a tree, and is often used for several years. However, within the confines of its territory, to which it remains faithful, it often builds several nests over a period, occupying them successively. The usual clutch of 2 eggs is incubated by the female for 44—45 days, the male occasionally relieving her so that she can stretch her wings. The food is hunted by the male, who passes it to the female to give to the nestlings, though when they are older he feeds them himself. The young take to the wing for the first time when they are between 71 and 81 days old, but remain in the company of their parents for a short time after. When they are fully grown they leave their home territory, often travelling great distances. The golden eagle hunts marmots, mountain hares, red grouse and ptarmigan; sometimes it will kill a young chamois, stray lamb or kid. Young eagles also eat amphibians, reptiles and large insects, and welcome fresh carrion.

Voice:
A noisy "kya" and a few whistling notes.
Length:
82 cm.
Wing span:
188 to 196 cm. The female is usually larger. The male and female have like plumage.
Size of egg:
70.1—88.9 × 51.0—66.0 mm.

# Buzzard
# or **Common Buzzard**
*Buteo buteo*

At the end of February the buzzard may be seen circling above a wood, suddenly plummeting to the ground and the next instant soaring up again. This large bird of prey is one of the most common raptors of Europe, where it is absent only in the northernmost regions. It frequents forests of all kinds, from lowland to mountain altitudes, preferring country where woods alternate with fields and meadows. It usually remains in its nesting territory throughout the year, which extends from three to four kilometres in diameter, or roams the countryside far and wide after fledging. Many inhabitants of northern Europe migrate southwest in winter. In April the buzzard builds its nest high in the treetops, though in England it will also build on cliffs. The structure is made of twigs and lined with leaves, moss and hair; the edge is often decorated with leaves, or seaweed. Both partners share the duties of brooding the two to four eggs for 28 to 49 days, though the female bears the brunt of the task. The nestlings are fed at first by the female, who first receives the prey from the male, but later he also feeds them. Fledging is after 41 to 49 days, but the chicks continue to be fed a further four weeks by the parent birds. The mainstays of the diet are field-mice and other small rodents. A buzzard will often wait on the ground outside the hole of a fieldmouse, sometimes without moving for hours, in order to outwit its wary prey.

Voice:
A long, plaintive "pee-o".
Length:
53 cm.
Wing span:
117 to 137 cm.
The male and female have similar plumage.
Size of egg:
49.8−63.8 × 39.1−49.0 mm.

# Kestrel

*Falco tinnunculus*

High above the field, as if pinned to one spot in the sky, hovers a small predator—the kestrel, its keen eye seeking the ground below for prey. The instant some careless fieldmouse emerges from its underground passage the kestrel quickly swoops down to catch it in its claws. Besides fieldmice it also hunts other rodents, as well as grasshoppers and other insects. It is easy to understand why the bird is the farmer's friend. In late April or early May it builds its nest on a rocky ledge, an abandoned crow's nest, a tree cavity or larger nest-box. The female lays 5—7 eggs which she incubates for 28—30 days. The young, covered with a thick layer of down, are fed by the male for the first few days and later by both parents. At about the age of one month the young kestrels leave the nest, remaining in the company of the older birds until autumn. Birds from northern and northeastern Europe migrate to southern Europe and north Africa for the winter. Populations inhabiting the other parts of Europe are either resident or roam far afield. Kestrels are also to be found in Asia and Africa.

♂

Voice:
A clear "kee-kee-kee" and a more musical double note "kee-lee".
Length:
male 32 cm, female 35 cm.
The male has the top of the head coloured blue-grey, the young resemble the female.
Size of egg:
31.9—47.2 × 22.1—36.3 mm.

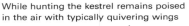

While hunting the kestrel remains poised in the air with typically quivering wings

♀

# Common Pheasant

*Phasianus colchicus*

The common pheasant was introduced to many parts of Europe in the Middle Ages. It quickly became acclimatized and was soon a common game bird, autumn pheasant shoots remaining popular to this day. Other subspecies from China were later introduced into Europe, where they interbred. The pheasant is generally found in light woods, field groves, thickets besides water, and also in large parks. It is particularly abundant in lowlands, but is common also in hill country. It is a resident bird, remaining in its territory throughout the year. During the spring courting season the cock utters his characteristic harsh note with head held erect, usually following this with a bout of wing fluttering. With a short hopping motion he then circles a chosen hen, or engages in battle with other cocks. After the courting season he pays no further attention to the hen or the young. The hen scrapes a simple hollow in the ground, which she lines with dry leaves or grass, and then lays 8—15 eggs which she incubates alone, generally for a period of 24—25 days. The chicks begin to fly at the age of two weeks and roost in the treetops with the hen. The diet consists of various seeds, berries, green plant shoots, insects, worms and molluscs. In winter it is necessary to put out food for pheasants wherever they occur in greater numbers. Many countries have established large pheasant preserves, where the birds are given partial freedom or kept in aviaries.

Voice:
The male's courting call is a harsh "korrk-kok".
Length:
male 79 cm, female 60 cm.
Marked sexual dimorphism.
Size of egg:
39.0—51.1 × 32.4—37.6 mm.

# Partridge
# or **Grey Partridge**

*Perdix perdix*

Over much of Europe the common partridge is a favoured game bird, and in some central European countries it is even trapped for live export. Resident throughout its European range, outside the breeding season the partridge is to be seen in small, usually family groups. Because it frequents snow-blanketed fields and meadows during the winter months, it relies to a considerable extent on food put out for it by humans. Early in spring, the family groups break up, young birds beginning their search for a mate, adults having already paired for life. In May or June the hen prepares the nest, lined with grass and leaves, in a deep hollow, concealed in a clump of grass or under a shrub. She incubates 8−24 eggs for 23−25 days while her mate stands guard close by. The nestlings, which feed themselves, are reared by both parents: if the hen dies then the male continues alone. At first the diet consists of insects and green leaves but later it is supplemented by seeds. The young birds fledge at 16 days. Adult birds feed on seeds, insects, worms, spiders and molluscs and also nibble greenery.

Among the European gallinaceous birds, the only migrant species is the quail *(Coturnix coturnix)*. Populations inhabiting southern Europe and Africa are resident.

*Perdix perdix:*
Voice:
A grating "krrr-ic" or "kar-wic".
Length:
29 cm.
Sexually dimorphic.
Size of egg:
31.6−40.4 × 24.1−29.4 mm.

*Coturnix coturnix:*
Voice:
"Whic-whic-ic".
Length:
17.5 cm.
Sexually dimorphic.
Size of egg:
25.0−33.9 × 20.0−25 mm.

Partridge

Quail

Quail

# Capercaillie
*Tetrao urogallus*

Largest of the European grouse, the capercaillie frequents woodlands (mostly conifer forests) with dense undergrowth in mountains and hilly country. In the north it may be also found in lowland areas. Native to Scotland, the Pyrenees, northern and central Europe, it remains in its breeding grounds throughout the year. Except during the courting season it is a very shy bird, adept at concealing itself. The spring courtship display, however, is conspicuous and remarkable and well known to sportsmen. During one phase of the display, which takes place while it is still dark, the cock is "deaf" and "blind" for a few seconds. When dawn breaks, he flies down to the ground, often engaging in battle with a rival. While this takes place the hens sit waiting on nearby branches, and are then led off by the victors. The nest is a hollow in the ground which the hen digs, usually at the base of a tree trunk, and is lined with grass and leaves. She incubates the five to eight eggs alone for 26 to 29 days, then leads the young, who can feed by themselves, in search of food. She also shelters them under her wings and generally gives them protection. The chicks are yellow-russet in colour with dark spots, and by ten days are able to fly about. The diet consists chiefly of insects, berries, buds and shoots of conifers. Capercaillie flesh tastes resinous, and for this reason the species is not one of the most popular game birds.

Voice:
The male's courting call begins with a rapidly accelerating "tik-up, tik-up, tik-up", ending with a "pop", followed by hissing and whispering; the hen's call is a "kok-kok" resembling the pheasant's.
Length:
Male 94 cm, female 67 cm.
Sexually dimorphic.
Size of egg:
50.8–62.2 × 39.0–43.5 mm.

# Black Grouse

*Lyrurus tetrix*

The black grouse inhabits northern, eastern and central Europe, nesting also in England. It is most abundant in the arctic tundra, but occurs in marshland with birch trees, light deciduous and mixed woods, as well as in mountain areas and among peat bogs. It also visits meadows and fields near woods, or forest clearings, where it performs its courtship display in the spring. As many as 100 cocks will arrive at the courting grounds before sunrise, where they perform all sorts of antics, hopping about, dropping their wings and uttering burbling sounds. To conclude, they leap up and attack one another with their beaks, but only rarely inflict serious wounds. As dawn breaks, the hens arrive on the scene and then fly off with their chosen partners, one cock being accompanied by several hens. Between the middle of May and June the hen scrapes a simple hollow in the ground, which she lines with leaves or grass before laying seven to 12 eggs. These are incubated for 25 to 28 days by the hen, the cock showing no further interest in the fate of his family. When the young hatch, the hen guides them in search of food and also protects them. The chicks, spotted yellow-black, grow very fast and by the end of October are almost the size of adult birds. A black grouse's diet consists of insects, worms, molluscs, seeds, berries, plant shoots and grass. This is a game bird, cocks being shot during the courtship display. Their lyre-shaped tails are prized trophies.

Voice:
The male utters a sound resembling "tchu-shwee" and a whistling sound when he takes to the air; the female's call is a loud "kok-kok".
Length:
Male 61.5 cm, female 42 cm.
Sexually dimorphic.
Size of egg:
46.0—56.3 × 33.4—38.5 mm.

# Crane
# or **Common Crane**
*Grus grus*

The large crane is today found only in north and northeast Europe and the northern parts of central Europe. At one time it was very plentiful throughout central and western Europe but civilization has caused its reduction. Cranes migrate as far as the Sudan and Ethiopia but some winter also in the Mediterranean. They leave their breeding grounds in September or October, returning again from the middle of March to April. They inhabit marshy areas with lakes, extensive meadows near large ponds and lakes, swamp areas and also marshy woodlands next to meadows. The birds pair after returning to their nesting grounds, each pair choosing and fiercely defending their own territory. The courtship antics are striking and vociferous. During the performance the cranes utter loud trumpet-like calls, leap high in the air and spread their wings, hop on one foot and run around in circles; in short they do a sort of dance. The nest of reeds and twigs is built on small flat islets, on broken and bent reeds in swamps, or on clumps of grass, and often in the same spot for a number of years. In dry locations the nest is low, in swamps it is high and broad. In April or May the female generally lays two, sometimes one or three eggs, which she and her partner take turns incubating 28−31 days. On hatching, the young cranes, which have a short bill at first, scamper about the neighbourhood; they are also able to swim. The crane feeds on seeds, grain, green plant parts, insects, molluscs, etc. and also occasionally captures small vertebrates.

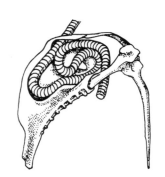

The coiled trachea in the breast bone serves as a resonator (sound amplifier)

Voice:
Loud trumpet-like calls, in the vicinity of the nest cries that sound like "kr-r-r".
Length:
male 122 cm, female 112 cm.
The male and female have similar plumage.
Wing span:
About 220 cm.
Size of egg:
85.0−109.0 × 56.0−67.0 mm.

# Coot

*Fulica atra*

The coot is the commonest member of the rail family and is found throughout all of Europe except the northernmost parts. Birds inhabiting eastern and northern Europe leave their nesting grounds in October to November and fly southwest, those from other parts of the continent are resident or dispersive. Coots arrive at their breeding grounds in March, and soon after the males wage fierce combats amongst themselves to win a mate. The paired birds then begin building a nest in reeds, rushes, grass or other vegetation. It is usually sited away from the water's edge, and leading to it from the water is a ramp of leaves. The structure itself is made of reeds and grasses and sometimes covered with a roof of broken plant stems. The female usually lays six to nine eggs, which she and her partner take turns incubating for about 22, sometimes as many as 24 days. The young hatch successively, the first being led out on the water by the male, who after a few hours swims back to the nest for the next. They are cared for by both parents. Their plumage is black but the head is orange-red. Adults place food directly inside their offspring's beaks. The diet consists mostly of green plant parts, but seeds are eaten in autumn, and during the nesting period includes insects and their larvae, molluscs, crustaceans, spiders and other small invertebrates.

Voice:
A clear "tewk" or "kt-kowk"; also a short, sharp "skik".
Length:
38 cm.
Male and female have similar plumage.
Size of egg:
40.0—61.0 × 31.2—40.6 mm.

The coot's toes are fringed with flattened lobes which have the same function as the webs on the feet of ducks and geese.

# Lapwing

*Vanellus vanellus*

The lapwing, one of the commonest of shorebirds is widespread throughout most of Europe, the only places where it does not nest being Portugal and Italy. Between August and October it migrates to southwest Europe and northwest Africa but south and west European populations are resident. The lapwing returns to its nesting grounds in March, though it has often arrived by the end of February, its favourite sites being damp meadows and fields near water. In spring the lapwings perform their characteristic courtship flights. The courtship display often takes place on the ground, the partners running around each other and the male often picking up a plant stalk with his bill and casting it behind him or to the side. In late March or April, sometimes also in May, the birds build a nest in a shallow depression in the ground in a meadow, field, on a raised spot in a swamp. etc. The structure is lined sparsely with leaves, plant stalks or small twigs. Like all shorebirds, the female usually lays four eggs, which she and her partner take turns incubating for 24—28 days. The speckled nestlings remain in the nest for a day or two and then scatter in the neighbourhood, concealing themselves in clumps of grass when danger threatens. They begin flying at the age of five weeks, forming large flocks and roaming the countryside until they leave for their winter quarters. The diet consists of insects and their larvae, spiders, molluscs and the like as well as small bits of green vegetable matter and various seeds.

Voice:
A ringing "peese-weet", during the courtship display a note that sounds like "pee-r-weet".
Length:
32 cm.
The male and female have similar plumage.
Size of egg:
37.8—60.4 × 27.8—36.1 mm.

# Black-headed Gull

*Larus ridibundus*

The black-headed gull is one of the commonest of European birds. It nests in central, western and eastern Europe, in Scandinavia and on the shores of Iceland. Northern and eastern populations fly south in July or August whereas gulls from the other parts of Europe may stay the winter or migrate to the Mediterranean. During the winter months the gulls seek out lakes and rivers that do not freeze over and often occur in large groups even in big cities, where people often feed them. They return to their breeding grounds in flocks, but already paired, during the months of March and April, nesting on lakes, ponds as well as the seashore. Black-headed gulls breed in large colonies comprising as many as a thousand birds. The nest is built by both parents on dry ground on islets or as a floating structure on water. The female usually lays three eggs which show marked variation in colour. These are incubated by both partners for 20—23 days. The speckled offspring remain in the nest a number of days, abandoning it sooner when disturbed, either concealing themselves in the surrounding vegetation or making their escape by swimming. Food is brought to the young by the male, who sometimes passes it first to the female to distribute. The young begin to fly at the age of five to six weeks, after which they roam the countryside in flocks. The diet consists of insects, worms, molluscs and other invertebrates as well as small vertebrates such as fish, frogs, etc. Sometimes the gulls also eat green plant parts and are fond of visiting cherry orchards for the fruit.

Voice:
A repated "kwarr" or short "kroup", etc.
Length:
37 cm.
The male and female have similar plumage.
The head is coloured white in winter.
Size of egg:
43.0—66.0 × 31.3—42.1 mm.

Young black-headed gull

# Turtle Dove

*Streptopelia turtur*

The purring call of the turtle dove may be heard on a warm April or May day, announcing its return from winter quarters in far-off tropical Africa. This species is plentiful throughout all of Europe, except Scandinavia, and is found also in northwest Africa and western Asia. The turtle dove frequents thin mixed woods with undergrowth, copses, thickets alongside rivers, streams and ponds, as well as parks with thick growths. During the courtship flight the male soars into the air, before gliding down with tail feathers spread wide. The nest, a simple structure of dry sticks and twigs arranged haphazardly on top of each other, is built by both partners, generally one to five metres above the ground, in bushes and treetops. The two eggs are incubated 14 to 16 days by both parents and both feed the young with "pigeon's milk", regurgitated from the crop during half-digested seeds and grain. The young leave the nest at the age of 14 to 16 days but continue to be fed by the parent birds a short while longer. When the first brood is fully mature, the adult birds have a second, usually in June or July. The turtle dove leaves the woods to visit fields in search of food, and in late summer they gather in small groups in the fields before leaving for the south. The turtle dove is considered a game bird in many countries, but is of little importance to hunters. Agile and swift in flight, it is adept at darting between branches in the treetops, and often eludes an attacking falcon.

The collared dove (*Streptopelia decaocto*) is a related species which is common throughout many parts of Europe, including Britain. Its original breeding area was in the Balkans but in the 1930s it began a spectacular northwestward spread which is still continuing.

One of the differences between turtle and collared doves is the extent of white band on the tail.

1 – *Streptopelia turtur*:
Voice:
A long-drawn-out "roor-r-r".
Lenght: 27 cm.
The male and female have similar plumage.
Size of egg:
27.0–34.6 × 20.0–24.6 mm.

2 – *Streptopelia decaocto*:
Voice:
Typical a deep "coo-coo-coo", in flight a nasal "kwurr".
Length: 28 cm.
Size of egg:
27.5 × 33.8 × 21.8–25.0 mm.

# Common Cuckoo
## or **Cuckoo**

*Cuculus canorus*

As early as the middle of April one may hear the familiar melodious call of the male cuckoo, returned to his breeding grounds from far-off tropical or southern Africa. The females, who arrive a week or ten days later, do not make this characteristic call, but a sound resembling that of the woodpecker. Cuckoos often return to the same breeding grounds for several years in succession, and may be found in woods, copses, large parks, overgrown graveyards as well as thickets beside water or even in large reed beds. The female roams her territory seeking small songbirds' nests and, when she finds one that is suitable, removes any eggs it might contain, depositing one of her own in their stead, usually similar in colouring to those of the host. From May to July one hen lays about 15—20 eggs, each in a different nest. An individual cuckoo lays eggs of like coloration, but often markedly different from those of other cuckoos. The period of incubation is twelve days and, on hatching, the young cuckoo soon evicts all the eggs and even the rightful progeny of its foster parents out of the nest. The newly hatched cuckoo is completely naked and has very sensitive sensory cells on its back that, during the first four days, react to contact with any foreign object in the nest, including both eggs and the hatched offspring of the foster parents. Adult cuckoos feed on hairy caterpillars. In late July or early August the adult cuckoos leave the breeding areas for their winter quarters. The young follow later, in early September.

Voice:
The male's call sounds like "cuc-coo", the female's like "kwickkwickkwick"; the cry of the young resembles "tseetseetsee".
Length:
33 cm.
The male and female have similar plumage.
Size of egg:
19.7—26.4 × 14.7—18.8 mm.

Young cuckoo throwing the eggs of its host out of the nest

# Long-eared Owl

*Asio otus*

The long-eared owl is common throughout Europe except for the most northerly parts. It occurs chiefly in small conifer and mixed woods, as well as in copses, large parks and overgrown gardens. It is faithful to its breeding grounds but many birds, especially inhabitants of northerly regions, sometimes form groups that travel southwest in winter, staying in places where field mice are plentiful, these being the mainstay of the long-eared owl's diet. At the end of March or in April it lays its eggs in the abandoned nests of crows, raptors, jays or the dreys of squirrels, adding only slight variations of its own. The hen incubates the 4—6 eggs herself for 27—28 days, beginning as soon as the first is laid, and so the young hatch successively. The male brings food for his partner and also the nestlings, but these are fed only by the hen. The male often stands beside the nest and claps his wings against his body with a sharp crack, thus revealing its location. The long-eared owl hunts only after dusk, concealing itself in the thick branches of spruce, pine and other trees during the daytime. Pressed motionless against a branch it often looks like a broken stump, escaping detection by all except an experienced ornithologist. Besides rodents, the long-eared owl hunts small birds and, when the young are being fed, it also captures countless insects, including such harmful pests as cockchafers. The young leave the nest at the age of 21—26 days and perch on neighbouring branches.

Voice:
During the courting season a penetrating "oo-oo-oo", also semi-whistling sounds.
Length:
34 cm.
Wing span:
85 to 90 cm.
The male and female have similar plumage.
Size of egg:
35.0—44.7 × 28.0—34.5 mm.

# Eagle Owl
*Bubo bubo*

This is the largest European owl, widespread throughout Europe except for the western parts. It is quite plentiful in some areas, numbers having increased in recent years, thanks to rigid protection laws. The species inhabits open woodland, rocky locations and scrub country. It is a resident bird or transient migrant and may be found in both lowland and mountain regions. Nesting is on cliff ledges, the walls of old castle ruins or simply the ground; in northern regions it often uses a tree cavity at ground level. The nest itself is simple, sometimes lined with only a few hairs and feathers from the owl's victims. Two to four eggs are incubated by the female for 32 to 37 days. During this time the male brings her food, which she takes from him at a short distance from the nest. The newly hatched nestlings are cared for by the hen, who also shelters them from rain and sun. At one to two months the young leave the nest and perch in its vicinity. By the time they are three months old they can fly well. The species requires a large territory, extending as far as 15 kilometres from the nest. It preys on vertebrates as big as hares or small foxes but will also feed on insects. The eagle owl is hated by predators and crows, a fact of which hunters once took advantage by using it as a decoy. This method of hunting is now forbidden in many countries with the aim of protecting birds of prey.

Voice:
A penetrating note which sounds like "coo-hu", and is sometimes followed by a guttural chuckle.
Length:
67 cm.
Wing span:
160 to 166 cm.
Male and female have similar plumage.
Size of egg:
51.2—73.0 × 42.0—53.7 mm.

# Kingfisher

*Alcedo atthis*

The kingfisher, one of the most attractively coloured of all birds, is found in all of Europe excepting the northernmost parts. In Scandinavia it occurs only in the south. It does not leave its breeding grounds for the winter but roams the countryside during the cold months, seeking water that does not freeze over, that is, generally flowing rivers and streams. During the breeding season the kingfisher occurs by standing as well as flowing water of all kinds as long as these are bordered by a steep bank or embankment in which it digs its nesting burrow, which is usually 40—100 centimetres long. Both partners share the task of digging the burrow, which takes several days, using their beaks as digging implements and their feet to scrape the loosened matter out. The nesting chamber is not lined, but within a short time it becomes filled with the indigestible fragments of bones, fish scales, beetles' elytra, etc., which the birds cast up. The pairs have one brood in April or June and a second in June or July. The clutch consists of six to seven eggs and the female begins incubating as soon as the first is laid. The young hatch after 18—21 days. During this period the male keeps his partner supplied with food and sometimes also relieves her. Both share the duties of feeding the young in the nesting chamber for 23—27 days, continuing to bring them food a few days longer when they have fledged. The kingfisher catches small fish and also crustaceans and water insects. When hunting prey it dives into the water.

Voice:
In flight a lengthy "chee-kee" or short "chee".
Length:
16.5 cm.
The male and female have similar plumage.
Size of egg:
20.3—24.8 × 16.7—20.0 mm.

# Hoopoe
*Upupa epops*

Hoopoes are native to practically all of Europe except northeastern Scandinavia and the British Isles and do not breed in Denmark or Iceland. The species does, however, occur accidentally in England and Finland. European populations leave in September for winter quarters in tropical Africa, returning to their breeding grounds in April. The birds are found in open country with extensive meadows, especially near ponds and lakes, and also in light, deciduous woods. The nest is made in a tree hollow, sometimes as high as six metres above the ground. It may also be made close to the ground among rocks. In May to June, sometimes also in July, the female lays six to seven eggs, which she alone incubates for 16 to 20 days. Because the female starts incubating as soon as the first egg is laid, the young hatch successively. Both parents feed their offspring in the nest for 24 to 27 days, doling out the food in the following manner: one nestling awaits the adults' arrival at the entrance hole and as soon as it receives its ration, the one behind pushes to the front; and so it continues, each returning to the end of the queue until its turn comes again. The hoopoe exists mostly on insects and their larvae, which it digs out of soil or cattle droppings with its long bill. Surface prey, such as locusts and spiders, are also taken.

Voice:
The characteristic "poo-poo-poo".
Length:
28 cm.
Male and female have similar plumage.
Size of egg:
23.1—30.3 × 16.3—19.8 mm.

♂

♀

# Great Spotted Woodpecker

*Dendrocopos major*

All of Europe, except Ireland and the most northern areas, provides a home for one of the most abundant of woodpeckers — the great spotted. It stays for the winter in most areas, though it is also a transient migrant out of the breeding season, but inhabitants of northern Europe sometimes journey south in large flocks. Why they undertake such a long trip is as yet not understood. The great spotted woodpecker occurs in woodlands of all types, in the mountains up to the tree line, but is also found in large numbers in parks and large gardens, orchards and tree avenues. In the winter it often roams the countryside in the company of nuthatches and tits, and will visit a garden bird table to nibble sunflower seeds or suet. In spring both partners, though mainly the male, drill a hole about 30 centimetres deep in the trunk of a deciduous or coniferous tree, often using the same cavity for several years. The female lays 5 to 6 eggs, which she and the male take turns incubating for 12 to 13 days. The parents feed the young from the beak, and consequently must bring food to the nest much more often than the green or black woodpecker. At first they make about 40 trips a day, but when the young are some 10 days old the daily trips can total 150 or more. For this reason, the prey must be hunted in the immediate neighbourhood of the nest. The diet consists mainly of insects and their larvae. At the age of 21—23 days the young abandon the cavity but remain in the vicinity of the nest. Adult birds also feed on various seeds and grain.

a ♂   b ♂   c ♂

Some of the other species of black and white European woodpeckers:

(a) white-backed woodpecker,
(b) lesser spotted woodpecker,
(c) middle spotted woodpecker

Voice:
A loud "kik" or "chick". In spring it drums with its beak on the trunks or branches of trees.
Length:
23 cm. The male has a red patch on the nape.
Size of egg:
20.0—29.5 × 15.4—21.8 mm.

# Common or Barn Swallow

*Hirundo rustica*

Throughout Europe the graceful swallow has left its native cliffside habitat and moved to the vicinity of buildings where it has found more favourable conditions. It generally arrives in early April but the vanguard may appear at the end of March, often to be caught by an unexpected snowfall. The swallow's favourite nesting sites are stables, sties, as well as passages in houses, where it builds its open nest of mud cemented with saliva and strengthened with plant stalks and straw. The female lines it with feathers before laying the eggs, five as a rule, which she incubates alone for 14−16 days, being fed meanwhile by the male. The young, which first leave the nest after 19−23 days, are fed by the parents on insects caught adroitly on the wing. On fledging, the swallows form large flocks that fly to neighbouring ponds in the evening, where they roost in the thick reeds. One fine day in September or October, however, the whole flock suddenly takes off on its long journey to the tropical parts of Africa or even as far away as South Africa. In Transvaal, for instance, a million swallows were once counted roosting in a single place at one time.

*Hirundo rustica:*
Voice:
Oft-repeated "tswit, tswit".
Song:
Delicate long and short twittering and warbling notes.
Length: 18 cm.
Size of egg:
16.7−23.0 × 12.2−15.0 mm.

*Delichon urbica:*
Voice:
A clear "tchirrip" or "tchichirrip".
Song:
Twittering.
Length: 13 cm.
Size of egg:
16.1−21.6 × 11.5−14.7 mm.

The common or barn swallow (a) is often mistaken for the house martin (*Delichon urbica*) (b), but they are quite easy to distinguish.

# Crested Lark
*Galerida cristata*

On the mainland of Europe one may sometimes come across a pair of crested larks running to and fro along a road, even in a busy city street. In winter the bird is often found in built-up areas, seeking for seeds on the ground. With the arrival of spring, sometimes even in early March, the birds (which pair for life) get ready to nest near rubbish dumps and highways, on railway embankments and in other localities resembling their original habitats on the eastern steppes, the region from which they spread to Europe in the fourteenth century. They were, for example, first sighted in Cologne on the Rhine in 1552. In Denmark they arrived much later, around 1850; and they have yet to make their appearance in the British Isles. The nest, a careless construction of stalks and roots, is built on the ground by the female, with the male in attendance. The four to five eggs hatch after twelve to thirteen days, incubation being undertaken principally by the hen, relieved by the male only occasionally. She likewise rears the young, which leave the nest when nine days old, as yet incapable of flight, fledging at the age of eighteen days. The crested lark is mainly a vegetarian, though the young are fed only on insects and worms.

Voice:
A liquid "twee-tee-too"
Song:
Slightly resembling that of the skylark with notes learned from other songbirds.
Length:
17 cm.
Distinguishing feature is the conspicuous crest.
The male and female have similar plumage.
Size of egg:
19.0—24.8 × 15.0—18.3 mm.

# Nightingale
*Luscinia megarhynchos*

Bushes on the edges of damp, deciduous woods, overgrown parks, gardens, hillsides and thickets, bordering rivers and ponds are favourite haunts of the nightingale. Its song, famed for strength, clarity and purity, is mostly at night, but also at intervals during the day. Not all nightingales have the same sweet song, and some are markedly more accomplished than others. They return to their breeding grounds, which embrace all of Europe except Scandinavia, Ireland and Scotland, from mid-April onwards, flying, as a rule, by night. First to arrive are the males, who immediately burst into songs. The females arrive several days later. A nest is built of grass, rootlets and dry leaves, close to the ground or on a pile of leaves, well concealed in thick undergrowth. The female lays three to six eggs which she incubates herself for 14 days. However, in rearing the young, which hop out of the nest at the tender age of 11 days (as yet incapable of flight), she is aided by the male. Both parents feed the young with insects, larvae and spiders. In late August or early September the nightingale leaves for its winter quarters in Africa.

Voice:
A liquid "wheet", short "tuc" and similar sounds.
Song:
Beautiful, rich and varied melodies alternating with joyous bubbling phrases; the song often includes phrases learned from other birds.
Length:
16.5 cm.
Male and female have similar plumage.
Size of egg:
18.2—24.7 × 13.9—17.0 mm.

# Robin

*Erithacus rubecula*

Deciduous, mixed and coniferous woods with thick undergrowth, from lowland to mountain altitudes, are the home of the robin over practically the whole of Europe except Iceland and northern Scandinavia. Its range extends eastwards as far as western Siberia, and it is also found in northwestern Africa. In western and central Europe it is plentiful in parks and cemeteries, preferring thickly overgrown, dimly lighted spots, which accounts for its conspicuously large eyes. Northern and eastern populations migrate in September and October to winter quarters in western and southern Europe, and northern Africa. Birds often fly to England in the autumn, sometimes catching a ride on ships crossing the channel. March marks the return to the breeding grounds, where in April the females begin building their nests of roots, plant stalks and moss. These are well concealed between stones, under protruding roots, in piles of underbrush or less frequently in a hollow stump, and are lined with thin roots, fine plant parts and sometimes with animal hairs. The three to six eggs are incubated by the hen only for 13 to 14 days, but the male asists her in feeding the young with insects, larvae and spiders. The young leave the nest at the age of 12 to 15 days, though as yet incapable of flight, and conceal themselves on the ground, where the parents bring them food.

Voice:
A ringing "tic" or "tsip".
Song:
Loud and melodious.
Length:
14 cm.
Male and female have similar plumage.
Size of egg:
16.9—22.2 × 13.8—16.3 mm.

# Blackbird

*Turdus merula*

The blackbird is found in all but the northernmost parts of Europe. In the central and western regions it is mostly resident, but more northerly populations winter in the Mediterranean. During spring, at dawn and even while it is still dark, one may hear the melodic song of the male perched on a rooftop, a tall post or a tree. His song may be interspersed with various unexpected passages for the bird is an expert mimic. As soon as the thickets show the first hint of green, he begins building his nest of roots, grass stems, bits of paper and rags, often using mud as well. The nest may be found in many different places — in thickets or trees, on a windowsill, wall or in a wood-pile. In the latter part of April the hen may already have started incubating her four to six eggs. The young hatch after 13 to 15 days, leave the nest two weeks later as yet incapable of flig t, and conceal themselves on the ground. The parent birds are tire-less providers of food, mainly earthworms, which they are very adept at pulling out of the ground. Blackbirds also feed on caterpillars, molluscs and, in autumn and winter, berries and household scraps. In winter they are frequent visitors to suspended feeders and bird tables in parks and gardens.

Gardens, parks and woods are the home of another excellent singer, the song thrush (*Turdus philomelos*).

*Turdus merula:*
Voice:
"Tchink, tchink, tchink"; an anxious "tchook".
Song:
Loud flutey, very melodic.
Length: 25.5 cm.
Sexually dimorphic.
Size of egg:
24.0—35.5 × 18.0—23.6 mm.

*Turdus philomelos:*
Voice:
A liquid "tchuck" or "tchick",
sometimes "dag-dag".
Song:
Flutey, whistling, very distinctive varied phrases.

Length:
23 cm.
Male and female have similar plumage.
Size of egg:
23.0—31.8 × 18.6—23.0 mm.

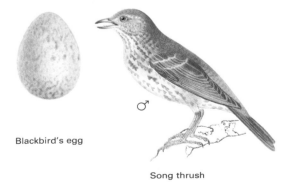

Blackbird's egg

Song thrush

# Chaffinch

*Fringilla coelebs*

One of our commonest birds, the chaffinch is found not only throughout Europe but also in northwestern Africa, the Middle East and Asia as far as western Siberia. Birds inhabiting northerly regions migrate to the Mediterranean in the autumn. Elsewhere they are resident or migrate only locally. The males stake out their breeding territory in February or March, the females arriving somewhat later to select a nesting site, usually in the fork of a tree, then building the nest, mostly alone, males assisting only for brief intervals. The nest itself is a neat, compact cup of moss, lichen and spiders' webs, often camouflaged with bits of bark from the tree in which it is placed. The chaffinch has one brood in April or May and a second in June or July. A clutch usually comprises five eggs, incubated for 12 to 14 days by the hen alone. Both partners, however, share the duties of rearing the young, feeding them mainly on insects and spiders for about two weeks in the nest, and for a short while after they abandon it. The diet of adult birds consists mainly of seeds. Outside the breeding season chaffinches form groups that roam the fields with other seed-eating birds or frequent parks and gardens where there are feeding trays or bird tables. They are also plentiful in thin woodlands.

Another seed-eating bird is the European gold-finch *(Carduelis carduelis)*, which lives in gardens, fields and meadows and feeds on thistle seeds.

Goldfinch

Chaffinch

*Fringilla coelebs:*
Voice:
The familiar "chwink-chwink".
Song:
Short, melodious and rattling;
terminates in a well
defined flourish
Length:
15 cm.
Sexually dimorphic.
Size of egg:
17.0—22.8 × 13.2—15.8 mm.

*Carduelis carduelis:*
Voice:
The twittering "swilt-witt-witt-witt".
Song:
Composed of similar notes to call.
Length:
12 cm.
Sexually dimorphic.
Size of egg:
15.6—20.0 × 12.3—14.3 mm.

# Bullfinch

*Pyrrhula pyrrhula*

During the winter months, especially when there is plenty of snow, one can come across a large number of brightly coloured birds in rowan woods, at the edges of forests, or in parks and gardens. They are bullfinches, which at this time fly to central and southern Europe in vast numbers from their homes in the north. Elsewhere, the bullfinch is distributed throughout most of Europe, except Spain, and in many places is a resident bird. It is found chiefly in coniferous forests with dense undergrowth, both in lowland country and in mountains, though it also frequents overgrown parks and large gardens. At the end of April, the female begins to build the nest in thick hedges or coniferous trees, quite close to the ground. It is woven of twigs and the hollow lined with hairs and lichen, or sometimes with fine roots. The male keeps his mate company during this period, both of them staying very quiet and unobtrusive, concealing themselves with some skill. The clutch, numbering five eggs, is incubated by the hen for 12 to 14 days; only sometimes is she relieved by the male. The young are fed in the nest by both parents for 12 to 16 days, chiefly on insects, and for a short while longer after they have fledged. In June or July there is usually a second brood. Bullfinches feed on seeds and berries, and in early spring devour the buds of flowering trees, especially fruit trees, which makes them extremely unpopular with gardeners.

Voice:
A soft, piping sound resembling "wheeb".
Song:
Composed of piping tones, including "teek-teek-tioo".
Length:
14.5—17 cm.
Sexually dimorphic.
Size of egg:
17.0—22.2 × 13.0—15.4 mm.

# Starling

*Sturnus vulgaris*

Early in spring one often hears strange and varied sequence of notes, including sounds resembling the cackling of a hen and flutey trills emanating from the top of a tree or from beside a nest-box. All are made by the starling, an excellent imitator of other birds' songs. It has almost entirely abandoned the deciduous woods that were its ancestral habitat and moved instead to towns and suburbs. There, from April to June, the female builds the nest of rootlets and dried grass, sometimes assisted by the male. Both share the duties of incubating the four to six eggs for two weeks, alternating at regular intervals, and both feed the hungry nestlings who welcome each meal of insects and their larvae, molluscs and worms with a harsh, rasping call. The older nestlings literally fight to be among the first to get to the entrance hole with their wide-open beaks. Not until three weeks do they find courage to venture from the nest for the first time. After they have fledged, starlings assemble in flocks that visit cherry orchards and in autumn they are frequent and unwelcome visitors to vineyards. Flocks roost in spinneys, reed-beds or on buildings, and move south and west to escape the cold weather. Some individuals winter in southern Europe and north Africa; Scandinavian populations winter in the British Isles.

♂

Voice:
A harsh, descending "tcheer".
Song:
Whistling and squeaky notes as well as imitations of the songs of other birds.
Length:
21 cm.
The female's plumage has a less metallic sheen that the male's and is more spotted.
Size of egg:
26.2—34.1 × 19.7—23.2 mm.

# Great Tit
*Parus major*

The great tit may be found in all parks and gardens, even in the immediate vicinity of buildings, as well as in woodlands. Its distribution includes the whole of Europe and a large part of Asia and North America. Most do not leave their nesting grounds even in winter and only tits inhabiting the northernmost areas sometimes fly southwest in small flocks in the autumn. As early as April and then again in June or July it builds its soft-lined nest in a tree cavity, a wall crevice or a nest-box. First it gathers bits of moss and lichen and then lines a deep hollow with fine hairs and feathers. When all is ready the hen lays one egg a day until there are eight to ten, at which stage she begins incubating. The male does not assist her in this task but brings her a juicy caterpillar at intervals to satisfy her hunger. The naked, helpless nestlings hatch after 13—14 days and the parent birds are kept busy supplying them with food, mainly caterpillars. During the first few days they make as many as 500 trips a day and before the nestlings are fledged even 800 a day. The young tits abandon the nest at the age of 16—21 days but perch on branches close by for several more days, continuing to be fed by the parent birds. In winter the great tit is one of the commonest visitors to bird tables.

Voice:
A clear "tsink, tsink", "tchair, tchair" or "chi-chi-chi".
Song:
Ringing "teechew, teechew, teechew."
Length:
14 cm.
The male and female have similar plumage.
Size of egg:
14.4—20.1 × 11.3—14.8 mm.

# Jay

*Garrulus glandarius*

All of Europe, excepting Iceland and northern Scandinavia, provides a home for the jay, which frequents woodlands with undergrowth from lowland to mountain elevations. It is most abundant, however, in woods where oak stands predominate. Mostly a resident bird, it roams the countryside after fledging, but inhabitants of northern Europe sometimes fly in large flocks to central Europe during the winter. The nest is built in spring, from April to May, generally amidst the dense branches of spruce trees on the margins of forests, at a height of four metres or more above the ground. It is usually constructed of dry twigs and a layer of plant stalks and roots, but sometimes is made of moss and lined with grass. The clutch, consisting of 5—7 eggs, is incubated by the female for a period of 16—17 days. Both parents feed the young until the age of 20—21 days when they leave the nest and roam the countryside. Several families will later combine to form a flock. When crossing open territory, however, the flocks break up and the birds fly singly and spaced far apart, converging again only after they have reached a forest. The diet consists of both vegetable and animal food and the jay is notoriously fond of birds' eggs. In the autumn flocks visit oak woods, where they collect acorns. The jay is an extremely wary bird and, on sighting a human being, immediately utters a loud cry. In the vicinity of the nest, however, it is very quiet and cautious. The jay can imitate various sounds and birds raised in captivity can be taught to mimic words.

Voice:
A penetrating "skraaak" and sometimes a mewing note.
Length:
34 cm.
Wing span: 54 cm.
The male and female have similar plumage.
Size of egg:
28.2—36.0 × 21.0—25.6 mm.

# Magpie
*Pica pica*

The magpie is notorious for its habit of collecting glittering objects, which it then conceals in various places. Whereas wild magpies are very shy and wary, individuals reared in captivity are quickly tamed and grow into entertaining companions, though one must be careful to keep objects such as spectacles, rings and spoons out of sight. The species is widespread not only in Europe but also in Asia, northwestern Africa and North America. It is always resident, roaming the countryside far and wide in small flocks of ten to 20 individuals. In Europe, its favourite haunts are shrub-covered hillsides, woods and the edges of ponds. In early April, individual pairs choose a tree or tall shrub in which to build their nest made of dry, mostly thorny twigs, lined with turf and loam with an inner layer of hairs and fine stalks. It is additionally protected by a dome of thorny twigs. The hen lays three to ten eggs which she incubates for 17 to 18 days, mostly on her own. The young are fed in the nest by both parents for 24 days and for a further short period after fledging. The diet consists of mice, fieldmice, lizards, insects and other invertebrates, as well as seeds, fruits and berries.

♂

Voice:
Raucous, barking cries such as "chak-chak-chak".
Length:
46 cm.
Male and female have similar plumage.
Size of egg:
27.3–41.9 × 21.2–26.4 mm.

# Crow
*Corvus corone*

The crow is widespread throughout the whole of Europe. There are two subspecies: the carrion crow *(Corvus corone corone)* (1), inhabiting western and southwestern Europe and part of central Europe; and the hooded crow *(Corvus corone cornix)* (2), which inhabits the remaining territory including Scotland and Ireland. Where their distribution overlaps, the two races may interbreed. The crow is a resident bird or a transient migrant, large flocks flying to central and western Europe from the north and east in winter. During the breeding season it frequents open woodlands, field groves and thickly overgrown parks in cities. It builds its nest in March, usually in trees at a height of five metres or more. The structure is made of dry twigs, mud and turf, and lined with moss, grass, hairs, sheep's wool and rags. A new nest takes some eight to ten days to build, but crows often use old nests. The female incubates the four to six eggs herself for 18 to 21 days, fed by the male. He only feeds the nestlings for the first five to seven days, after which both partners share the duties of attending the young. At 28 to 35 days they leave the nest. Flocks of crows visit the edges of ponds, lakes and rivers, where they find plentiful food remnants. They are omnivorous birds, collecting seeds, berries, beech nuts, insects and their larvae, molluscs and carrion, besides which they also hunt fieldmice and other small vertebrates.

Another smaller corvine bird is the jackdaw *(Corvus monedula)* which lives in parks, quarries, old castle ruins and church steeples.

Jackdaw

Crow

Voice:
A deep "kraa" or croaking "keerk".
Song:
Composed of similar notes and heard in the spring months.
Length:
47 cm.
Wing span:
95 to 100 cm.
Male and female have similar plumage.
Size of egg:
35.5—52.7.×26.0—29.7 mm.

# Horsfield's Tortoise
*Testudo horsfieldi*

# Spur-thighed
or **Common European Tortoise**
or **Grecian Tortoise**
*Testudo graeca*

Horsfield's tortoise is a small terrestrial tortoise living in the lower Volga region, in Turkestan, Iran, Afghanistan and north Pakistan. Its carapace is markedly flat and the tail ends in horny spike. It lives in steppe and semi-desert regions and in some places reaches considerable altitudes — over 1,200 metres above sea level. It survives the winter and the driest summer days in underground shelters. Mating time is in spring. Approximately two months later; the female lays three to five eggs that hatch in August. The newly hatched young are three to five cm long.

The spur-thighed tortoise has an ivory-yellow to olive-green carapace marked with dark spots, and only a single plate above the tail. The tail itself is rounded and has no horny spike at the tip. The insides of the thighs bear horny projections.

It occurs in the low-lying shrubby areas of southern Europe, north Africa and southwestern Asia.

1 — *Testudo graeca:*
Length:
25—30 cm.
Egg-laying period:
May and June.
Hibernation period:
November to March.

2 — *Testudo horsfieldi:*
Length:
16—20 cm.
Egg-laying period:
May and June.
Hibernation period:
November to March; often aestivates in dry summers.

1

2

# Kotschy's Naked-toed
## or **Kotschy's Gecko**
*Cyrtodactylus kotschyi (Gymnodactylus kotschyi)*

# Turkish Gecko
*Hemidactylus turcicus*

Kotschy's naked-toed gecko has a grey or brown, often cross-barred back with small round and larger granulated scales; its belly is porcelain white. The pupils contract to vertical slits. There are no suction pads on the tips of its fingers and toes.

It lives in southern Europe as well as in the temperate zone of western Asia, its favourite habitat being rock fissures, stone piles and buildings where it is often seen swiftly climbing along walls and ceilings. It is most active in the evening and by night, hunting insects and spiders. Towards the end of spring, the female deposits usually two eggs in various crevices; the young geckos hatch in summer.

In the Turkish gecko, the ground colour of the back varies from greyish to brown and bears irregularly arranged dark spots. It can quickly change its colour depending on its surroundings. Two longitudinal rows of suction pads are located on the underside of the tips of its fingers and toes.

Its original habitat is the Mediterranean region but it has been accidentally carried by ship as far away as North America and Cuba. It seeks similar shelters as Kotschy's naked-toed gecko. It is capable of making relatively loud sounds.

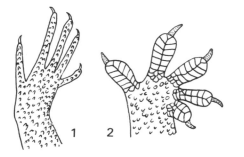

1 — *Cyrtodactylus kotschyi:*
Length:
8—10 cm.
Egg-laying period:
April and May.
Hibernation period:
beginning of December to March.

2 — *Hemidactylus turcicus:*
Length:
8—10 cm.
Egg-laying period:
April and May.
Hibernation period:
November to March.

# Sand Lizard

*Lacerta agilis*

The coloration of this species is highly variable. The brownish or grey-brown back and sides are usually strewn with dark circular patches which have whitish centres. In spring and summer, the sides of the male's body are grass-green and sometimes the back assumes a green colour, while in the females brownish hues predominate. Sometimes the back of either sex may be brown or red.

It is distributed throughout Europe as well as in western and central Asia and inhabits both lowlands and hilly regions. In Britain it is confined to a few, scattered, sandy locations; on the continent it prefers sunny, sheltered places at the edge of woods and meadows, slopes covered with grass or shrubs, wasteland and old quarries; it is also plentiful in gardens and parks. The sand lizard's diet consists of locusts, flies, beetles, spiders and other arthropods. It spends the winter underground. Towards the end of spring or at the beginning of summer the female lays 5—15 longish eggs, provided with a leathery cover, in a shallow hole in the earth. In about six to eight weeks, the young lizards measuring three to four cm hatch out. There are many subspecies.

Length:
16—20 cm.
Egg laying period:
May and June.
Hibernation period:
October to end of March.

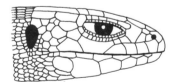

1♂

2♀

3

# Green Lizard

*Lacerta viridis*

The grass-green back of the male is densely covered with small black spots. The females' upper surface is brown-green, the young are brownish, sometimes marked with longitudinal streaks. In the breeding season, the throat in males is bright blue. The ventral side is yellow-white or yellow. The tail is twice the length of the rest of the body.

It occurs at lower elevations in central and southern Europe and Asia Minor, but in the southernmost parts of its range, it may be found in mountainous regions up to 1,700 metres. It prefers dry places overgrown with shrubs but is also abundant in light, sunny woods, at field edges and in vineyards. Insects, small lizards and rodents are its chief food.

It usually mates in April, soon after coming out of hibernation, and between late May and July the female lays 6—20 eggs; the young that hatch 6—8 weeks later are 4 cm in length. Several subspecies of the green lizard occur in the Balkans and on some Mediterranean islands.

Length:
30—50 cm.
Egg-laying period:
end of May to July.
Hibernation period:
depends on the climate; in central Europe end of October to April.

1, 2 — adults
3 — young

# Viviparous Lizard

*Lacerta vivipara*

The back of this lizard varies in colour from grey-brown to dark brown; a slightly darker streak may run along the spine and is flanked by an even darker discontinuous stripe. A continuous dark band bordered by light-coloured spots appears on either side of the body. The belly is yellowish or grey in females; in males it varies from yolk yellow to orange, spotted with black. The tail is relatively short and thick.

It occurs throughout Europe and Asia — in damp places at high elevations up to 3,000 metres, and in the north even on low-lying land. Its movements are relatively sluggish and it spends the hibernation period in underground shelters, usually in very deep burrows. Mating takes place in May or June and three months afterwards the female gives birth to three to ten young measuring three cm. The viviparity of this species is an adaptation to a cold environment: in the lower altitudes of southern Europe it is sometimes oviparous. It feeds mostly on insects.

Length:
15—16 cm.
Time of bearing young:
August and September.
Hibernation period:
September or October to March or April, according to locality;
in warmer regions it remains active throughout the winter.

1, 2 — adults
3 — young

Eggs with hatching young

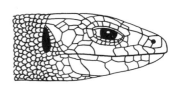

# Wall Lizard

*Podarcis muralis (Lacerta muralis)*

A slender lizard with a flat, pointed head and a narrow tail which is almost twice as long as the rest of the body. Its grey-brown back bears dark spots or a dark recticular pattern. In females the spots are frequently joined up into rows, forming a dark band bordered on either side by lighter streaks. The flanks also have conspicuous rows of dark patches. In males, blue spots are present between the sides and belly.

Its habitats are sunny, stony areas of southern and central Europe and Asia Minor. It can run amazingly quickly and is an excellent rock climber. Various arthropods, particularly insects, provide the main source of its food. Two or three times a year the female deposits her two to eight eggs in a little hole dug in the soil. On hatching two months later the young are two to three cm long. In Europe it exists as several subspecies, especially on the Mediterranean islands such as the Baleares.

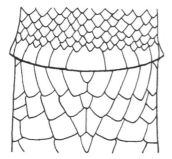

Scales on the throat form a characteristic collar

Length:
18—25 cm.
Egg-laying period:
May to July (two or three times).
Hibernation period:
in central Europe November to March, in southern Europe it remains active throughout the year.

# Balkan Wall Lizard
## or Grass Lizard
*Podarcis taurica (Lacerta taurica)*

# Snake-eyed Skink
## or Balkan Lidless Skink
*Ablepharus kitaibelii*

The Balkan wall lizard is a variegated lizard with a short, slightly pointed head and a relatively long, narrow tail. It is abundant in the Ukraine and the Balkan Peninsula, ranging northwards as far as Hungary and Rumania. Steppe localities overgrown with grasses and low shrubs are its usual habitat. It feeds on small insects. The female lays two to six eggs in the late spring and the young hatch in the summer.

The snake-eyed skink is a slender animal with a lustrous dorsal surface varying from greyish to brown-red. Two broad, dark streaks run along the sides of the body. The belly is grey-white, the legs are short, and the distance between fore legs and hind legs is relatively great. The tail is very long.

It is distributed throughout western Asia and penetrates into Europe on the Balkan Peninsula. Northwards it reaches the southern parts of Czechoslovakia. It lives on dry, stony slopes, frequently under oaks. In the daytime it keeps hidden under the stones but after nightfall it goes out hunting small insects on which it lives. Unlike most skinks, which lay eggs, it is viviparous.

1 — *Podarcis taurica:*
Length:
15—18 cm.
Egg-laying period:
May and June.
Hibernation period:
December to February.

2 — *Ablepharus kitaibelii:*
Length:
10—11 cm.
Egg-laying period:
May and June.
Hibernation period:
in northern regions November to March, in the south December to February.

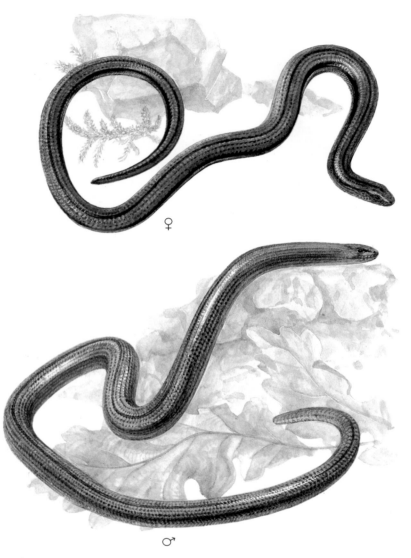

♀

♂

# Slow-worm
*Anguis fragilis*

This is a legless lizard with a grey, brown or olive green upper surface; a dark central dorsal band is present in females and in the young. In old males, azure-blue scales are sometimes scattered on the back and sides among the normally coloured ones.

It is distributed almost throughout the whole of Europe (northwards up to southern Sweden and Finland), in southwestern Asia and northwestern Africa. It is found in lowlands as well as mountains and it lives under fallen leaves, logs, stones, and in crevices. Its diet consists of earthworms, slugs and insect larvae, which it hunts both underground and on the surface. Like the other lizards, it can shed its tail when in danger.

It frequently stays in its underground winter shelters until April. The breeding season starts a short time afterwards. At the beginning of summer, the female bears 8—20 young. These are wrapped at birth in a transparent membrane which breaks almost immediately. There are several subspecies.

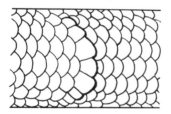

Scales in the anal region

Length:
40—45 cm.
Time of bearing young:
June and July.
Hibernation period:
November to March, April.

# Aesculapian Snake

*Elaphe longissima*

This is a large colubrid snake with a light brown or dark brown back covered with white-flecked scales. The belly is white-yellow. In younger individuals, the rear part of the head may be marked with yellow or orange crescent-shaped areas, occasionally edged with black.

It is widespread throughout southern Europe and southwestern Asia; in central Europe it occurs only in isolated populations, the most northerly of these being in Poland. It shows a preference for sunny, sheltered places in dry regions, especially on bushy and stony slopes in light and warm deciduous woods. It climbs expertly in trees and shrubs where it hunts birds, dormice and squirrels. Mice and voles, however, are the chief item of its diet. It kills prey by coiling around and constricting it.

Mating takes place in April and May; at the beginning of summer the female lays five to eight eggs; the young hatch in September and measure about 20 cm. There are several subspecies.

Length:
180–200 cm.
Egg-laying period:
June and July.
Hibernation period:
end of October to end of March.

Young

Scales in the anal region

# Smooth Snake

*Coronella austriaca*

This is a small, grey, brown or black-brown snake with two to four rows of dark markings, frequently confluent, extending along its back. On either side of the head a dark band runs from the nostrils to the throat, and there is another dark area at the back of the head. Because of these markings it is often mistaken for an adder but the spots are never arranged in the zigzag line characteristic of adders; moreover, the smooth snake's head is much narrower than that of an adder and the body is much more slender.

It inhabits central and northern Europe, but is only locally distributed in southern Britain, showing a preference for dry places abounding in stones and gravel. It is an exclusively diurnal snake. When young its diet is small lizards, small mice, young snakes and slow-worms. It coils in several loops around the captured prey, constricts and subsequently devours it. When attacked, it defends itself by vigorously biting the aggressor.

Mating takes place early in spring; towards the end of summer the female gives birth to two to twelve young which emerge from the eggs at the moment of birth. Thus the smooth snake is ovoviviparous. The young are 13—18 cm long.

Smooth snake

Adder

Length:
70—80 cm.
Time of bearing young:
August and September.
Hibernation period:
November to March.

# Grass Snake
## or **Ringed Snake**
*Natrix natrix*

The back of this snake is coloured greyish-brown, sometimes with a bluish or greenish tinge, and may be decorated with four to six longitudinal rows of black spots which sometimes tend to fuse. The belly is yellow-white, checkered with black; in some individuals it may be completely black. At the back of the head there are two whitish or yolk-yellow crescent-shaped markings edged with black.

It is distributed throughout most of Europe, northwards as far as Scandinavia, in Asia as far as Siberia, and also in northwestern Africa. It is a typical inhabitant of richly overgrown banks along stagnant and sluggish waters. Being an excellent swimmer, it can also skilfully hunt in water. When young it feeds on tadpoles and small frogs, but when older it prefers fish and adult amphibians, including toads.

It emerges from hibernation in March or April depending on the climatic conditions; it mates a short time afterwards, and in summer the female lays clusters of elongate, soft-shelled eggs among the decaying plant litter. Sometimes several females lay eggs in the same place. The newly-hatched young measure 15—20 cm. There are several subspecies.

Length:
130—150 cm.
Egg-laying period:
July and August.
Hibernation period:
end of October to March or April.

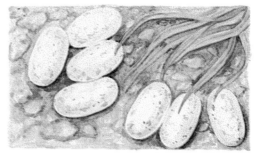

Eggs

# Adder or Common Viper or Northern Viper

*Vipera berus*

The coloration of this species is highly variable — from light grey or yellow-grey through various shades of brown to entirely black. The males are usually grey, the females brownish. A conspicuous broad and dark, zigzag band, indistinct in black forms, runs the full length of the back. When viewed from above, the broad head is triangular in shape and clearly distinct from the powerful body. Large fangs are located at the front of the upper jaw.

Except in the extreme south, this species is distributed throughout Europe and ranges all the way across Asia to Japan; it inhabits lowlands as well as mountains where it occurs at considerable altitudes. It likes to bask in the sun on elevated places — stones, stumps, etc. The chief items of its diet are small mammals which it kills by striking them with lightning speed. It is shy and, unless accidentally disturbed, it shuns human beings. It sometimes bites in self-defence, however, and it is then necessary for the victim to see a doctor immediately as the venom is very strong indeed.

It hibernates in underground shelters, mates early in spring, and the female gives birth to 5—20 young, measuring 15—20 cm, at the beginning of summer.

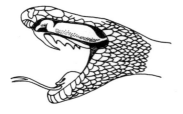

Exposed venom sac

Length:
75—90 cm.
Time of bearing young:
June and July.
Hibernation period:
October, November to February, April.

# Nose-horned Viper
# or **Sand Viper**
# or **Horned Viper**

*Vipera ammodytes*

The ground colour of this species varies from light grey to reddish-brown or dark brown. A dark zigzag band, which, in males, is usually black, extends along the middle of the back. The body is wide and flattened. The typical broad, flat head is triangular in shape and the upper end of the snout bears a characteristic little horn. Hollow fangs are located at the front of the upper jaw.

It occurs in southeastern and central Europe, the northern limit being Hungary and Austria; it is also found in the southwestern parts of Asia. Its favourite spots are sunny places overgrown with bushy vegetation, rocky hillsides, stone piles, etc. It can be found at most altitudes.

Depending on the climate, it hibernates until February or April; mating takes place soon afterwards, and, in late summer or autumn, the female bears fully developed young measuring 15—20 cm. The first food of the young includes small lizards, shrews and small voles, while the adults hunt voles, mice, moles and small birds which they kill by striking them with their fangs. Its venom can be lethal to man.

Length:
90—100 cm.
Time of bearing young:
August and September.
Hibernation period:
according to climatic conditions;
October, November to February, April.

165

# Fire Salamander
## or **European Salamander**

*Salamandra salamandra*

It has a glossy black body with marked ribbing and irregularly scattered spots ranging in colour from yolk-yellow to orange; in west European individuals, these spots can fuse into longitudinal streaks. The skin is smooth; on either side of the rear part of the head there are two crescent-shaped skin glands which contain a venomous secretion. Body and head are dorso-ventrally flattened; the blunt tail is circular in cross-section.

In ranges throughout the hills and mountains of southern and central Europe, eastern Asia and northwestern Africa, where it lives in damp, deciduous woods to altitudes of more than 1,000 metres, in the vicinity of clean and cool streams. Throughout the day it stays under stones, bark or leaves, coming out of hiding only in the evening, at night or in rainy weather. It feeds on various invertebrates — worms, slugs and insects — and hibernates in underground shelters which it leaves in March or April. The mating period starts shortly afterwards. The female enters water to bear 50 or more larvae with four fully developed limbs and branchial gills. There are several subspecies.

Another species in the genus is the alpine salamander (*Salamandra atra*) which occurs in the Alps, the French Jura and the mountains of western Yugoslavia and Albania. Unlike the fire salamander it gives birth to fully developed young, but usually only two.

The alpine salamander

Length:
20—28 cm.
Breeding season:
March and April;
eggs are often fertilized in the following year;
the larvae hatch in spring and metamorphose after 2—3 months.

1 — western form
2 — eastern form

# Smooth Newt
# or Common Newt

*Triturus vulgaris*

The basic colour of the body is olive-brown speckled in males with circular black spots. In the breeding period, males are adorned with a high, unbroken crest starting immediately behind the head and terminating at the end of the tail where it is developed on both dorsal and ventral edges. In the smaller females the crest is absent and the colour varies from brownish to yellowish-brown.

The smooth newt is distributed throughout Europe, ranging from the British Isles to central Siberia, northwards as far as southern Scandinavia; it avoids, however, regions covered with continuous forests. It can be found even in the smallest pools and lives on a large variety of invertebrates. As early as the end of February it leaves its winter shelters and pairs in water. The female attaches the 200—300 eggs to water plants; the aquatic larvae complete their development in about three months, though they may take somewhat longer in cold waters. Soon after mating the adult newts leave the water to live in damp places nearby. Under natural conditions, the smooth newt sometimes successfully interbreeds with the Carpathian newt *(Triturus montandoni)*. There are many subspecies in southern Europe.

Length:
8—10 cm.
Breeding season:
April and May;
larvae metamorphose in June and July.

1, 2 — adults, aquatic stage
3 — terrestrial stage
4 — larva

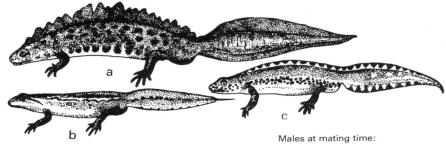

Males at mating time:
a — Warty newt (*T. cristacus*)
b — Carpathian newt (*T. montandoni*)
c — Alpine newt (*T. alpestris*)

# Fire-bellied Toad
*Bombina bombina*

# Yellow-bellied Toad
or **Variegated Fire Toad**
or **Mountain Toad**
*Bombina variegata*

The dorsal side of the fire-bellied toad is greyish-black or greyish-brown with dark spots. The black belly is marked with red or orange speckles.

It lives in central and eastern Europe and is abundant in lowlands, inhabiting both small pools and larger ponds. It is an excellent swimmer. Larvae of gnats and midges, aquatic crustaceans and molluscs constitute its diet. When in danger it sometimes assumes a warning position: it turns on its back, arches its body and exposes its brightly coloured belly towards the enemy. Its skin secretions are venomous and distasteful.

The back of the yellow-bellied toad is grey to dark brown, frequently dark-speckled. The yellow belly is adorned with black or bluish spots.

It is widespread in southern and eastern Europe, except in the Iberian Peninsula; mostly in mountains where it reaches the elevation of 1,800 metres. Its biology is similar to that of the fire-bellied toad. A number of subspecies occur in Europe.

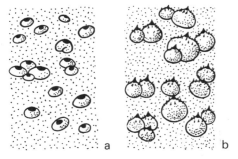

Skin papillae on the back of (a) the fire-bellied toad and (b) the yellow-bellied toad

1 — *Bombina bombina*, dorsal side
2 — *Bombina bombina*, ventral side
3 — *Bombina variegata*

1, 2 — *Bombina bombina:*
Length:
4.5 cm.
Breeding season:
throughout April and May; tadpoles metamorphose in September and October.

3 — *Bombina variegata:*
Length:
5 cm.
Breeding season:
March to May; tadpoles metamorphose in September.

# Marsh Frog
# or Croaking Frog
*Rana ridibunda*

This large frog resembles the edible frog, to which it is closely related. Both have a grass-green or olive back marked with dark spots, and frequently a longitudinal yellowish-white dorsal band. The vocal sacs of males, located at the corners of the mouth, vary from greyish to black. The skin is warty and females exceed males in size.

Its range extends from northern, central and south-eastern Europe to the entire temperate zone of Asia, eastwards as far as Japan. It shows a preference for places near stagnant or sluggish warm waters; in central and northern Europe it is found at lower elevations but in southern Europe it occurs in mountains up to about 2,000 metres. It feeds on a wide variety of invertebrates and small vertebrates. In the fry ponds of fish farms, it can damage the young fish populations. In hibernates at the bottom of deeper waters and is active from April to October or November. It breeds in spring and three or four months later the tadpoles metamorphose into minute froglets. In Europe, this frog occurs as two sub-species. It can successfully interbreed with the edible frog under natural conditions.

Length:
females 12 cm, exceptionally 15 cm;
males 9—10 cm.
Breeding season:
April and May; tadpoles metamorphose in July and August.

Tadpole

# Common Frog
*Rana temporaria*

This frog's back is brown and usually dark-spotted; its dirty-white belly bears greyish-brown spots. A light longitudinal streak may run along the centre of the back and a dark blotch extends behind the eyes to the fore limbs. It differs from the moor frog in having a rounded head and obtuse snout. Its hind legs are shorter than those of other true frogs.

The area of distribution of the common frog is discontinuous, being divided into two distinct areas. The western part covers central and northern Europe, and the eastern part covers the Far East, northeastern China and northern Japan. It inhabits woods, fields, meadows and peat-bogs — always in a moist environment near water. In southern regions it prefers foothill and mountain regions, while in the north it occurs also in the lowlands. Its food consists of slugs and various arthropods. Large numbers of these frogs often gather in the mud at the bottom of ponds to hibernate. Mating takes place very early in spring, often at a time when the water surface is still partly covered with ice. The eggs usually float in large clusters at the water surface. After two to three months the tadpoles metamorphose into frogs.

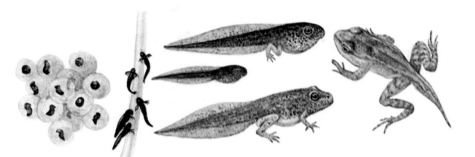

The stages of metamorphosis

Length:
8—10 cm.
Breeding season:
March and April, but later in higher altitudes; tadpoles metamorphose in June and July.

# Agile Frog
## or **Dalmatian Frog**
*Rana dalmatina*

# **Moor Frog** or **Field Frog**
*Rana arvalis*

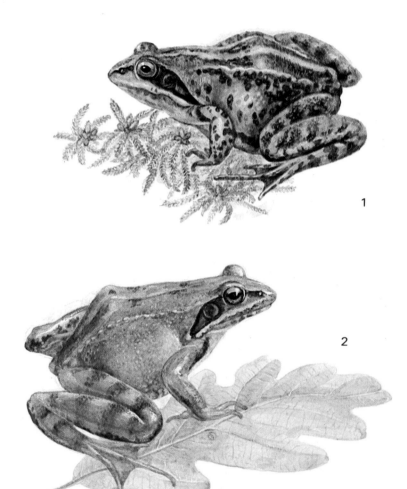

1

The colour of the back of the agile frog usually varies from a uniform light brown to rose-brown. A conspicuous dark spot is situated between the eyes and fore limbs. Extraordinarily long hind legs allow it to make long leaps of as much as two metres.

It occurs throughout southern and central Europe and in northwestern Asia and shows a liking for light, deciduous lowland woods. It returns to water only to mate. Earthworms, spiders and small insects constitute its diet. Females lay clusters of eggs early in spring. Towards the end of summer the tadpoles metamorphose into small froglets that reach maturity in three or four years.

The moor frog has a brown back and sides, often spotted with black. A relatively broad, light band runs along the centre of the back, edged on either side with narrow dark streaks. The front of the snout is long and pointed and a dark patch can be seen behind each eye. It resembles the common frog.

Its home is in central and northern Europe, where it lives in lowlands up to an elevation of about 600 metres, in peaty and swampy districts. It feeds on various arthropods and slugs. It breeds in spring and the tadpoles metamorphose in summer into little frogs about one cm in length; these take three years to mature.

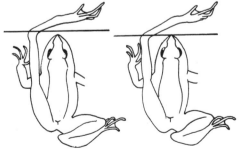

2

1 — *Rana arvalis:*
Length:
6—7.5 cm.
Breeding season:
March to May;
tadpoles metamorphose in July and August.

2 — *Rana dalmatina:*
Length:
7—9 cm.
Breeding season:
March and April;
tadpoles metamorphose in August.

Unlike the moor frog (right), in the agile frog the heel joint reaches beyond the nose

# Common Tree Frog or **Green Tree Frog**

*Hyla arborea*

A slender, broad-headed frog whose digits end in suction discs. A dark lateral streak, edged with white above, runs along each side of the body. The skin is grass-green and smooth on the back, pale grey and finely granulated on the belly. The male has a vocal sac on his throat which inflates into the shape of a large bladder when he is croaking.

It lives in the temperate zone of Europe and Asia as well as in northwestern Africa, moist areas with lush vegetation being its favourite habitat. While in spring it keeps close to water, in summer and autumn it prefers to stay on shrubs and trees where it is an excellent climber thanks to the suction pads on its digits. Its perfect camouflage makes it invisible against the tree foliage: it can quickly change its colour from green to grey or even brown. Small insects and spiders are its favourite food. Mating takes place in spring and the females lay their eggs in small clusters. Newly metamorphosed individuals are 15—20 mm long.

Southern Europe is the home of the closely allied stripeless tree frog *(Hyla meridionalis)* which, in contrast to the common tree frog, has no dark lateral bands along its sides.

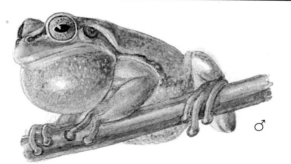

♂

Croaking male

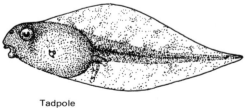

Tadpole

Length:
5 cm.
Breeding season:
April to June;
tadpoles metamorphose in August and September.

# Common Toad

*Bufo bufo*

The common toad is a powerfully built animal with a massive, broad head. The ground colour is grey or brown to brownish-black and the back and flanks are covered with abundant tubercles. The belly is yellowish or dirty white-grey, and the eyes are copper-coloured. Two large crescent-shaped glands which secrete an irritating exudation are located behind the head. Males are substantially smaller than females.

The common toad is found all over Europe, both in lowlands and mountains. It lives in fields, gardens, parks, meadows, and frequently even in human settlements. The adults are active in the evening or by night, when they hunt slugs, earthworms and arthropods which they consume in large quantities. They leave their underground winter shelters at the beginning of March and make for water to mate. The female lays her eggs in strings, three to five metres long, which she coils about water plants. The newly-hatched tadpoles are very small, measuring only about 0.5 cm. Their metamorphosis takes about four months. Several subspecies exist in Europe.

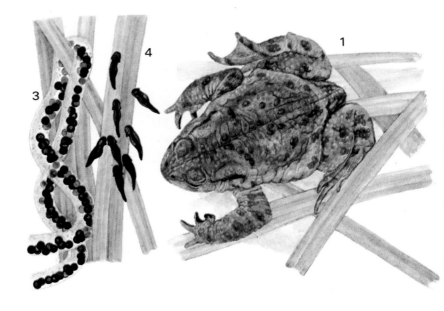

Length:
males 8 cm, females 13 cm.
Breeding season:
March; tadpoles metamorphose in June and July.

1, 2 — adults
3 — string of eggs
4 — tadpoles

Tadpole at an early stage of hind limb development

# Common Spadefoot or **Garlic Toad**

*Pelobates fuscus*

This species has a smooth skin and a light brown or grey back adorned with red dots and spots varying from olive-green to chestnut-brown. The belly is greyish-white, sometimes marked with dark speckles. The bulging eyes have a vertically contracting pupil. The inner side of each hind leg bears a conspicuous horny projection which the animal uses to bury itself rapidly in the ground.

It ranges from central Europe to western Asia and lives in lowland sandy regions. During the day it lies hidden in its underground shelter but comes out after nightfall to hunt for worms, molluscs and other invertebrates. In the breeding season it makes for water where the female winds a long string of several thousand eggs around water plants. Tadpoles hatch several days after the eggs have been laid, and their metamorphosis usually takes three to four months. Sometimes, however, they hibernate in water as tadpoles and do not develop further until the following spring. In this case they reach an abnormal length of about 17 cm.

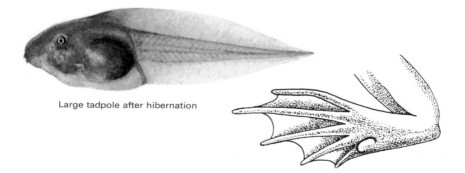

Large tadpole after hibernation

Length:
5—8 cm.
Breeding season:
March and April;
tadpoles metamorphose in June and July, sometimes in the following spring.

1 — adult
2 — string of eggs
3 — tadpoles

# Sea Lamprey

*Petromyzon marinus*

This fish is the largest of the lampreys. Adult individuals, often up to one metre in length, migrate in spring from seas into rivers, where they can be seen from March to June. Between May and July they gather in the shallow parts of the river, where the water current is strong and the bottom covered with stones. With the help of their sucking mouth the females remove stones from the water bed and prepare the spawning ground. The digestive system of adult lampreys degenerates during their journey upriver, so that they cannot eat and die soon after spawning. The lamprey larvae have eyes covered with skin and their mouth is toothless but has distinctive fringed lips. They live in freshwaters in river bottom mud for about four years and then change into adult fish and migrate back to the sea. The mouth of the adult lamprey is funnel-shaped and armed with fine horny teeth; in addition it has a large fleshy tongue, which works in and out like a piston rod. In the sea, lampreys live parasitically on various species of fish, sucking their body juices and crushing their muscles, so that they often leave deep circular wounds of the bodies of their prey.

The sea lamprey lives close to the European coastline from Scandinavia as far as the eastern shores of Italy. It also inhabits the western Atlantic ranging from Nova Scotia to Florida. It is this lamprey which entered the Great Lakes (through the Welland Canal) and became a serious pest to the native fishes.

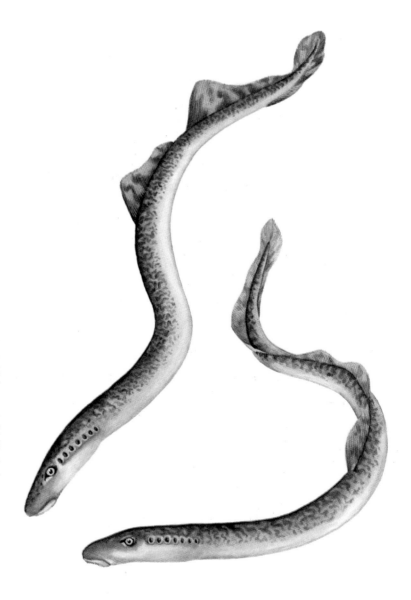

Length:
100 cm.
Weight:
1 kg.
Identifying characteristics:
diagnostic tooth arrangement on the mouth funnel; dorsal fin divided into two parts, the back part of it joined to the caudal fin.

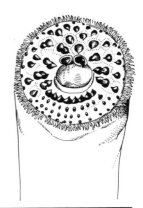

Detail of mouth sucker

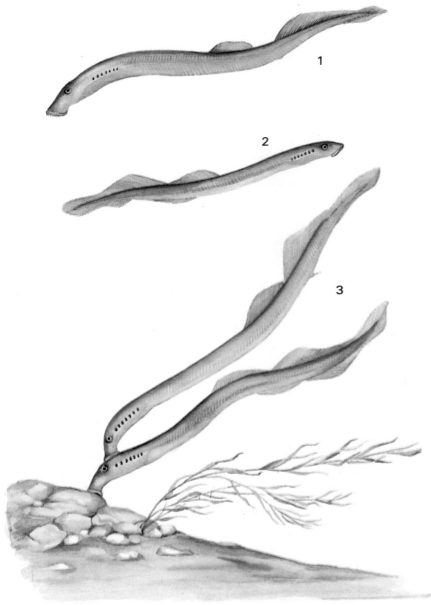

# Danube Lamprey
*Eudontomyzon danfordi*

# Brook Lamprey
*Lampetra planeri*

The Danube lamprey, which is about 20 cm long, inhabits both mountain streams and larger rivers. Prior to spawning both partners dig circular hollows in the sandy bed and into these the female lays her eggs. The male gyrates around her and fertilizes the spawn. The larvae live between four and five years in the sandy, humus deposits and feed on organic debris and diatoms. The adult lamprey attacks other fish, at first cutting their skin with its sharp teeth and then feeding on their blood. In contrast to other related species, it usually lives another two to three years after spawning. It lives in the tributaries of the Danube and the rivers flowing into the Black Sea south of the Danube; however, it is not found in the upper reaches of that river.

The small, non-parasitic freshwater brook lamprey is about 15 cm long and spawns from May to June in mountain streams. It can be distinguished from the Danube lamprey by a different teeth arrangement in the funnel-shaped mouth. As in the previous species, the larvae are larger than the adult fish. After reaching adulthood, they develop a sucker disc, their digestive tract is reduced and they mature sexually. Adult brook lampreys die after spawning. This species inhabits the rivers flowing into the North and Baltic Seas and the Adriatic Sea.

A similar non-parasitic species, the American brook lamprey *(L. lamothenii),* lives in the eastern United States.

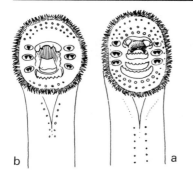

Detail of the mouth funnel in (a) Danube lamprey (b) brook lamprey

1 – *Eudontomyzon danfordi:*
Length:
20 cm.
Weight:
100 g.
Identifying characteristics:
separation of dorsal fin parts.
Lives permanently in freshwaters.

2 – *Lampetra planeri:*
Length:
15 cm.
Weight:
50 g.
Identifying characteristics:
both parts of the dorsal fin connected.
Non-migratory.

3 – spawning of *L. planeri*

# Mackerel Shark
*Lamna nasus*

# Fox Shark
or **Thresher Shark**
*Alopias vulpinus*

# Lesser Spotted Dogfish
*Scyliorhinus caniculus*

The mackerel shark is quite rare and lives in the central Atlantic, in the English Channel, the North and the Mediterranean Seas and in the western part of the Baltic. It spends its life in the upper layers up to a depth of 150 metres. The mackerel shark is a good swimmer; it hunts in shoals of herrings and mackerel most frequently in groups. In summer the female produces between one and five young, each about 60 cm long. The mackerel shark is dangerous to man.

The fox shark or thresher shark lives in the Mediterranean Sea, in the Atlantic Ocean and the North Sea. In summer the female produces from two to four young which may be encountered close to the shore. Adult individuals live near the water surface in the open sea. They feed mainly on smaller pelagic fish. When hunting they circle around a shoal and keep the fish together by beating their tails. This shark is not dangerous to man.

The lesser spotted dogfish is common in the Mediterranean and North Sea, in the English Channel and the Atlantic Ocean. It lives close above the sandy or muddy sea bed at depths ranging from 300—400 metres. This shark lives on small fish, crustaceans and molluscs. It is an oviparous animal. Embryos take from eight to nine months to develop in the eggs. Man is not attacked by the lesser spotted dogfish.

Eggs of the lesser spotted dogfish

1 — *Lamna nasus:*
Length: 3—4 m.
Weight: 100—150 kg.
Identifying characteristics:
high, strong body with a crescent-like tail fin.

2 — *Alopias vulpinus:*
Length: 3—4 m.
Weight: up to 500 kg.
Identifying characteristics:
slim body, short head with small, single pointed teeth. Tail fin has a largely extended upper lobe. Pectoral fins are long.

3 — *Scyliorhinus caniculus:*
Length: 60—100 cm.
Weight: up to 9 kg.
Identifying characteristics:
slim, elongated body, short rounded nose. Upper lobe of the tail fin is only slightly raised above the vertical axis of the body.

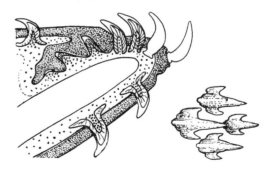

Placoid scales in cross section and from above. They correspond with true teeth — they are formed of dentine and enamel.

# Spur Dog
*Squalias acanthias*

# Thornback Ray
*Raja clavata*

# Marbled Electric Ray
*Torpedo marmorata*

The spur dog lives close to the muddy shores of the Atlantic Ocean, the English Channel, and in the North, Mediterranean, Black and Baltic Seas. Its shoals can be found at depths of up to 950 metres. They live on smaller pelagic fish, crustaceans, etc. The females produce from four to eight young, each about 20 cm long. The young are born in summer, close to the shore. The spikes on the back fins of the spur dog contain poisonous glands.

The thornback ray has the back of its body covered with numerous fine, typically formed placoid scales. These tooth-like scales form a row along the lateral axis of the body. Its pectoral fins are large, wing-like and form the typical body shape characteristic of all the members of the genus *Raja*. The thornback ray is the most common ray in European seas. It lives at depths of 20−500 metres, and it is active at night. It is oviparous; the young hatch after five months.

The marbled electric ray lives in shallow water from 2−20 metres. Usually it rests either partly or completely buried in the sand or mud. It is viviparous, the female produces 5−35 young. Along the spine in the front part of the body it has a pair of electric organs able to produce an electric discharge of 40−220 volts and of 7−10 amps intensity.

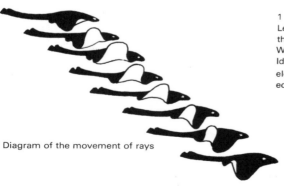

Diagram of the movement of rays

1 − *Squalias acanthias:*
Length: up to 1.2 m; males are smaller than females.
Weight: 10−12 kg.
Identifying characteristics:
elongated body with flattened head. Front edges of the back fins have spikes.

3 − *Torpedo marmorata:*
Length: up to 1.5 metres.
Weight: over 30 kg.
Identifying characteristics:
disc-shaped body with strong tail. Pectoral fins are fleshy and form a rim around the outer edge of the body; skin is smooth, without spikes.

2 − *Raja clavata:*
Length: up to 1.2 m.
Weight: 20−30 kg.
Identifying characteristics:
rhomboid body with a whip-like tail and a pointed nose;
dorsal side covered with spikes.

# Sturgeon
# or **Atlantic Sturgeon**

*Acipenser sturio*

The sturgeon is a large, migratory fish, weighing sometimes more than 300 kg. It enters the rivers in April and May. Its sides are covered with about 30 plates, the number of the dorsal plates varies from 9 to 13. It spawns between June and July in deep hollows in fast running water. It lays a large number of eggs, which can rise to as much as two and a half million. The adult fish and the embryos stay in freshwater for only a short time. They live on various marine invertebrates, such as crustaceans, worms and molluscs, whilst large sturgeon even hunt fish that live near the sea bed.

It lives along the whole of the European coast from the North Cape as far as the Black Sea. It used to migrate up the Rhine to Basle, up the Elbe and into the Vltava as far as Prague, also up the Oder to Wrocław and up the Vistula to Cracow. It also lives in the Danube delta.

Its economic importance in Europe is negligible, although at the end of the last century it used to be abundant in all large rivers. Its gradual disappearance has been the result of intensive fishing and river pollution, as well as the result of increasing number of large water constructions, which have made it impossible for the fish to migrate upstream.

A closely similar species *(A. oxyrhynchus)* lives along the American Atlantic coastline from the St. Lawrence to the Gulf of Mexico. It too is now relatively rare.

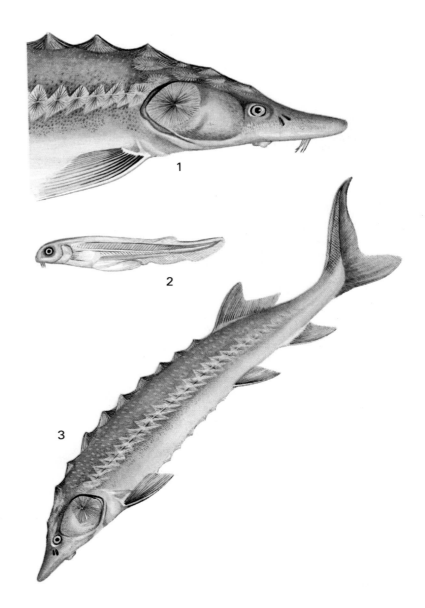

Length:
300 cm.
Weight:
300 kg.
Identifying characteristics:
About 30 lateral plates, 9—13 dorsal plates. Barbels not branched, semicircular in cross-section. Snout relatively flat.

1 — Head from side
2 — Larva
3 — Adult fish

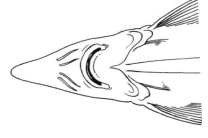

Head from below

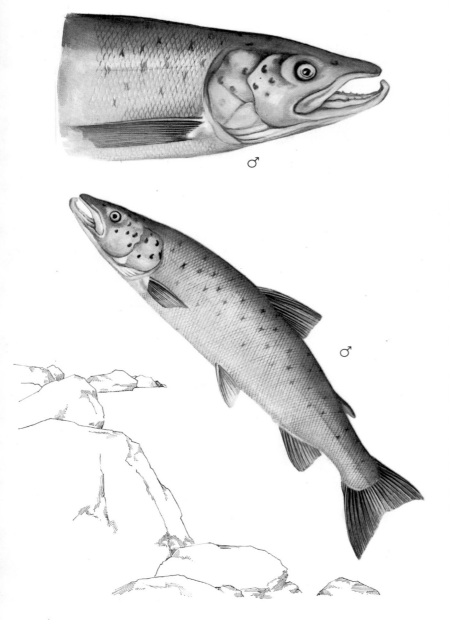

# Salmon

*Salmo salar*

The salmon migrates in the summer and autumn months high upstream against the current to spawn. During migration the males become darker and their sides are decorated with red and orange spots, whilst the belly becomes pink. The females do not change their appearance when they migrate and remain a silvery grey. During their journey they have to overcome strong currents, rapids, weirs and other obstacles as the spawning grounds are located in the upper reaches of rivers in clean and well oxygenated waters. Here the females excavate large hollows (called redds) in which they deposit their eggs which the males fertilize, after which they are covered with gravel. During migration they do not eat and therefore many die after spawning through sheer exhaustion. The young salmon stay in the river for two or three years and only then migrate to sea as smolts. They live in the sea one to three years and grow very rapidly. In freshwaters they feed on small invertebrates, but in the sea solely on fish.

Salmon migrate *en masse* to spawn in the European rivers extending from the mouth of the Pechora in the Barents Sea to the rivers of northwestern Spain. They are also very numerous in the rivers of Iceland, Greenland and along the Atlantic coast of North America, southwards to the Hudson River. However, during the last century they have become scarcer in a number of European and North American rivers as a result of the construction of irrigation and dam installations and the progressive pollution in the lower rivers.

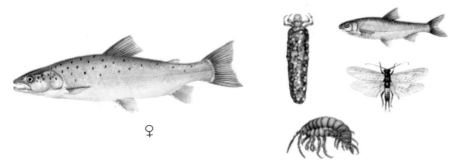

Length:
150 cm.
Weight:
50 kg.
Identifying characteristics:
cross- or star-shaped black spots scattered on the sides. Adipose fin plain grey. Upper jaw bone reaches only to the rear of the eye, section of the body in front of tail fin very narrow.

Food items

# Brown Trout

*Salmo trutta fario*

The brown trout is a typical fish of the salmon family inhabiting mountain streams, rivers and lakes, characterized by its vivid and variable colouring. Immature fish have large, conspicuous grey-blue spots on their sides, while the maturer individuals have small, red flecks, often edged with light shades. The belly is yellow-white to yellow. In autumn and winter it migrates upstream to spawn. The fertilized eggs are deposited by the female into a bowl-shaped depression on the river bed. The size of this trout is closely related to its habitat; in the fast-flowing waters of mountain streams they can reach a length of about 20 cm and weight about 100 g; however, in lowland rivers rich in food they grow to a length of 60 cm and a weight of about 2 kg. It lives predominantly on water insects and their larvae, as well as other small water animals, whilst the larger specimens often hunt for other fish, including members of their own species.

The brown trout lives in mountain and submountain waters all over Europe, but is differentiated according to the river of its origin. North and Baltic Sea river types are classified as a different subspecies to those originating in the rivers flowing into the Black Sea. However, differences can only be detected after a close anatomical analysis and are not noticeable externally. The brown trout has been introduced to many parts of the world, North America, South America, New Zealand, Australia and elsewhere, on account of its sporting qualities.

Length:
60 cm.
Weight:
2 kg.
Identifying characteristics:
back dotted with numerous dark spots; spots on the sides reddish, with lighter edges. Adipose fin light with dark edging and sometimes red at the end.

1 — adult fish
2 — alevin
3 — one-year-old fish
4 — two-year-old fish

Food items

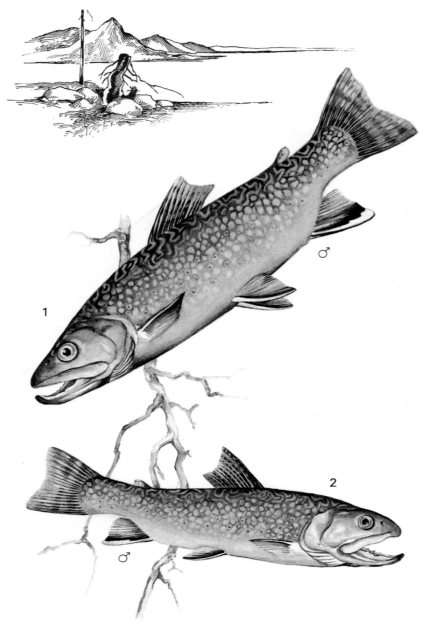

1

2

# Brook Trout
*Salvelinus fontinalis*

This trout was imported into Europe from North America with other fish species at the end of the last century. In the American populations both permanently freshwater as well as migratory forms are known. The brook trout has an olive back with light marbling pattern and the body covered with red, yellow and blue spots. The fins are pale yellow to reddish, whilst the first rays of its pelvic, pectoral and anal fins are white and black. The biology of the brook trout is similar to that of the brown trout and the charr and thus it can easily be interbred with them. The hybrids are known as zebra-trout, when interbred with the trout. It will also hybridize with the Arctic charr. The progeny of both crosses are infertile. It habitually spawns during the winter months when the female excavates a suitable spawning bed. It has a very similar diet to that of the brown trout and the charr.

It has been introduced into some British lakes and in Europe into several Alpine lakes, but has disappeared from many of them. It has only become effectively acclimatized in a few lakes and in some streams high up in the mountains. Generally in Europe it reaches a length of about 50 cm and weighs about 1 kg. However, in North America the brook trout is much larger and heavier and is a popular angling fish.

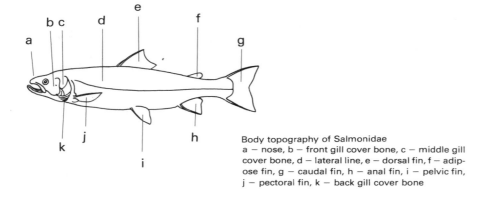

Body topography of Salmonidae
a — nose, b — front gill cover bone, c — middle gill cover bone, d — lateral line, e — dorsal fin, f — adipose fin, g — caudal fin, h — anal fin, i — pelvic fin, j — pectoral fin, k — back gill cover bone

Length:
65 cm.
Weight:
3 kg.
Identifying characteristics:
olive-coloured back with light marbling, red, yellow and blue spots on the sides. Fins pale yellow to reddish; first rays of pectoral, pelvic and anal fins white and black.

1 — adult fish
2 — starved form from mountain lakes

# Grayling or Comnion European Grayling

*Thymallus thymallus*

The grayling is a schooling fish which inhabits the submountain regions of rivers with sandy or stony beds. It spawns in spring, when it leaves its home territory and migrates upstream to the areas with a more gravelly river bed. The spawning grounds are prepared by the males, which often chase and attract several females onto them. By comparison with members of the salmon family, the grayling has a relatively small head, which has a small mouth with a fleshy, overhanging snout. It has impressively large scales and a high, long and vivid dorsal fin. It measures up to 50 cm and can weigh 1 kg or sometimes even more. The young fish are a light silvery green and often have bluish spots on the sides.

The grayling inhabits the submountain rivers of Europe from Wales and France, across Europe southwards to northern Italy and the basin of the River Po. However, it is not normally found in southern Europe or the northern parts of Scandinavia and Ireland. In the Alps it swims upriver to an altitude of 1,500 metres above sea level and in the Carpathians up to about 1,000 metres.

The grayling subspecies *Thymallus arcticus baicalensis,* which is a native of Lake Baikal and its tributaries, has been introduced relatively successfully in some European valley reservoirs. It is distinguished by an overall darker colouring and a larger mouth. Another subspecies is found in North American rivers and lakes.

Length:
60 cm.
Weight:
1.5 kg.
Identifying characteristics:
fish with large scales, small mouth and adipose fin; dorsal fin strikingly high and brightly coloured.

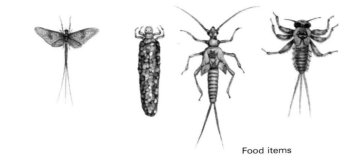

Food items

# Pike

*Exos lucius*

The pike is the only representative of its family to be found in European waters. It has a characteristically depressed head and jaws with large teeth, the dorsal and anal fins are close to the tail fin. The pike has a grey-green or brownish back, greenish sides with yellow spots or stripes and a white belly with light grey spots. Exceptional individuals can reach a length of 150 cm and weigh up to 35 kg. However, pike longer than one metre and heavier than ten kg are quite rare.

It is a predatory fish, which from an early age lives on the fry of other fish and later on adult fish and other aquatic vertebrates. It lives mainly in the lower reaches of rivers but also penetrates high upriver against the current. In waters with a plentiful supply of relatively small fish it grows quite quickly. Its economic value for breeding in ponds as well as in open waters has increased considerably. It is often introduced into carp ponds, where it reduces the supply of small, unwanted fish. In many countries in Europe it is artificially reared and the fry are then transferred to ponds, rivers, dams and lakes. It usually spawns in early spring on the flooded vegetation of river meadows.

It can be found throughout Europe with the exception of the Iberian Peninsula, the southern Balkans, southern Italy and the western shores of Norway. It is a species which is indigenous to the temperate and northern zones of the whole northern hemisphere. It is also found in Asia and North America (where it is known as the northern pike).

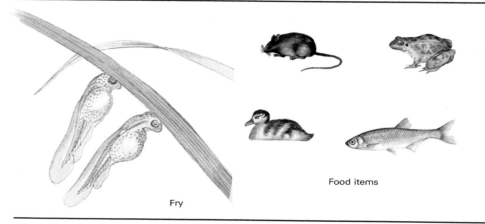

Length:
150 cm.
Weight:
35 kg.
Identifying characteristics:
body long and cylindrical; rearwards placed dorsal fin; large mouth with numerous backwardly inclined teeth.

1 — adult fish
2 — young fish

Food items

Fry

# Moderlieschen

*Leucaspius delineatus*

# Bitterling

*Rhodeus sericeus*

The moderlieschen has a slender body, flattened at the sides and with easily detached scales. The lateral line is visible only on the first scales towards the front of the body. It may reach a length of between seven and nine cm, although it is usually much shorter. It lives in large schools in stagnant or slow-flowing waters which have become overgrown with vegetation. It spawns in April and May, when the female lays her eggs in strips around the stems of water plants and the male fertilizes and subsequently guards them. Its main diet consists of plankton.

The moderlieschen is indigenous to the whole of central and eastern Europe, from the Rhine as far as the watershed of the Volga; it can be found as far north as the rivers of southern Sweden.

The bitterling is a small fish with a high-backed body. It is quite abundant in the stagnant waters of the lower reaches of rivers, in shallow creeks, in old river backwaters and pools. However, it lives only in waters inhabited by the freshwater mussel, into which the bitterling lays its eggs between April and June.

It is found all over Europe from northeastern France as far as the Caspian Sea, but is not present in Denmark, Scandinavia, or the Mediterranean countries. It has been introduced into a number of waters in north-west England. It lives on planktonic crustaceans, insect larvae and worms.

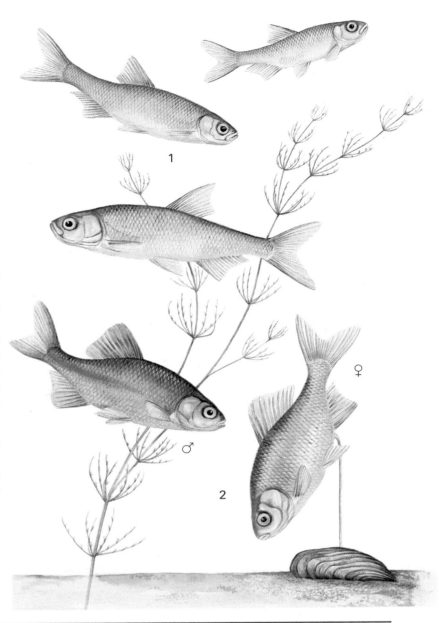

1 – *Leucaspius delineatus:*
Length:
9 cm.
Weight:
10 g.
Identifying characteristics:
mouth slants upwards, scales large and easily shed. Lateral line developed only on the first 7–13 scales.

2 – *Rhodeus sericeus:*
Length:
8 cm.
Weight:
15 g.
Identifying characteristics:
a blue-green stripe on the sides, widening towards the back. During mating female with long ovipositor, male reddish-purple on sides. Mouth in semi-inferior position; lateral line extends to only 5–6 scales.

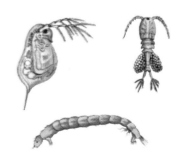

Food items

# Asp

*Aspius aspius*

The asp has a long body and a wide mouth, which extends behind its eyes. Its upper jaw has a small depression into which the protruding lower jaw fits. It has a grey-blue back and silvery sides. Its dorsal fin is placed behind the imaginary vertical line projected from the base of the pelvic fins. Behind its pelvic fins it has a scale-covered keel.

The asp is a predatory fish, which inhabits the lower reaches of large rivers and sometimes also lives in oxbow lakes. It prefers upper water layers, where it feeds on small fish, which it often attacks noisily, sometimes even jumping out of the water. It also catches insects fallen onto the water surface. It spawns between April and June on the stony bed whilst swimming against the current. The fry at first eat plankton, small insect larvae, the fry of other fish, and later progress to a diet of small fish.

In Europe it inhabits rivers to the east of the Elbe and those opening into the Baltic, Black and Caspian Seas. It is not found in France, Britain, Denmark, Switzerland, the Iberian Peninsula or in the southern part of the Balkan Peninsula. Its economic value grows proportionally as one moves eastwards through Europe, where it is also a favourite quarry of anglers.

Cycloid scale

Length:
1.2 m.
Weight:
14 kg.
Identifying characteristics:
upper jaw has depression into which protruding lower jaw slots. Large mouth reaches behind eyes. Scale-covered keel behind pelvic fins.

# Barbel
## or **Common Barbel**
*Barbus barbus*

# Southern Barbel
*Barbus meridionalis*

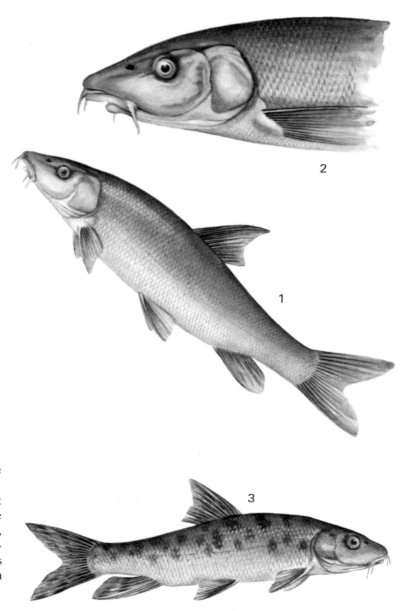

The barbel grows up to one metre in length and is a sturdy fish. It lives close to the river bed in strong currents and has a long, spindle-shaped body and a characteristically ventrally positioned mouth with four barbels. The long spine in the dorsal fin has a saw-like edge. The long-rayed anal fin nearly reaches the tail fin. It spawns in May and June and migrates upstream to areas with a sandy or stony water bed. It is a schooling fish and feeds on the animals and plants of the water bed.

It inhabits western and central Europe, but is not found in Ireland, Denmark, Scandinavia and Italy. In the peripheral areas of its habitat it has produced numerous subspecies, for example in Spain, Dalmatia, eastern Bulgaria and the basins of the rivers Dniester, Dnieper and Bug.

The southern barbel is a smaller fish, which grows to a length of about 30 cm. This also lives close to the river bed amongst strong, clean currents. The large spine in the dorsal fin is smooth-edged, the anal fin is high and when depressed it touches the base of the tail-fin.

It is confined to certain areas in the northern part of the Iberian Peninsula (which is inhabited by the subspecies *B. meridionalis graellsi*), southern France, northern Italy, Albania and Greece. Another subspecies, *B. meridionalis petenyi*, lives in the rivers Oder, Vistula, Danube, Dniester, Vardar, Strymon and Maritsa.

1, 2 — *Barbus barbus*:
Length:
1 m.
Weight:
15 kg.
Identifying characteristics:
long spine of dorsal fin has serrated edge. Anal fin does not reach caudal fin. Mouth ventral, with four fleshy barbels.

*Barbus meridionalis*:
Length:
30 cm.
Weight:
500 g.
Identifying characteristics:
long spine in dorsal fin smooth. High anal fin reaches tail fin when depressed.

3 — *Barbus meridionalis petenyi*

Cross section through skin showing lateral line

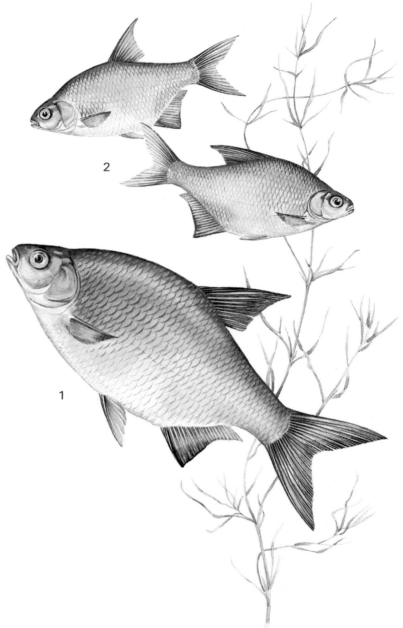

# Silver or White Bream

*Blicca bjoerkna*

The silver bream has a very deep body, which is flattened at the sides; the mouth is in a semi-ventral position and the eyes are relatively large. Its back is scaleless towards the front of its body, as is also its keel behind the pelvic fins. Older specimens have dark, grey-green back, silvery sides and a white belly. The fin edges are grey and the bases of the pectoral and pelvic fins are red or orange. Occasionally the silver bream reaches a length of 35 cm.

It is a generally abundant inhabitant of the river bed in the lower reaches of large rivers, in old river backwaters and pools, in creeks and even in some lowland ponds. It spawns from the end of April to June on aquatic plants. Its food consists of planktonic organisms, algae and the larvae of water insects.

It is found in Europe to the north of the Alps and the Pyrenees as far as southern Scandinavia. It also inhabits the eastern parts of England and the northern Danubian tributaries of the Black Sea.

It interbreeds in some localities with other fish such as the bream and the roach, but these hybrids are sterile. Economically it is relatively unimportant and is only caught in large quantities in a few rivers and ponds. In terms of fishery management it represents an undesirable fish species, as it sometimes multiplies excessively, although it grows relatively slowly.

Food items

Length:
35 cm.
Weight:
1 kg.
Identifying characteristics:
high, laterally flattened body; eyes relatively large.
Sides strikingly silvery and bases of paired fins reddish.

1 — adult fish
2 — young fish

# Carp

*Cyprinus carpio*

The domesticated carp displays a number of variations in the nature of the scale covering of its body. The most common pond variety is the mirror carp, whose body is irregularly covered with scales of different sizes. Another variety has a row of scales along the sides of the body and sometimes a similar line of scales on the base of the dorsal fin, whilst the leather carp either has no scales at all or only a few individual scales below the dorsal fin and along the base of other fins.

The carp is a most valuable fish, which is readily appreciated also by anglers, on whose behalf it is stocked in open waters. The ponds used for carp breeding are looked after in the same way as fields or other agricultural areas.

The original home of the carp is the watershed of the Black and Caspian Seas, but as it has become a most popular pond fish, it has slowly been dispersed all over Europe. During the past century it has also been introduced to the United States, as well as parts of Africa, Australia, and New Zealand. In the warmer parts of the USA it has multiplied exceedingly, often to the detriment of native fishes and aquatic vegetation. It can be as much as 120 cm long and can weigh over 30 kg. The original wild form of the carp *(Cyprinus carpio)* has a long, cylindrical, scaly body. This lives in the Danube and some of its tributaries. Spawning takes place between May and June. The fry lives on zooplankton and when two cm long, progresses to a diet of bottom-living invertebrates, whilst in overgrown waters the carp also lives on water plants.

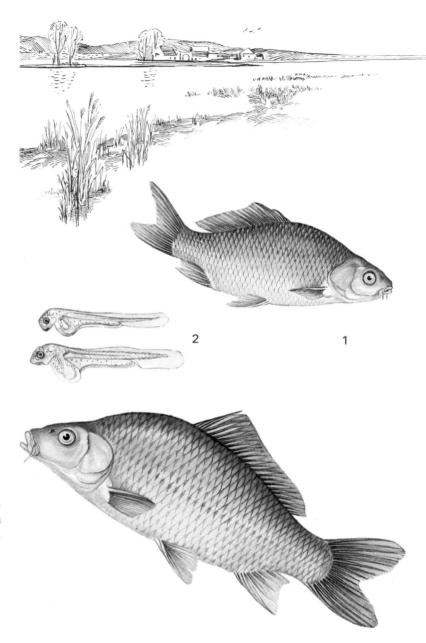

2          1

Length:
120 cm.
Weight:
30 kg.
Identifying characteristics:
large scales, long dorsal and short anal fins. Mouth has four fleshy barbels.

1 — pond form with scales
2 — fry

(a) mirror form and (b) leather form

# Weatherfish
*Misgurnus fossilis*

# Stone Loach
*Noemacheilus barbatulus*

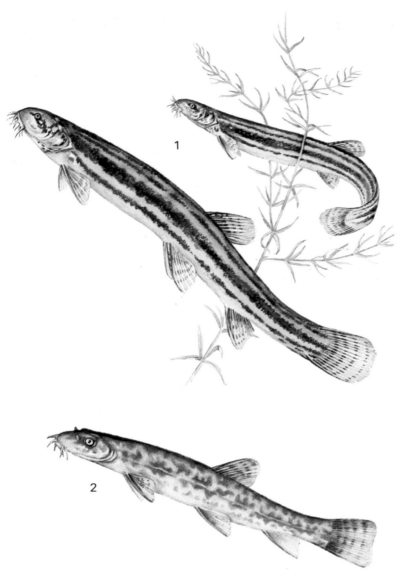

The weatherfish is a long-bodied fish with the body compressed at the sides and with ten barbels at the sides of its mouth. It lives in muddy, stagnant waters, in river backwaters and also in ponds. In any sudden change of air pressure it will swim close to the water surface and move about briskly. If oxygen is sparse in the water, it will gulp in air and absorb the oxygen through the lining of its gut. It spawns in May and the embryos have special external, web-like gills which soon disappear. In Europe it can be found from the Seine to the Neva and from the Danube to the Volga. However, it does not live in rivers flowing into the Arctic Ocean or in rivers in England, Scandinavia, Finland and southern Europe.

The stone loach is a small, 10—18 cm long fish with a cylindrical, dark-marbled body and with six barbels at the mouth. The back is greenish or brownish, the sides are yellowish with irregular black-brown spots. The belly is whitish grey, sometimes with a pinkish tint. The fish keeps close to the bottom, in rivers as well as in ponds and lakes, and usually hides under stones and roots. It spawns in spring during the month of May on sandy or stony shallows. Its diet consists chiefly of the larvae of water insects, such as the red midge. It is most active at night or in the twilight. It occurs all over Europe with the exception of northern Scotland, northern Scandinavia, southern and central Italy and Greece.

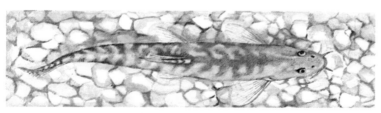

Noemacheilus barbatulus from above

Weatherfish fry

1 — *Misgurnus fossilis:*
Length:
35 cm.
Weight:
150 g.
Identifying characteristics:
long body, compressed sideways. Ten barbels at the mouth. Lateral longitudinal stripes.

2 — *Noemacheilus barbatulus:*
Maximum length and weight:
18 cm, 80 g.
Identifying characteristics:
elongated, cylindrical body with dark marbling. Six barbels at the mouth. Scales very small.

# Wels or European Catfish

*Silurus glanis*

The wels is a large fish with a long, scaleless body, a very small dorsal and a rounded caudal fin, which touches the long anal fin. Its mouth is equipped with three pairs of barbels; the one located on the upper jaw is very long. The back is plain, either olive-green or blue-grey, but the sides often have a marble-like pattern. The wels lives close to the bottom in the deep waters of large rivers, reservoirs and lakes. It spawns from May to July in the shallows, where the female constructs a kind of nest. After mating the male guards the spawn and later the fry. During the day the wels usually hides close to the bottom, but is active at night, when it seeks its food on the water surface. It feeds on various types of small fish, small mammals and water birds. It grows very quickly and in Europe achieves a length of about 2 metres and a weight of over 50 kg, although in some regions, for example in the Danube basin, it grows still larger. Young wels often live in schools and only become solitary when adult.

In Europe it can be found to the east of the upper reaches of the River Rhine, in the River Elbe and in rivers flowing into the Baltic Sea and in the tributaries of the Black and Caspian Seas; it is local in Sweden, and has been introduced into England. Its relative, *Silurus aristotelis*, lives in Greece.

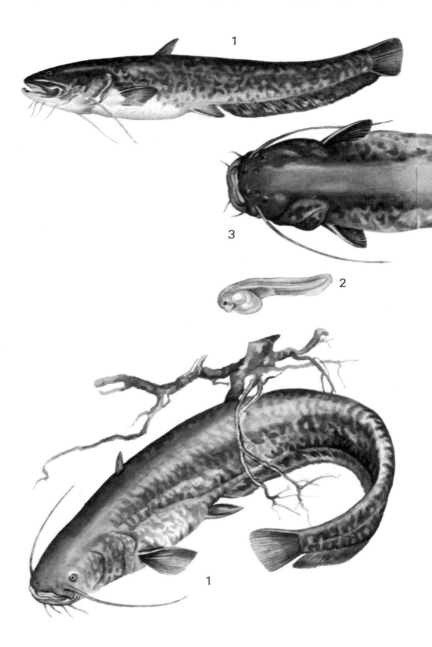

Length:
3 m.
Weight:
300 kg.
Identifying characteristics:
scaleless body with small dorsal fin; rounded caudal fin touches anal fin. Three pairs of barbels; pair on upper jaw very long. Mouth wide, head depressed from above.

1 — adult
2 — fry
3 — detail of head

Food items

# European Eel

*Anguilla anguilla*

The European eel has a long, snake-like body without pelvic fins. It has small scales, which are so deeply embedded in the skin as to be virtually invisible. Its extremely long dorsal and anal fins merge with the caudal fin and thus form a continuous edging to the whole of its body. It spawns in the Atlantic Ocean in the region of the Sargasso Sea, east of the Bermudas and Bahamas. The larvae differ considerably from the adult fish as they look like transparent willow leaves. For about three years they are slowly carried by the Gulf Stream towards the European continent, where they change into minute, snake-like elvers. Young eels have dark green or brown-black backs and their bellies and sides are yellowish or white. The females then travel upriver, while the males remain in the river estuaries. At the start of their breeding migration the adult fish have large eyes, shiny, metal-coloured sides and a silvery white belly. The females live in freshwater for twelve years or more and then return to the Atlantic Ocean, where after spawning they are believed to die.

The European eel lives close to the river bed under roots and in other hideouts, only becoming active at night. Many travel short distances overland (usually on wet nights) to get to isolated ponds. They are usually 100 to 150 cm long and weigh up to 4 kg, although in exceptional cases they grow to 2 m in length and achieve a weight of 7 kg.

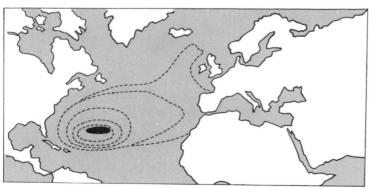

Spawning region in the Atlantic

Length:
2 m.
Weight:
7 kg.
Identifying characteristics:
snake-like body; no pelvic fins. Dorsal, caudal and anal fins form a continuous fin edging. Minute scales deeply embedded in skin.

# Perch or European Perch
*Perca fluviatilis*

The perch is one of the most abundant of European fish and is characterized by its oblong body, which is flattened at the sides and has two dorsal fins (the first strongly spiny) and ctenoid scales. The top half of the body is a dark grey to blue or olive green, the belly is lighter. It grows to a length of 30 to 50 cm and averages a weight of 1 to 2 kg, although in exceptional conditions this rises up to 5 kg. It lives in both flowing and stagnant waters, but especially likes to linger in creeks close to banks overgrown with water vegetation in the middle and lower river reaches, in old water ways, in ponds, lakes and lowland reservoirs. It usually remains near the river bed and spawns between April and May. Its eggs are laid and fertilized in long strips which are wrapped round the remains of water plants and submerged tree branches. These strips of spawn are often one to two metres long and one to two cm wide.

Young perch usually form small schools, but older fish are much more isolated and independent. Perch living in enclosed waters frequently overmultiply to such an extent that they squeeze out other fish species and then themselves become stunted individually. They feed on aquatic invertebrates and small fish, although older and larger perch live exclusively on fish.

It is found all over Europe with the exception of Scotland, the Iberian Peninsula, Italy, the western Balkans, the Crimea and northern Norway. It is closely related to the North American yellow perch *(Perca flavescens)*.

Length:
60 cm.
Weight:
5 kg.
Identifying characteristics:
a black spot at end of first dorsal fin and 6—9 dark transverse stripes on sides. Pelvic and anal fins reddish.

Food items                          Ctenoid or comb-edged scale

# Burbot

*Lota lota*

The burbot is the only freshwater representative of the cod family. It has a long body, which is compressed at the sides towards the rear. The pelvic fins are located in front of the pectoral pair and their second ray has a thread-like protrusion. The centre of the chin bears a single barbel. The burbot has two dorsal fins, of which the second is very long, as is also its anal fin. The belly is whitish; the back and sides are grey-brown, the body and fins have a striking, marble-like pattern. It rarely reaches a length of over 1 metre or a weight of over 20 kg. The burbot hides close to the river bed or under overhanging banks in the trout, grayling and barbel zones of European rivers, although it is sometimes found in their lower reaches and in lakes or ponds. It is a predatory fish, which feeds predominantly on fish, frogs and other larger vertebrates. It spawns in winter and produces a large number of eggs, sometimes as many as a million. These are deposited onto shallow stony beds.

It is found over almost all of northern Europe to the north of the Balkans and the Pyrenees and in Italy to the basin of the Po. In England it has become very rare and is possibly extinct. In some places, especially in northern zones, it is an economically important fish, as its meat and liver have a great protein value.

Food items

Length:
1 m.
Weight:
20 kg.
Identifying characteristics:
Pelvic fins in front of pectoral pair; anal fin and second dorsal fin very long. One barbel in middle of chin.

# Common Edible European Urchin

*Echinus esculentus*

## *Echinocardium cordatum*
## *Asterias rubens*
## *Ophioderma longicauda*

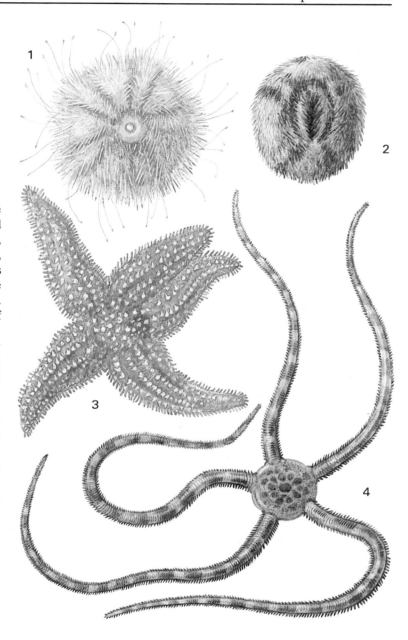

The common edible European urchin has a ray-like symmetrical body. It has a ventral mouth equipped with a complex organ consisting of five strong teeth, known as Aristotle's lantern. The shell is calcareous, composed of plates and covered with skin. The plates are perforated and through the holes tube feet can be extended — the locomotor organs of the sea urchin. The tube feet are linked to the ambulacral system of water canals which are used for moving and breathing. The females lay eggs which are fertilized in the water by the males. Bilaterally symmetrical free-swimming larvae (pluteus) hatch from the eggs, later settle, and after an elaborate period of development they become radially symmetrical.

*Echinocardium cordatum* has a bilaterally symmetrical body. The opening of the mouth is without Aristotle's lantern. The animal spends its time in a small hole dug out about 20 cm below the sea bed and connected with the water by a vertical canal.

*Asterias rubens* has a body made of a disc and several arms. The ambulacral system is used for breathing and locomotion.

The arms of *Ophioderma longicauda* are flexible and mobile, hence the ambulacral system is not used for locomotion. The madreporite is located on the underside of the disc.

1 – *Echinus esculentus*:
Diameter:
10 cm, rarely up to 17 cm.
Distribution:
the Atlantic from Portugal
to Norway, the English Channel,
North Sea.

2 – *Echinocardium cordatum*:
Diameter:
up to 9 cm.
Distribution:
North Sea, Atlantic Ocean,
the English Channel, Mediterranean Sea.

3 – *Asterias rubens*:
Diameter:
30–50 cm.
Distribution:
Atlantic Ocean, the English Channel,
North Sea, western part of the Baltic Sea.

4 – *Ophioderma longicauda*:
Diameter:
25–30 cm.
Distribution:
Mediterranean Sea, Atlantic Ocean.

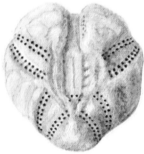

Sea-urchin tests with spines removed

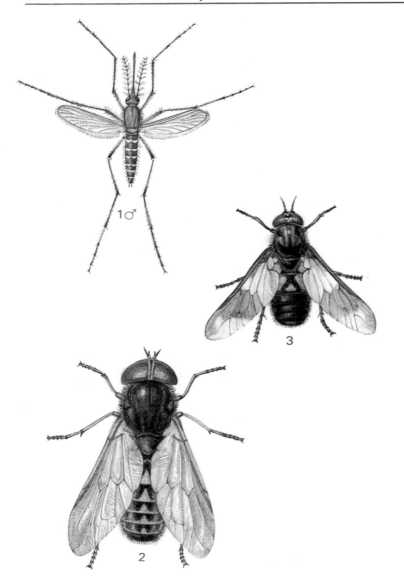

1♂

3

2

## *Aëdes vexans*
## **Common Gadfly**
### *Tabanus bovinus*

## **Blind** or **Thunder Horsefly**
### *Chrysops caecutiens*

Like all other mosquitoes *Aëdes vexans* has relatively long and narrow wings which it never folds over its body. The wing veins are covered with small brown scales. It has a biting mouth. The females have very short antennae next to the proboscis; the ends of the antennae of the males are comb-like and longer than the proboscis. Females suck the blood of mammals, the males suck the juices of plants. The females lay their eggs on periodically flooded soil. The larvae live in water and breathe atmospheric oxygen while suspended by the end of the tube under the surface film. They filter food from the water.

The larvae of common gadflies and blind or thunder horseflies live on the muddy banks of still water. After laying the eggs on plants the females die. On hatching the larvae crawl into the water where they live as predators. Their bodies are cylindrical, with false legs and a respiratory tube. Adult females of both species attack mammals, by piercing their skin and sucking their blood. The males, however, live on plant juices.

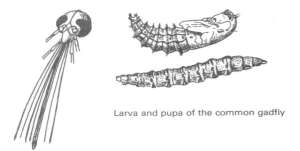

Larva and pupa of the common gadfly

The mouth parts of a mosquito

1 – *Aëdes vexans:*
Length:
5–6 mm.
Habitat:
close to water, in human dwellings and animal sheds.

2 – *Tabanus bovinus:*
Length:
20–24 mm.
Habitat:
males on flowers, females on the trunks of trees in forests, close to roads.

3 – *Chrysops caecutiens:*
Length:
8–11 mm.
Habitat:
water sides, close to roads.

# Assassin Fly or Robber Fly

*Asilus crabroniformis*

# Dronefly

*Eristalis tenax*

# Yellow Dung Fly

*Scatophaga stercoraria*

# Common Housefly

*Musca domestica*

The assassin fly or robber fly has a fairly elongated body with a powerful thorax, a pointed abdomen and strong legs. Its head is large and very mobile, the forehead between the eyes is indented hence the eyes do not touch each other. The assassin fly is a skilful flier and feeds on insects which it hunts in the air. The female lays eggs in the soil, its larvae living on the larvae of other insects.

The dronefly slightly resembles the honey-bee. Its abdomen is arched and it has a strong square shield and strong legs. The cylindrically-shaped dronefly larvae develop in stagnant water. They have a breathing tube at the rear end of the body. They pupate on walls and the stems of plants.

The yellow dung fly can live even at very high altitudes (in the Alps up to 3,000 metres).

It flies slowly and feeds on small insects which it finds on faeces, carrion and waste.

The common housefly is an important domestic species. The proboscis is bent downwards. Its tip is broad and cushionlike and is adapted for licking and sucking. The female lays about 150 eggs into rotting matter. The eggs quickly develop into larvae, which pupate underground.

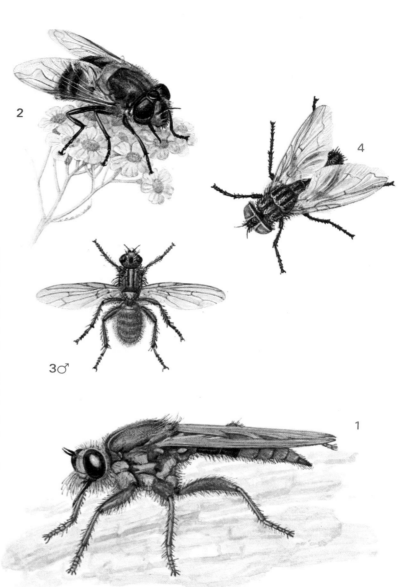

1 — *Asilus crabroniformis:*
Length:
17—30 mm.
Habitat:
forest clearings.

2 — *Eristalis tenax:*
Length:
15—19 mm.
Habitat: on flowers (also in Man's dwellings).

3 — *Scatophaga stercoraria:*
Length:
9—11 mm.
Habitat:
on fresh dung and surrounding plants, on carrion.

4 — *Musca domestica:*
Length:
7—9 mm.
Habitat:
near human habitation.

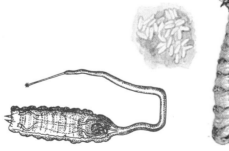

The rat-tailed larva of *Eristalis tenax*

Development of the common housefly

# Swallowtail

*Papilio machaon*

Tha swallowtail is undoubtedly one of the best known species of the butterflies in Europe. It does not occur in Ireland and in England it is rare and local, its range of distribution being limited only to the Norfolk Broads. Its occurrence in central Europe has also decreased markedly during recent decades, although it is still quite abundant in some areas. The swallowtail occurs in north Africa, Europe, the temperate zone of Asia and some parts of North America. It is found high up in the mountains, even at altitudes of about 2,000 metres in the Alps and 4,500 metres in Tibet. A great number of types and geographical races have been described. The home of the *gorganus* subspecies is central Europe, that of the *britannicus* subspecies is England, and that of the *aliaska* and two other subspecies is North America. The caterpillar has a very variegated appearance. When disturbed, it protrudes from the front part of the body a fleshy orange-red forked organ called the osmeterium. The pupa is usually green or grey-brown. In central Europe the pupal stage lasts two or three weeks. In hibernating pupae it may last six months. In the mountains and in northern regions the butterfly has only one generation a year.

Pupation (metamorphosis of a caterpillar into a pupa)

Adult:
IV—VI; VII—VIII, in the south, part of a third generation (IX—X).
Caterpillar:
VI; VII—IX, sometimes also X.
Foodplants:
fennel, carrot, dill, celery, parsley, and a number of other umbelliferous plants. In the Near East an allied species causes damage to citrus trees.

1 — caterpillar
2 — adult
3 — pupa

# Scarce Swallowtail

*Iphiclides podalirius*

The scarce swallowtail is found in gardens, fields, open woodlands. You can come across it in places with thickets and particularly orchards. It is widespread throughout Europe with the exception of the northern parts. Its range extends northwards to Saxony and central Poland and eastwards across Asia Minor and Transcaucasia as far as Iran and western China. A few individuals of the scarce swallowtail have been reported from central Sweden and England but they were probably only strays and not migrants. In the Alps it can be found up to altitudes of 1,600 metres. In some years the scarce swallowtail is quite abundant. The caterpillars spin little pads on leaves and grip them firmly. The newly hatched caterpillar is dark in colour with two smaller and two bigger greenish patches on the dorsal side, later they are greenish with yellowish dorsal and side stripes. The summer chrysalides are green as a rule, the hibernating ones are brown. A number of hibernating chrysalides fall prey to various enemies. The scarce swallowtail is getting rarer as the blackthorn bushes are being cleared; and it is now protected in some central European countries.

Adult:
end of IV − beginning of VI; VII − beginning of IX.
Caterpillar:
V−IX, (development takes about 5−8 weeks).
Chrysalis hibernates. The stage of chrysalis lasts 3−5 weeks, the extremes being 7 days to one year.
Foodplants:
Blackthorn, hawthorn, bird cherry and fruit trees.

1 − adult
2 − caterpillar
3 − pupa
4 − form *undecimlineatus*, adult

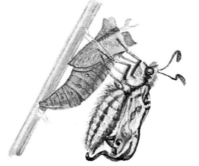

Freshly emerged butterfly

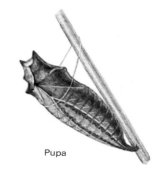

Pupa

1♂

2♀

3

# Apollo

*Parnassius apollo*

The apollo is indubitably one of the prettiest butter-flies and for this reason it is very much sought after by collectors. Its popularity is partly due to its immense variability. About six hundred different forms have already been described. The apollo inhabits valleys, hillsides and mountain meadows. In the Alps it is found at altitudes of about 2,200 metres and in the Asian mountains even higher. The vast area of its distribution includes the Pyrenees and Iberian Peninsula, the Alps, the Carpathians and the Caucasus, extending as far east as the Altai mountains. It is not found in Ireland or in Britain. In some parts of central Europe it has disappeared entirely or is getting noticeably rare; it is therefore protected in a number of European countries. It flies slowly, flutteringly and gliding, and likes to settle on flowering thistles. It is not shy. The full grown caterpillar is up to 50 mm long. It is velvet black with small steel blue raised dots and flanked with many orange spots. The chrysalis stage lasts from eight days to several weeks. The fat, blunt-ended pupa is tinted blue.

Pupa

Adult:
VI—IX, in central Europe VII—VIII.
Caterpillar:
VIII—VI or III—VI; sometimes hibernates; is heliophilic, that is in the absence of sunshine it hides under stones and does not feed.
Foodplants:
houseleek and various species of stonecrop, etc.

1, 2 — adults
3 — caterpillar

# Large White

*Pieris brassicae*

The large white is widespread throughout Europe, in north Africa and even as far east as the Himalayas. Most often it can be found in gardens, but it also inhabits fields, meadows, woodland margins and mountain valleys. The female lays 200—300 orange-yellow eggs, which are glued in clusters to the underside of leaves. The caterpillar hatches after four to ten days; it starts to eat the leaves from the centre, only beginning to nibble the edges several days later. It moults four or five times during its development, which lasts three to four weeks or sometimes even longer, depending on the climatic conditions of the habitat. Before pupating, caterpillars leave the foodplant and search for sheltered places in the neighbourhood. They pupate underneath window ledges and the eaves of houses, on fences, milestones, etc. The pupa is usually yellow-green with dark spots. Among the caterpillars preparing for pupation there are always a number which are killed by the parasitic larvae of the braconid wasp *(Apanteles glomeratus)*. Instead of turning into a pupa, the caterpillar dies, surrounded by the yellow cocoons of the parasites which have been feeding inside its body.

1♀

2♀

3♂

4

Adult:
IV — beginning of VI, half of VII—VIII; partial 3rd generation in IX—X.
Caterpillar:
VI—VIII; VIII—IX.
Pupa hibernates.
Main foodplants:
cauliflower, cabbage, radish, cress, etc. In central and northern Europe it causes damages to vegetable production.

1, 3 — adults
2 — underside of wings
4 — caterpillar

Pupa

# Orange Tip
*Anthocharis cardamines*

The orange tip is a lovely butterfly of spring meadows, fields and forest pathways. The male can be easily recognized at a considerable distance by the conspicuous orange patches on its forewings. This species has only one generation in central Europe. In the Alps it can be found even at altitudes exceeding 2,000 metres. The distribution area of the orange tip includes the whole of the palearctic region from the British Isles to Japan where, however, it is very rare; it was discovered there as late as 1910 by the collector Nakamura. The female lays eggs on the underside of leaves and also often on flowers. The egg is barrel-shaped with 11 to 13 grooves on its surface. At first yellow-white, it turns orange and then grey before hatching in about two weeks. The development of the caterpillar takes approximately five weeks. In captivity it has often been possible to breed a second generation which also appears spontaneously in the individuals inhabiting the south of Europe. The pupa is usually attached to the stalk of a foodplant. The newly pupated chrysalis is green and later turns buff. In rare cases the pupa maintains its green colour until the imago has emerged.

Topography of a caterpillar body:
a — head, b — thoracic legs, c — abdominal legs,
d — stigma, e — claspers, f — tail segments,
g — ocelli

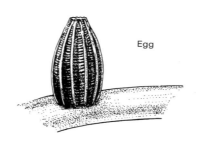

Egg

Adult:
IV—VI (in the mountains also VII).
Caterpillar:
V—VIII.
Chrysalis hibernates.
Foodplants:
great variety of plants, for example garlic mustard, rock-cress, lady's smock, penny-cress.

1, 2 — adults
3 — caterpillar
4 — pupa
5 — underside of wings

# Brimstone

*Gonepteryx rhamni*

Although the brimstone is not a very variable species, nevertheless twelve subspecies have so far been designated, only one of which lives in Europe. The brimstone is widespread throughout north Africa and western Europe, extending through Asia Minor and Asia proper as far as the eastern parts of the palearctic region. The brimstone is well known in western and central Europe especially because the butterfly hibernates and leaves its winter shelter early in spring, when there are still the last remnants of snow lying in the shaded places. The next generation of butterflies hatches out in June or early July and they can be seen on the wing until September, when they go into hibernation. The eggs are not laid until the spring, when the buckthorn bushes begin to come into leaf. The individuals that have hibernated may be found up to the end of May and at higher altitudes even later. Its distribution in time fluctuates, according to climatic conditions and the altitude of habitat. The development of the green caterpillar lasts three to seven weeks. It feeds on leaves, initially eating the centres and later nibbling the edges. The pupa hangs in the tree from a leaf or twig and is extremely well camouflaged.

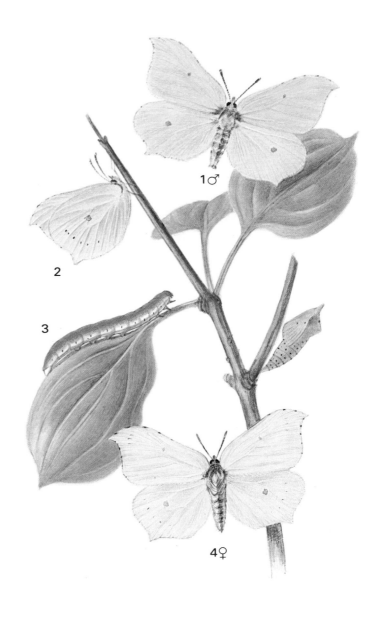

Adult:
From VI—V. next year.
Caterpillar:
V—VIII. Partial second generation in VII—IX in north Africa.
Foodplant:
buckthorn.

1, 4 — adults
2 — underside of wings
3 — caterpillar

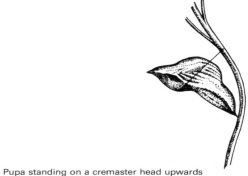

Pupa standing on a cremaster head upwards

# Lesser Purple Emperor

*Apatura ilia*

This butterfly, as well as the purple emperor, resembles the brightly coloured tropical species. Light reflection on the scales of the male's forewings causes a pretty violet-blue iridescence. The lesser purple emperor is widespread throughout western and central Europe, across Asia Minor and the temperate zone of the palearctic region as far as Japan, in which area several geographical races can be distinguished. It does not occur in England nor in some of the islands in the Mediterranean. One of the best known forms is the form *clytie* with yellow spots in the corners of the forewings, illustrated here. In some places this form is much more abundant than the nominate one, originally described near Vienna. The lesser purple emperor is most commonly found by ponds and streams where the foodplants of the caterpillar grow. It lives both in lowlands and in the hills, but it avoids higher mountains. A second generation may occur in southern Europe; in central Europe only one generation is the rule.

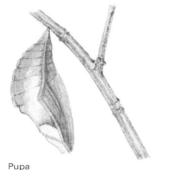

Pupa

Adult:
V—VII (in the south also VIII—IX).
Caterpillar:
VII—V.
Pupal stage lasts 2—3 weeks; it is usually found in VI.
Caterpillar hibernates.
Foodplants:
aspen, poplar, sallow, various species of willow, etc.

1 — adult
2 — caterpillar
3 — form *clytie*

# Purple Emperor

*Apatura iris*

The area of distribution of this species ranges from England throughout the whole of the temperate zone of the palearctic region as far as Japan. The butterfly inhabits deciduous woods and is also found along streams. It likes to settle on muddy woodland rides to drink. Both species of European emperors are shy butterflies, and for this reason they are not easy to capture. The butterfly loses its shyness when thirsty. The purple emperor is one of the very common butterflies in some parts of deciduous forests in Europe. It flies about woodland rides, where it can find horse dung and carrion, which attract these beautiful butterflies from the whole neighbourhood. It prefers lowlands and is only rarely found at altitudes of more than 1,300 metres. As a rule, only the males are captured, as the females stay at the tops of high trees. The female glues her eggs to willow leaves. The caterpillar is at first brown, later turning green with yellowish spots and a side stripe. It hibernates after the second moulting. The best known and most conspicuous form is the form *iole,* which lacks most of the white markings.

Adult:
VI—VIII.
Caterpillar:
VIII—V.
It hibernates in a spun nest on a twig or a leaf near a bud.
The pupal stage lasts 2—3 weeks; it is usually found in VI.
Foodplants:
various species of willow and aspen.

1 — adult
2 — caterpillar
3 — pupa
4 — form *iole*

Head of a caterpillar

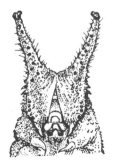

Egg

# White Admiral
*Limenitis camilla*

# Southern White Admiral
*Limenitis reducta*

The two species look much alike but still they can be easily distinguished. The white admiral has two rows of black spots on the outer underside margin of the hindwings in contrast to the southern white admiral, which has only one.

The white admiral occurs all over central Europe as well as in England and southern Sweden, penetrating as far as Japan. It is found in woodland rides and clearings and in the Alps it reaches altitudes of about 1,500 metres. Generally, single specimens are to be seen, only in some localities do they appear in larger numbers. The caterpillar is yellow-green with white dots and brown bristles. The pupa is green with two small horns and spattered with silvery spots.

The southern white admiral inhabits the sunlit scrub-covered hillsides and forest margins. It occurs in southern Europe, Asia Minor, Transcaucasia and Iran. In some places it is fairly abundant and regularly has two generations during one year. Only one generation appears along the northern boundary of its distribution, which passes through central Europe. In the south it produces up to three consecutive generations in a year. On the southern slopes of the Alps it is found at altitudes of about 1,300 metres. The caterpillar has two rows of red spikes. The pupa is grey-brown with metallic spots.

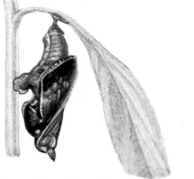

Pupa of *Limenitis camilla*

*Limenitis camilla:*
Adult:
V—VII.
Caterpillar:
as *L. reducta*.
Foodplants:
as *L. reducta*.

1 — adult
2 — underside of wings

*Limenitis reducta:*
Adult:
V—IX (usually in two generations).
Caterpillar:
VII—V.
Pupates after hibernation, usually in V.
The pupal stage lasts less than two weeks.
Foodplants:
different species of honeysuckle.

3 — underside of wings
4 — adult

# Poplar Admiral
*Limenitis populi*

The ground coloration of the male is dark brown or black. It has a few white spots on the forewings and several brick-red half-moons along the outer margin of the wings. The ground colouring of the underside is light brown and the white spots have grey-green or bluish iridescence. Sometimes it is possible to come across a male without the white spots on the upper-side of the wings (form *tremulae*); in some places it is even more common than the nominate form. The female has a much more conspicuous white design particularly on the hindwings. The poplar admiral inhabits deciduous and mixed forests of almost the entire temperate zone of Eurasia. It is widespread in central Europe but never found in large numbers. It is rare in the Netherlands and Denmark and does not occur in Great Britain. The butterfly frequents the banks of streams and rivers where the trees needed by the caterpillar grow. Most of the time the butter-flies fly about at the tops of trees, coming down to the ground only to drink. They settle on muddy roads and on various kinds of decaying matter (for example fruit and food refuse, animal dung and carrion). The pupa is yellow-brown with black spots. The butterfly emerges in three to four weeks.

Adult:
VI–VII (sometimes also VIII).
Caterpillar:
until V.
Hibernates and pupates on the upperside of a leaf.
Foodplants:
aspen, poplar, usually bushes and small trees.

1 — underside of wings
2 — caterpillar
3 — adult

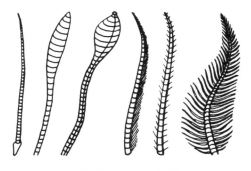

various types of antennae

# High Brown Fritillary

*Fabriciana adippe*

This butterfly is widespread throughout the vast area extending from north Africa over western Europe as far as Japan. It has a large number of geographical races. The nominate form was described near Vienna. The subspecies *bajuvarica* occurs in the German and Austrian Alps, *norvegica* breeds in the north of Europe. Many geographical races have been described in eastern Asia, particularly in the extensive regions of China and Japan. Worth a special mention is the form *cleodoxa*, which lacks the silvery spots on the underside of hindwings, so that the olive-green or yellow-green colouring with a greenish sheen predominates. In many localities in south-eastern Europe this form is evidently more common than the nominate one. The high brown fritillary occurs in habitats similar to those of the related species, mostly in woodland rides and clearings. The butterfly can be well identified by the pattern on the underside of the hindwings. The female lays eggs which are at first greenish and later turn red. The caterpillar is grey-black with rusty-brown spikes. The pupa is brown-grey with blue and silvery spots.

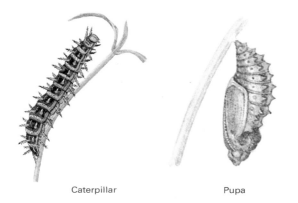

Caterpillar          Pupa

Adult:
VI—VIII (sometimes even IX).
Caterpillar:
in some localities from VIII to V; according to other observations the caterpillar hatches as late as in III feeding until V—VI when it pupates.
Foodplants:
different species of violet.

1, 4 — adults
2 — underside of wings
3 — form *cleodoxa*, underside of wings

# Silver-washed Fritillary

*Argynnis paphia*

The species was described from specimens found in Sweden. In the north of Europe it occurs in central Finland and Sweden and in southern Norway. From there the distribution area extends across Denmark and northwest Germany as far as the Mediterranean. In north Africa it is reported from Algeria. It penetrates eastwards through the extensive regions of Siberia, as far as Japan. In this vast territory it forms a great number of geographical races which are not, as a rule, very sharply separated. The island race *immaculata,* from Corsica and Sardinia, is worthy of interest because of the reduced number of silver bands on the underside of the hindwings. Sometimes a dark form of the female, also illustrated here, may occur among the normally coloured individuals. It is well known among collectors as the form *valesina.* The female nearly always lays eggs on the trunks of trees, generally oak, sometimes also on low growing plants near the base of the trunk. The full-grown caterpillar is brownish-black, with a wide yellow dorsal stripe and black and yellow spots on the sides of the body. The pupa is dark brown with yellow dots. The species has only one generation.

Adult:
VI—IX.
Caterpillar:
VIII—VI. It pupates after hibernation, usually in V, at higher altitudes in VI. The period of pupa lasts approximately three weeks.
Foodplants:
different species of violet, especially common dog violet.

1, 2 — adults
3 — form *valesina*
4 — caterpillar

Underside of the wings

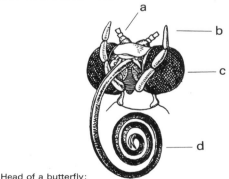

Head of a butterfly:
a — antennae (incomplete), b — labial palps, c — compound eye, d — proboscis

# Map Butterfly

*Araschnia levana*

This species inhabits woodland rides, parks, edges of meadows and shaded corners overgrown with the stinging nettle. Most often it occurs only sporadically, in some places, however, being very abundant. It can be found throughout the area extending from western Europe as far as Japan, excepting Britain. The map butterfly is renowned for its seasonal variability. The ground colour of the wings in the spring specimens *(levana)* is brick-red with dark markings. The summer generation specimens *(prorsa)* are black with light spots (whitish or yellowish). Occasionally a partial third generation appears but it is difficult to confirm its occurrence in central Europe conclusively, as the development of the caterpillar is very uneven and a possibility of later hatched second generation specimens cannot be excluded. The female lays greenish oval-shaped eggs, attaching them to the underside of leaves joined in columns in a chain-like fashion. At first the caterpillars stay together but later they split up and wander away from each other. When disturbed, they drop off the foodplant.

Eggs and newly-hatched caterpillars

Pupa of a butterfly:
a — head section, b — sheath of antennae, c — sheath of the front wing, d — abdominal segments, e — cremaster or hooks for attachment

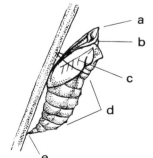

Adult:
IV—V (locally also in VI); VII—IX; possibly a 3rd generation even later.
Caterpillar:
VI—VII; VIII—IX.
Development lasts about 4 weeks.
Foodplant:
stinging nettle.

1 — *levana* (spring form)
2 — caterpillar
3 — *prorsa* (summer form)
4 — *porima* (autumn form)
5 — *levana*, underside of wings
6 — pupa

# Painted Lady

*Vanessa cardui*

The painted lady inhabits fields, heaths, steppes and meadows, avoiding forests. It is one of the best known migrant butterflies, arriving in central and western Europe from the south, usually in June. The migration of this species has been observed high up in the mountains. There are many detailed records concerning the immigration of the painted lady in English literature. A large invasion of the species was recorded in 1948; also in 1952, the species being conspicuously abundant in western and northern Europe. The geographical distribution of the painted lady covers an extensive area. It occurs almost universally throughout the world, the exception being South America. It is one of the few butterflies found in Iceland and Ireland. The female lays single eggs on leaves of the foodplant of the caterpillar. The caterpillar is spiny, grey or brownish with yellow stripes. The pupa is greyish or brown, with shiny golden spots. The butterfly hatches in about two weeks.

Adult:
arriving from the south coast from IV—VI, next generation until X.
Caterpillar:
VI—IX.
Foodplants:
different plants, chiefly thistle, burdock, stinging nettle, etc. It may be a pest on globe artichokes in the south.

1 — underside of wings
2 — adult
3 — pupa
4 — caterpillar

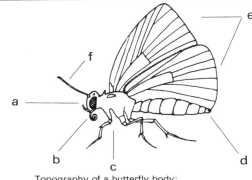

Topography of a butterfly body:
a — head, b — proboscis, c — thorax with legs, d — abdomen, e — wings, f — antennae

# Camberwell Beauty

*Nymphalis antiopa*

The Camberwell beauty enjoys much attention from the collectors because of its suitability for experiments concerning the influence of temperature on the wing pattern. The well-known form *hygiaea* is illustrated here. It occurs in deciduous forests both in the lowlands and quite high up in the mountains, and prefers riversides, streams and river banks with abundance of the caterpillar's foodplants. With the first sunny spring days the Camberwell beauty leaves the sheltered places where it hibernated. It is fond of sucking sap oozing from injured trees or the sweet juice from over-ripe fruits. This large butterfly inhabits Europe, Asia and North America but does not breed in England or Ireland. The nominate form was described from specimens captured in Sweden. It occurs in central and western Europe and is common in parts of North America, where two other geographical races are found (the subspecies *hyperborea* and *lintnerii*). Further subspecies have been described in east Asia. The butterfly is still abundant in some places but it seems to have decreased in number during the last few decades.

Suspended caterpillar ready for pupation

Adult:
VI—IX and after hibernation from III or IV to V, the mountain specimens to VI.
Caterpillar:
VI—VII.
Foodplants:
willow, sallow, birch, poplar, elm.

1 — adult
2 — caterpillar
3 — form *hygiaea*
4 — pupa

# Peacock Butterfly

*Inachis io*

Owing to its interesting wing design, the peacock butterfly is so conspicuous that it cannot be mistaken for any other species. It occurs throughout most of Europe and the temperate part of Asia including Japan. Only a few geographical forms are recognized in this extensive area. Like other related species, the peacock butterfly produces different forms if the fresh pupa is subjected to sudden changes in temperature. The butterfly is almost everywhere; it can be found in lowland forests, parks, gardens and high up in the mountains where it likes to settle on flowering plants, particularly thistles. It hibernates in lofts, cellars, caves and similar sheltered places and leaves them in early spring. The peacock and the small tortoiseshell feeding from the catkins of a sallow bush are a characteristic feature of spring. The female lays eggs in batches on the undersides of leaves of the caterpillar's foodplants. The young caterpillars crawl to the top of the plant where they spin a communal nest. They live gregariously. The pupa has two forms, grey or yellowish-green.

Adult:
VII—IX, after hibernation from III to V, in the mountains also in VI.
Caterpillar:
from V to VI and then from VII to IX.
The egg stage lasts about a week; caterpillar 2—3 weeks; pupa 10—14 days.
Foodplants:
almost exclusively on stinging nettle, rarely on hop.

1 — underside of wings
2 — adult
3 — pupa
4 — caterpillar

Emerging butterfly

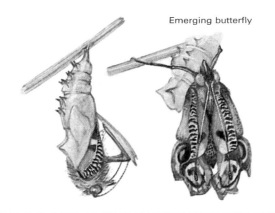

Detail of eye-spot on the left hind wing

# Comma Butterfly

*Polygonia c-album*

The comma butterfly has a small white spot in the shape of a 'C' on the underside of the hindwings. Many separate forms have been described, the distinctive element being the shape of this spot, which is very variable. These forms have little taxonomic significance, but for interest's sake, some of them should be mentioned: *o-album, delta-album, j-album, f-album, g-album,* etc. However, the specimens lacking this spot did not escape the attention of collectors and they can be found in many collections under the names *c-extinctum* or *extincta.* The comma butterfly hibernates, the hibernating specimens being only those of the typical form. The specimens hatching in summer are partly typical, partly much lighter in colour (form *hutchinsoni*). The butterflies of the typical form hibernate, while the light specimens breed again; their offspring, which appear in August or September of the same year, are typical and hibernate. Consequently, it is only typically coloured specimens that appear in spring, never the form *hutchinsoni.* The distribution area of the comma butterfly extends from the British Isles as far as Japan.

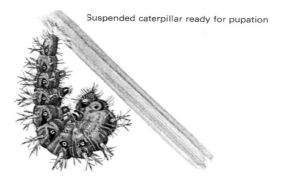

Suspended caterpillar ready for pupation

Adult:
VI-VII; VII—V or VIII—V.
Caterpillar:
V—VII, but also in VII—VIII.
Foodplant:
stinging nettle, hop, elm, gooseberry, currant, etc.

1 — adult
2 — pupa
3 — underside of wings
4 — caterpillar
5 — form *hutchinsoni*

# Speckled Wood

*Pararge aegeria*

The speckled wood is an inconspicuous brown butterfly inhabiting woodland rides, clearings, parks, etc. It can also be found fluttering along less frequented country lanes. Its flight is slow, hesitant, and it often settles on low branches or even on the ground. Its distribution area is quite extensive, from western Europe and north Africa as far as central Asia. In the Alps it ascends to altitudes of about 1,500 metres and in African mountains even higher. There are a considerable number of geographical races. The nominate form was described in southern Europe. The spots on the wings are orange, in contrast to those of the specimens from central Europe which are yellowish. The nominate form lives in southern Europe and north Africa (Morocco, Algeria, Tunisia). The subspecies *tircis* is reported from Britain and Ireland; *insula* was described in St. Mary's Island (Scilly Isles) in 1971. The west-European populations known as *tircis* and the central-European ones known as *aegerides* are considered by some to be identical.

Adult:
III—VI; VII—IX, sometimes also X.
Caterpillar:
VI—VII and from IX to the next year's spring. The butterfly breeds continuously through the summer and hibernation takes place either in the caterpillar or pupal stage.
Foodplants:
couch grass, meadow grass, etc.

1 — adult
2, 3 — subspecies *tircis*
4 — caterpillar

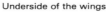

Underside of the wings

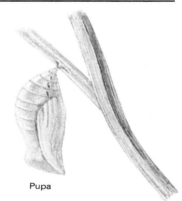

Pupa

# Woodland Ringlet
*Erebia medusa*

# Scotch Argus
*Erebia aethiops*

The woodland ringlet is one of the most widespread European species of the genus *Erebia*. It occurs both in the lowlands and in the hills and even quite high up in the mountains. In the Alps it is found at altitudes of about 2,600 metres; in the Carpathians 1,600—1,900 metres. The species was first described near Vienna. It forms several important geographical races, for example, the subspecies *hippomedusa*, found at higher elevations in the Austrian and Italian Alps. The butterflies are commonly found in damp meadows.

The Scotch argus prefers hilly regions, and is often found in the mountains. At higher altitudes (1,700—2,000 metres) smaller specimens occur with much reduced red-brown pattern. (form *altivaga*). The distribution range extends from western Europe as far as east Asia. It is absent from Scandinavia. The caterpillar stays in concealed places. The pupa is brownish-yellow in a lightly spun cocoon.

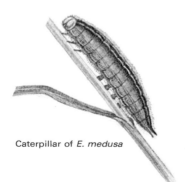

Caterpillar of *E. medusa*

Scent scales of *Erebia aethiops*

*Erebia medusa:*
Adult:
V—VI, in the mountains to VII.
Caterpillar:
from summer to spring.
Foodplants:
hairy finger-grass.

1 – adult
2 – underside of wings
4 – pupa

*Erebia aethiops:*
Adult:
VII—IX.
Caterpillar:
from IX to VI.
Foodplants:
meadow grass, bent, cocksfoot grass, etc.

3 – adult

# Marbled White

*Melanargia galathea*

It is impossible to mistake this species for any other butterfly in central Europe. There are, however, several similar species in southern Europe, Asia Minor and north Africa. The distribution area extends from western Europe as far as Iran and north Africa. It is found at altitudes of about 1,700 metres in the mountains and in the Atlas Mountains even higher. The butterfly inhabits woodland clearings, rides and margins, railway banks and grassy hillsides, in some places being very abundant. It likes to settle on flowers of the field scabious. The female is larger than the male. It lays its eggs loosely, so that they fall off the grass or often even releases them while in flight. The caterpillar feeds only at night, remaining hidden during the daytime. The marbled white is very variable, both individually and geographically, and so it is not surprising that many subspecies have been described. The nominate form lives in central Europe; the subspecies *lucasi* is the form found in north Africa. The form *procida* with a reduced pale wing pattern is one of the more conspicuous individual forms. It occurs in different types of habitat, being most abundant in the south.

Adult:
VI—VIII.
Caterpillar:
From summer to V—VI.
Foodplants:
timothy grass, meadow grass, cocksfoot grass, and other species of grass.

1, 2 — adults
3 — caterpillar
4 — yellow form

Pupa

# Purple Hairstreak
*Quercusia quercus*

# Brown Hairstreak
*Thecla betulae*

The purple hairstreak is an inhabitant of oak forests. It is difficult to see it in high woods because it stays, as a rule, round the tops of trees, fluttering about and settling from time to time on the leaves. The distribution area extends from north Africa and western Europe including England and southern Ireland to Asia Minor and Transcaucasia. The female has a shiny violet patch on the upperside of the forewings, while the male has an overall purplish sheen on a grey-black ground colour. The red-brown caterpillar has yellow or red dots along the black dorsal stripe. The pupa is brown, with dark spots and dots. The pupal stage lasts about 2 weeks.

The brown hairstreak lives in deciduous forests, parks and town cemeteries. In the mountains it is not found at altitudes higher than 1,000 metres. It is widespread in the area extending from western Europe, including England and Ireland, as far as Mongolia, China and Korea. It is never numerous in its habitats and usually only single individuals can be found. The female has a large rich orange patch on the forewings. The characteristic coloration of the underside of the wings also simplifies the identification of the brown hairstreak. The green caterpillar has a brown head and a double yellow dorsal stripe. The pupa is brown with yellow markings. The pupal stage lasts 15 to 21 days.

Egg of *Thecla betulae*

*Quercusia quercus:*
Adult:
VI—VIII.
Caterpillar:
IV—VI.
The egg overwinters.
Foodplant:
oak.

1, 2 — adults
3 — underside of wings

*Thecla betulae:*
Adult:
VII—X.
Caterpillar:
V—VI.
The egg overwinters.
Foodplants:
blackthorn, birch, etc.

4 — adult

# Adonis Blue
*Lysandra bellargus*

# Chalk-hill Blue
*Lysandra coridon*

The adonis blue inhabits uncultivated fields, railway banks, dry hillsides and downland. It is distributed throughout Europe and Asia as far as Iran. It occurs in the south of England but is absent from Ireland. The species is sometimes fairly abundant in fields of flowering clover, or lucerne; the butterflies stay on flowers overnight. The blue-green caterpillar has dark dorsal and side stripes and red-yellow spots. The pupa is green-brown.

The chalk-hill blue chooses habitats similar to those of the adonis blue, particularly on chalk and limestone downland. The two species are often found together. It occurs throughout most of Europe, with the exception of Ireland, Scandinavia, Denmark and Portugal. The species is very much sought after by collectors in England; this is why hundreds of different forms have been described and named. As in many other species of this family, there is a marked difference in colouring between the male and the female. The species was originally described from specimens found in Austria (Graz). The blue-green hairy caterpillar has yellow stripes and rows of yellow dots. The pupa is yellowish-brown.

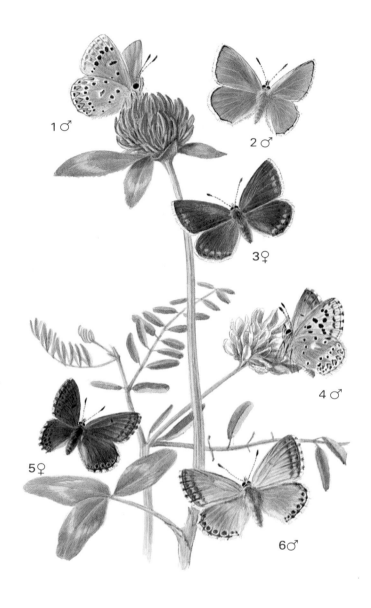

*Lysandra bellargus:*
Adult:
V–VI, VII–VIII.
Caterpillar:
VII, then from autumn to V.
Foodplant:
horseshoe vetch.

1 – underside of wings
2, 3 – adults

*Lysandra coridon:*
Adult:
VI–VIII.
Egg:
from autumn to IV.
Caterpillar:
IV to VI.
Foodplant:
horseshoe vetch.

4 – underside of wings
5, 6 – adults

♀

*Lysandra bellargus* f. *ceronus*

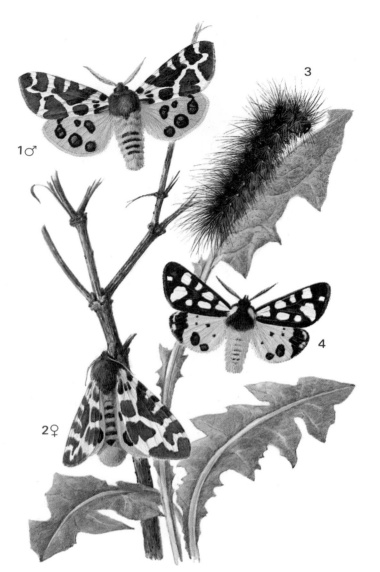

# Garden Tiger
*Arctia caja*

# Cream-spot Tiger
*Epicallia villica*

Tiger moths are among the most brightly coloured of moths. They do not rank among those with a great number of species but are represented in nearly all parts of the world. Small species are usually classed in separate families — the Nolidae and Lithosiidae. The larvae of all species are hairy.

The garden tiger is a markedly variable species — practically no two individuals have the same pattern. The forewings vary in the intensity of their coloration. The number of blue spots also varies. This moth is found both in lowlands and in mountains even above the tree line, but it is most plentiful at altitudes of about 600 meetres. It is distributed throughout all of Europe and Asia as far as Japan, and also in North America.

The cream-spot tiger shows just as much variation in pattern as the preceding species. A striking moth is the form *radiata,* which is marked with bands instead of spots, and also the form *paucimaculata* in which the spots on the forewings are almost non-existent. The cream-spot tiger is found in the warmer regions of Europe and Asia and is quite plentiful in all the places it inhabits.

Both of the illustrated tiger moths are attracted to light, but they are not active until about midnight.

The colourful hindwings of the garden tiger are normally hidden when the moth is at rest.

Pupa of the garden tiger

*Arctia caja:*
Adult:
VII—VIII.
Caterpillar:
IX—VI.
Foodplants:
various plants.

1, 2 — adults
3 — caterpillar

*Epicallia villica:*
Adult:
V—VI.
Caterpillar:
VII—IV.
Foodplants:
various plants.

4 — adult

# Red Underwing
*Catocala nupta*

# Dark Crimson Underwing
*Mormonia sponsa*

These two moths are examples of the 20 or so species of red-winged underwings found in Europe and Asia. In the daytime these large moths rest on the trunks of trees with folded wings which blend perfectly with the background; they are an inconspicuous grey with a darker irregular pattern resembling the cracked bark of oaks, alders and the like. If some bird does succeed in discovering it then the moth quickly spreads its forewings to disclose the red hind wings which acts as a deterrent. At other times the moth takes advantage of the moment of surprise and flies off rapidly following a zigzag course.

The red underwing is found in Europe, in hardwood forests and damp valleys with rich vegetation. Further east its range extends across European Russia to the Caucasus and across Siberia to the Far East. In Europe it is the commonest underwing of late summer. It may be easily captured at a light.

The dark crimson underwing is a warmth-loving species found in the oak forests of central and southern Europe; in the east the Urals and Caucasus mark the boundary of its range. It differs from other species in that the hind wings are a bright crimson.

*Catocala nupta:*
Adult:
VII—X.
Caterpillar:
V—VII.
Foodplants:
willow, poplar.

1 — *adult*
2 — *caterpillar*

*Mormonia sponsa:*
Adult:
VII—IX.
Caterpillar:
V—VI.
Foodplant:
oak.

3 — *adult*
4 — *caterpillar*

Pupa of *Mormonia sponsa*

Red underwing in resting position

# Gipsy Moth
*Lymantria dispar*

# Red-tail Moth
*Dasychira pudibunda*

# Vapourer Moth
*Orgyia antiqua*

The family of tussock moths includes some 1,800 known species. They are moderate-sized insects with broad wings and marked sexual dimorphism. The males are differently coloured from the females and have differently shaped antennae. The family includes many serious pests.

The gipsy moth is now distributed throughout the northern hemisphere. In 1869 it was introduced into North America where it spread rapidly and has become a very serious pest. In the warmer parts of Europe it is a pest of oak trees and sometimes also fruit trees. In years of overpopulation the trunks of trees are dotted with eggmasses covered with pale hairs from the female's abdomen.

The red-tail moth is distributed in the temperate zone from Europe to Japan. The adult is inconspicuously coloured but the caterpillars, coloured bright yellow with black rings, can be seen from afar on broadleaved trees.

The vapourer moth is one of the species in which the female has a bizarre shape and vestigial wings. She is in fact a small walking barrel filled with eggs. The flying male can be seen even during the day in a swift, zigzag flight. The strikingly multi-coloured caterpillar is covered with tough, bristle-like hairs. This moth is widespread throughout temperate Eurasia except the warmest parts of Europe and north Africa.

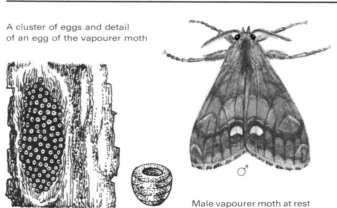

A cluster of eggs and detail of an egg of the vapourer moth

Male vapourer moth at rest

*Lymantria dispar:*
Adult:
VI—VIII.
Caterpillar:
IV—VII.
Egg overwinters.

1, 2 — adult
3 — caterpillar
4 — pupa

*Dasychira pudibunda:*
Adult:
IV—VII.
Caterpillar:
VII—X. Pupa overwinters.

5 — adult
6 — caterpillar

*Orgyia antiqua:*
Adult (2 generations):
VI—VII. and VIII—X.
Caterpillar:
IV—VI and VII—X.
Egg overwinters.
Foodplants (all species):
broadleaved trees and shrubs.

7 — adult
8 — adult female without wings
9 — caterpillar

# Great Peacock Moth

*Saturnia pyri*

The family Saturniidae includes some of the largest moths in the world with a wingspan of more than 20 cm. Most have a striking eye-spot near the centre of each wing and in some species the hind wings form long spurs. The mouthparts are generally atrophied and the males have long comb-like antennae. Some species from eastern Asia were reared for the fine silken fibre produced by their caterpillars. The ravenous caterpillars of some species are dangerous pests to fruit trees.

*Saturnia pyri* is the largest European moth with a wingspan of up to 16 cm. The males can be distinguished from the females by the prominently comb-like antennae; they are also somewhat smaller but their coloration is identical. This is a warmth-loving moth and central Europe marks the northern limits of its distribution. It frequents forest-steppe regions with thickets, and in urban areas, parks and gardens with fruit trees. In Europe *Saturnia pyri* may be seen early in spring (April to May), often circling round street lamps at night and looking more like a bat than a moth. In the daytime it may be found resting with wings slightly spread out on a tree trunk or on a wall lit by a street lamp at night. The stout larvae covered with coloured warts consume a large quantity of food. They pupate in late summer in large bottle-shaped cocoons of coarse fibres located in the trunks and in the branches of fruit trees, for example walnut, apricot, cherry etc.

1 ♂

2

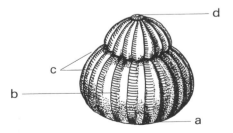

4

3

Adult:
IV—VI.
Caterpillar:
V—VIII.
Pupa overwinters.
Foodplants:
fruit trees of the family Rosaceae.

1 — adult
2 — caterpillar
3 — cocoon
4 — pupa

Topography of a moth egg:
a — base, b — longitudinal ribs, c — transverse ribs, d — micropylary zone with opening for spermatozoa

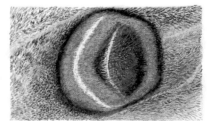

Detail of eye-spot

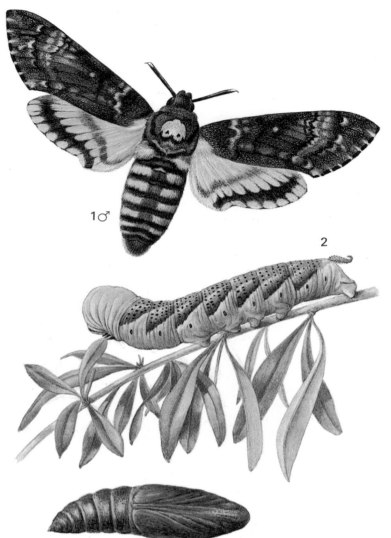

1♂

2

3

# Death's Head Hawk
*Acherontia atropos*

There are more than 800 known species included in the family Sphingidae, represented in Europe by only a small fraction — about 20 species. Some hawk moths are the largest moths in the world with a wingspan of as much as 20 cm. They are distinguished by a stout, long spindle-shaped body and narrow forewings, which are much larger than the hind wings and have strong venation. Hawk moths are the fastest fliers of all insects and the shape of their body is adapted accordingly. They are not only capable of fast but also sustained flight and travel distances of thousands of km. There is no difference between the sexes in coloration nor in the shape of the antennae. The proboscis is generally developed to a great length and curled into a spiral when not in use. Hawk moths imbibe nectar on the wing. They are able to stop abruptly and move to another spot in a flash. The larvae are smooth, extremely variegated as a rule with a projecting horn at the end of the body. Pupation takes place in the ground or on the surface in plant debris.

The death's head hawk acquired its name from the pattern on the thorax which resembles a human skull. It is distributed in Africa and southwest Asia whence it migrates far north to establish a summer generation. The pupae may often be found when harvesting potatoes. Adult moths may be obtained from these pupae if they are kept in a warm place. However, in the wild they rarely complete their development in the cold autumn weather. Beekeepers sometimes find this moth inside their hives, to which it has been attracted by the scent of the honey.

Appearance of adult in normal resting position

A caterpillar builds a clay case in the ground within which it pupates

Adult (2 generations):
V—VI and VIII—XI.
Caterpillar:
VII—VIII. Migrant.
Foodplants:
nightshades and related plants.

1 — adult
2 — caterpillar
3 — pupa

# Privet Hawk
*Sphinx ligustri*

# Convolvulus Hawk
*Herse convolvuli*

The privet hawk is one of the few species that have remained in the genera established and described by Linnaeus which is of interest for the simple reason that most other species have been classed in other, newly established genera by the further elaboration of the system of classification. The privet hawk is widespread and quite common throughout temperate Eurasia, excepting the coldest parts. It flies there from the south for the summer, but it does not stay for the winter. Adult moths may be seen on warm May evenings when they fly about sucking nectar from the trumpet-shaped blossoms of various flowering shrubs. The larvae appears in parks but are hard to locate in the branches. Their presence is revealed only by the large black faeces, which are quite conspicuous on the clean pathways.

In Europe the convolvulus hawk is a visitor from the south for its home is in tropical Africa, Asia, Australia and also America. Migratory journeys of thousands of km are a regular life habit and occur every year. The summer generation develops in Europe. The moths emerge in the autumn and their numbers are apparently augmented by further arrivals from the south. The convolvulus hawk is on the wing at dusk in August and September, when it generally visits phlox flowers, sucking nectar from the blossoms with its ten cm-long proboscis. The pupa of this hawk is interesting. It is about six cm long, coloured a glossy brown, and has a large spirally coiled proboscis casing.

*Sphinx ligustri:*
Adult:
V–VII.
Caterpillar:
VII–IX.
Pupa overwinters.
Foodplants:
lilac, privet, snowberry etc.

1 – adult
2 – caterpillar

*Herse convolvuli:*
Adult (2 generations):
V–VI (migrant) and VIII–IX.
Caterpillar:
VI–VIII.
Foodplants:
convolvulus.

3 – adult
4 – pupa

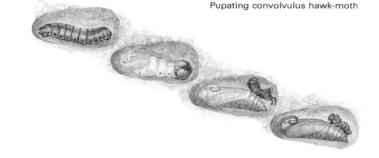

Pupating convolvulus hawk-moth

# Spurge Hawk
*Celerio euphorbiae*

## *Celerio lineata*

The spurge hawk, which inhabits the temperate and subtropical regions of Europe and central Asia, was at one time the commonest hawk of central Europe. At harvest time one could find its variegated larvae on cypress spurge *(Euphorbia cyparissias)* all over hedge banks. Today the species has disappeared almost entirely from many places and is plentiful only in more southerly regions where some of the population hibernate, their numbers otherwise being swelled by new arrivals from the warm south. In warmer summers there may be a second generation. The adult moths are on the wing in the late afternoon when they visit trumpet-shaped flowers, but they are also active all night. About midnight they are attracted in large numbers to ultraviolet light. The spurge hawk is a variable species. There is a pink form — *rubescens,* and the rarer form *latifolii* with yellow hind wings. These forms are infrequently met with in the field, being more easily obtained by breeding. Household conditions are apparently propitious to their development.

Members of the large genus *Celerio* are distributed throughout the entire world. *Celerio lineata* is represented in Europe by the subspecies *Celerio lineata livornica,* which is found in Africa, southern Asia and Australia, whereas the type species *Celerio lineata lineata* is distributed throughout North America. It is a very active moth and an excellent flier. In years when it overpopulates in its native habitat (the larvae cause damage to grapevines) it flies great distances in all directions.

Egg of the spurge hawk with the caterpillar head showing through

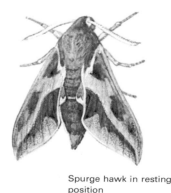

Spurge hawk in resting position

*Celerio euphorbiae:*
Adult (2 generations):
IV—VI and VII—VIII.
Caterpillar:
V—VII and VIII—X.
Pupa overwinters.
Foodplants:
spurge.

1 — adult
2 — caterpillar

*Celerio lineata:*
Adult (2 generations):
V—VI (migrant) and VII—IX.
Caterpillar:
VI—VIII.
Foodplants:
vine, bedstraw, willow herb.

3 — adult
4 — caterpillar

# Elephant Hawk
*Deilephila elpenor*

## *Deilephila porcellus*
## *Proserpinus proserpina*

The elephant hawk is a native of Europe but is also found in all of Asia excepting the northernmost parts. It is most plentiful at moderate altitudes and in the foothills, but may be encountered even high up in the mountains. In warm southern regions it is not so plentiful. The adult moths fly at dusk round flowering willow herb, wild thyme and other nectar-rich flowers. Most often found on willow herb and rose-bay willow herb in mid-summer are the larvae, which occur in two forms, green and brown.

*Deilephila porcellus* may be found in May and June in grassy localities with profusely flowering herbs. It flies in the late afternoon like other hawks round flowering campions and other flowers and is particularly abundant in the lowlands. It is distributed in Europe and Asia like the preceding species. The coloration shows marked variation, ranging from green to a rich carmine.

*Proserpinus proserpina* is a rare species occurring mostly in lowlands, alongside rivers and ponds, where the plants it feeds on grow. In recent years its numbers seem to have dwindled rapidly. The centre of its European distribution is in the south, to which it came via the warmer parts of Asia.

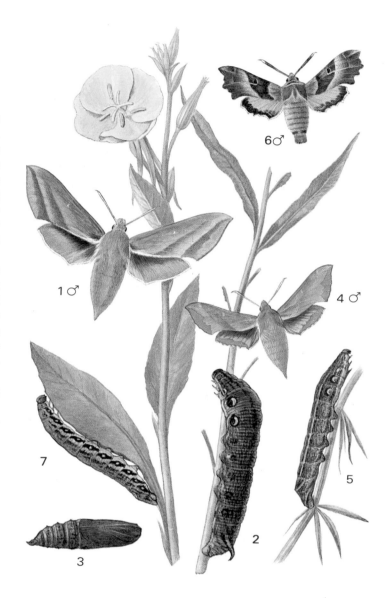

*Deilephila elpenor:*
Adult:
V–VII.
Caterpillar:
VI–IX.
Pupa overwinters.
Foodplants:
mostly rosebay and other willow herbs, bedstraw.

1 – adult
2 – caterpillar
3 – pupa

*Deilephila porcellus:*
Adult:
V–VII.
Caterpillar:
VII–IX.
Pupa overwinters.
Foodplants:
as *D. elpenor*.

4 – adult
5 – caterpillar

*Proserpinus proserpina:*
Adult:
IV–VI.
Caterpillar:
VII–VIII.
Pupa overwinters.
Foodplants:
evening primrose.

6 – adult
7 – caterpillar

Elephant hawk feeding

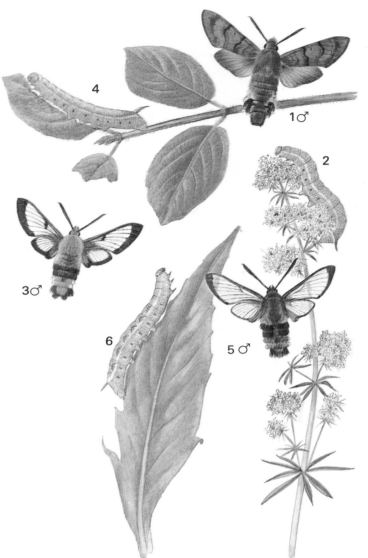

## *Macroglossum stellatarum*
## *Hemaris fuciformis*
## *Hemaris tityus*

The species illustrated on this page are small, diurnal moths which, like all hawk moths, have an exceptionally powerful flight. Besides having a streamlined body the apex of the abdomen in *Macroglossa* and *Hemaris* is provided with an extensile, truncated tuft of hairs reminiscent of the tail feathers of birds. *Macroglossum stellatarum* is a migrant which inhabits the warmer parts of temperate Eurasia and recently appeared also in North America. It does not overwinter in the temperate zone of Europe and Asia for the pupae would not survive the winters there, but there may be exceptions to the rule if the winter is uncommonly mild. The adult moths may be encountered even on alpine meadows at the highest altitudes where plants still grow, where they fly to feed when the meadows are in full bloom. In some years this moth is very plentiful in the autumn, often sucking the nectar of flowers in city parks when the supply in the field is meagre.

*Hemaris fuciformis* and *Hemaris tityus* are likewise diurnal moths, on the wing on sunny days in May in the vicinity of flowering sage and catchfly. Their powerful flight enables them to travel high up into the mountains. They are not uncommon moths but very shy. Both are distributed in Europe and in western and central Asia.

Pupa of *M. stellatarum*

*Hemaris fuciformis*
in resting position

| *Macroglossum stellatarum:* | *Hemaris fuciformis:* | *Hemaris tityus:* |
|---|---|---|
| Adult (2 generations): | Adult: | Adult: |
| V—VII (migrant) and VIII—X. | V—VII. | V—VII. |
| Caterpillar: | Caterpillar: | Caterpillar: |
| VI—VIII and IX—X. | VII—VIII. | VII—VIII. |
| Pupa overwinters. | Pupa overwinters. | Pupa overwinters. |
| Foodplants: | Foodplants: | Foodplants: |
| bedstraw, woodruff. | honeysuckle, snowberry. | teasels. |
| | | |
| 1 — adult | 3 — adult | 5 — adult male |
| 2 — caterpillar | 4 — caterpillar | 6 — caterpillar |

# Magpie Moth
*Abraxas grossulariata*

## *Abraxas sylvata*
## *Ennomos autumnaria*
## *Ourapteryx sambucaria*

The feeding damage caused by the larvae of the magpie moth on current and gooseberry bushes in Europe is practically a thing of the past, for this species is no longer as plentiful as it once was, though it is still distributed throughout the whole of temperate Eurasia. It was in this species that scientists first noted that unlike most animals, in which the male's sperm determines the sex of the offspring, it was the eggs from the female which determined the offspring's sex. This phenomenom is now known to occur in all butterflies and moths, and also in birds.

*Abraxas sylvata* is a woodland species with a similar range of distribution.

*Ennomos autumnaria* is a common moth of early autumn, widely distributed north of the tropics from lowlands to mountains wherever suitable trees grow. It is attracted to light, and in the morning, near these trees, one may find several individuals on a wall illuminated by the light of a lamp.

*Ourapteryx sambucaria* is one of the largest of European geometrid moths, though at first glance it does not even look like one. It is a European species, widely distributed in lowlands and warmer regions. In Asia its distribution is discontinuous.

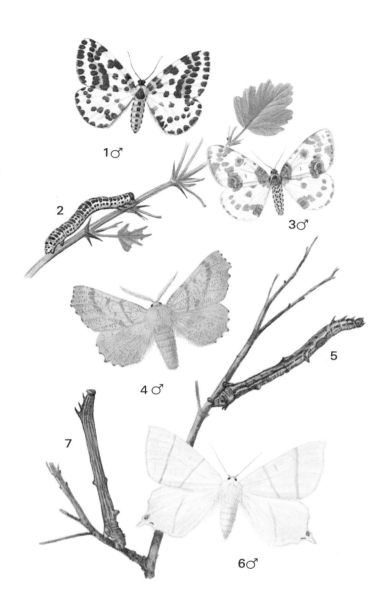

*Abraxas grossulariata:*
Adult: VI—VII.
Caterpillar: VIII—VI (hibernates).
Foodplants:
broad-leaved trees and shrubs.

1 — adult
2 — caterpillar

*Abraxas sylvata:*
Adult: VI—VIII.
Caterpillar: VIII—IX.
Pupa overwinters.
Foodplants:
broad-leaved trees and shrubs.

3 — adult

*Ennomos autumnaria:*
Adult: VIII—X.
Caterpillar: V—VII.
Egg overwinters.
Foodplants:
broad-leaved trees and shrubs.

4 — adult
5 — caterpillar

*Ourapteryx sambucaria:*
Adult: VI—VIII.
Caterpillar: VIII—V (hibernates).
Foodplants:
broad-leaved trees and shrubs.

6 — adult
7 — caterpillar

When at rest, the fore wings of *Abraxas* species do not completely overlap the hindwings

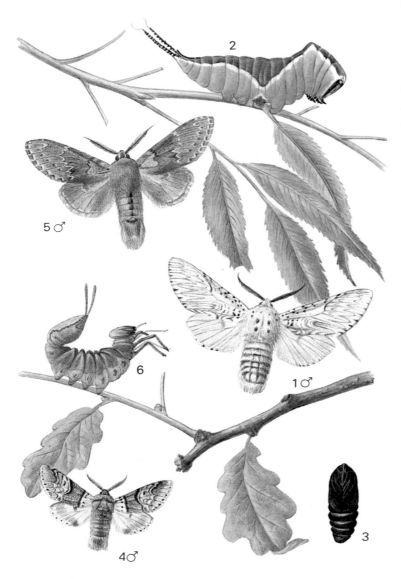

# Puss Moth
*Cerura vinula*

# *Stauropus fagi*
# *Harpyia hermelina*

The family Notodontidae includes some 2,000 species of moderate-sized moths distributed throughout the world, but chiefly in South America, Africa and the Middle East. Of particular interest in this family are the larvae which are either smooth and of bizarre shape with tooth-like prominences, or cylindrical and hairy. In most instances they are very brightly coloured. The dorsal hairs of adult moths are arranged in tooth-like tufts when at rest.

The species illustrated here are found in Europe and Asia. Of them all the puss moth occurs farthest east, as far as Japan, and *Harpyia hermelina* as far as the Altai. Both are comparatively rare. The moths are attracted to light. The stout colourful larvae, which have two long slender processes on the terminal segment, may be found on willows, sallows and alders. They extend the processes only when irritated. The larva of *Stauropus fagi* is also remarkable on account of the great length of the thoracic legs and the fact that the raised abdomen is sometimes curved forward towards the head which makes it look like a large spider when at rest. In the temperate zones of Europe and Asia *S. fagi* occurs in the hardwood forest regions. In southern Asia it sometimes over-multiplies causing damage.

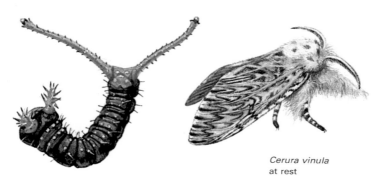

A freshly hatched caterpillar of the puss moth with the typical fork at the end of the tail

*Cerura vinula* at rest

*Cerura vinula:*
Adult: IV—VII.
Caterpillar: VI—IX.
Pupa overwinters.
Foodplants:
willow, poplar.

1 — adult
2 — caterpillar
3 — pupa

*Stauropus fagi:*
Adult: IV—VIII.
Caterpillar: VI—IX.
Pupa overwinters.
Foodplants:
  broad-leaved trees,
  mostly beech, hornbeam.

4 — adult
5 — adult male

*Harpyia hermelina:*
Adult: V—VIII.
Caterpillar: VII—IX.
Pupa overwinters.
Foodplant:
poplar.

6 — caterpillar

# Six-spot Burnet
*Zygaena filipendulae*

## *Agrumenia carniolica*
## *Polymorpha ephialtes*

The family Zygaenidae includes some thousand species found in practically all parts of the world excepting North America. They are not very big moths, many are brilliantly coloured and there is a great diversity in structure. The wing venation is very primitive, the antennae may be comb-like but are more often club-shaped. The proboscis is generally well developed. The short and stout larvae covered with fine short hairs have a small, retractable head. The pupae are enclosed in glossy, parchment-like spindle-shaped cocoons cemented lengthwise to grass or plant stems. The abdominal segments are mobile and the appendages are encased separately. The moths fly in the daytime but are usually to be seen resting on the blossoms of plants of the family Dipsacaceae and Compositae.

There are numerous red-coloured species of Zygaenidae. They are most common in lowlands as well as in mountains up to an altitude of 2,000 metres. The six-spot burnet extends into western Europe including Ireland. It frequents chalk downs and cliffs on warm sunny days.

*Agrumenia carniolica* is also a warmth loving species abundant in steppe areas, particularly on limestone, in Europe and central Asia. Both are of Oriental origin. The Eurosiberian burnet *Polymorpha ephialtes* is of interest on account of its remarkable variability, both individual and geographical, and it is no wonder that it has been widely studied by population geneticists.

<table>
<tr><td>

*Zygaena filipendulae:*
Adult:
VI—IX.
Caterpillar:
VIII—V (hibernates).
Foodplants:
birds foot trefoil, vetches etc.

1 — adult
2 — caterpillar
3 — cocoon

</td><td>

*Agrumenia carniolica:*
Adult:
VII—VIII.
Caterpillar:
IX—V (hibernates).
Foodplants:
birds foot trefoil, sainfoin.

4 — adult

</td><td>

*Polymorpha ephialtes:*
Adult:
VI—VIII.
Caterpillar:
VIII—V (hibernates).
Foodplants:
crown vetch.

5 — adult, typical form
6 — adult, form *peucedani*
7 — adult, form *icterica*
8 — caterpillar

</td></tr>
</table>

*Agrumenia carniolica* feeding

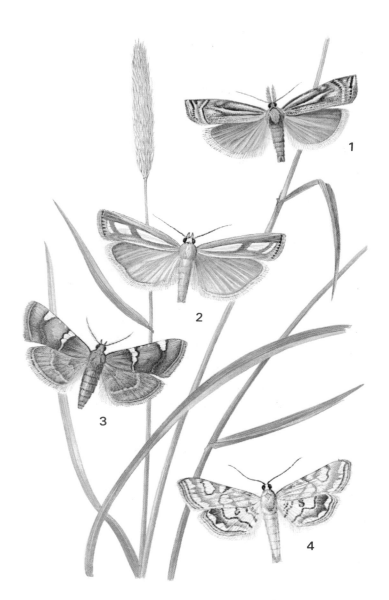

## Crambus nemorellus
## Catoptria permutatella
## Pyralis regalis
## Nausinoë nymphaeata

The family Pyralidae includes more than 20,000 species of small to moderate-sized moths distributed throughout the world. Many are serious pests of storehouses and field crops.

*Crambus nemorellus,* classified until recently under the name *Crambus pratellus,* is one of the commonest and most widely distributed species of the subfamily Crambinae. The moths are striking on account of their long forwardly extended labial palps and having their wings folded to encompass the body when at rest. They are nocturnal and are often attracted to light. The larvae generally feed on grasses.

*Pyralis regalis* resembles the common meal moth *(Pyralis farinalis)*, a pest of stored corn and flour, but is more variegated. In the wild it is found in dry and warm localities. Its distribution in Europe and Asia has been determined on the basis of captured moths, the larva having been discovered only recently.

*Nausinoë nymphaeata* is one of the few species that are distinguished by a habit quite unusual amongst moths in that the larvae live underwater and feed on aquatic plants.

The meal moth

Crambus nemorellus:
Adult:
V—VII.
Caterpillar:
VIII—V (hibernates).
Foodplants:
grasses.

1 — adult

Catoptria permutatella:
Adult:
VI—VIII.
Caterpillar:
VIII—V (hibernates).
Foodplant: moss.

2 — adult

Pyralis regalis:
Adult:
VII—VIII.
Caterpillar:
IX—V (hibernates).
Foodplants: faded and dry leaves.

3 — adult

Nausinoë nymphaeata:
Adult:
VI—VIII.
Caterpillar:
VIII—V (hibernates).
Foodplants: aquatic plants, for example water lilies.

4 — adult

# Pandemis corylana
# Archips piceana
# Green Oak Tortrix Moth
*Tortrix viridana*
# Hedya nubiferana

The Tortricidae is a huge family of small and moderate-sized moths numbering some 5,000 species with a worldwide distribution, mostly outside the tropics. Characteristic features are the shape of the wings and the developed mouthparts. These moths are long-lived and the adults of some species hibernate. The larvae live exposed, in curled leaves, buds, flowers, and in seed vessels. Some are serious pests of forest and fruit trees.

*Pandemis* and *Archips* are larger, common moths with a rich network of veins.

The green oak tortrix moth is a serious pest of oak forests, often completely defoliating whole sections. Such destruction became more frequent when chemical insecticides began to be used indiscriminately in forests thus killing the moths' natural enemies and leaving it to multiply unchecked.

*Hedya* is a common moth of fruit orchards. The grey-green larvae feed on the young leaves and shoots. When resting the adult moths resemble bird faeces thus escaping insect-eating birds.

*Pandemis corylana:*
Adult:
VII—IX.
Caterpillar:
V—VII.
Egg overwinters.
Foodplants:
broad-leaved trees
and shrubs.

1 — adult

*Archips piceana:*
Adult:
VI—VII.

Caterpillar:
IX—V (hibernates).
Foodplant: conifers.

2 — adult

*Tortrix viridana:*
Adult:
VI—VII.
Caterpillar:
IV—VI.
Egg overwinters.
Foodplant:
oak.

3 — adult
4 — caterpillar

*Hedya nubiferana:*
Adult:
VI—VIII.
Caterpillar:
IV—V.
Egg overwinters.
Foodplants:
broad-leaved trees
and shrubs, fruit trees.

5 — adult

Pupa of the green
oak tortrix moth

Tortrix moth at rest

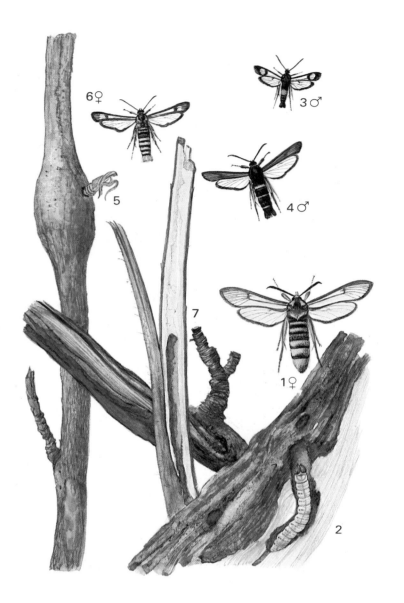

# Hornet Moth
*Sesia apiformis*

## *Aegeria myopaeformis*
## *Sciapteron tabaniforme*
## *Bembecia hylaeiformis*

Clearwings are remarkable moths both in appearance and habits. In body shape and coloration they resemble various, mainly hymenopterous insects such as bees, wasps, hornets, ichneumons, etc. but unlike these they are defenceless. On the narrow wings, which often have a metallic sheen, there are often large translucent patches without any scales. The abdomen is usually conspicuously striped black and yellow or red and is terminated by a characteristic tuft of long hairs. Most clearwings are on the wing in the daytime in sunny weather. They may often be seen resting on the leaves of bushes or the flowers of Umbelliferae. The larvae feed in the wood of trees or in the stems and root-stocks of plants. The larval stage lasts one to several years. Many species are pests, mainly of fruit trees. Rearing clearwings is very difficult and collecting the larvae as well as moths requires special techniques.

The moths illustrated are examples of some of the 800 or so species distributed chiefly in South America, as well as in Asia and Africa. Some 220 species are found in western Eurasia and over 30 species have been found in central Europe. The life habits of many have as yet to be studied more thoroughly.

*Sesia apiformis* in resting position

**Sesia apiformis:**
Adult:
V—VII.
Caterpillar:
VII—V (hibernates twice).
Foodplant:
poplar, in the wood.

1 — adult
2 — caterpillar

**Aegeria myopaeformis:**
Adult:
V—VIII.
Caterpillar:
VIII—V (hibernates).
Foodplants:
in wood of fruit trees, mostly apple trees.

3 — adult

**Sciapteron tabaniforme:**
Adult:
V—VIII.
Caterpillar:
VII—V (hibernates once or twice).
Foodplant:
poplar, in wood.

4 — adult male
5 — gall with exuviae of cocoon

**Bembecia hylaeiformis:**
Adult:
VI—VIII.
Caterpillar:
VIII—V (hibernates).
Foodplants:
raspberry.

6 — adult
7 — feeding damage

# Hyponomeuta cagnatellus
# Hyponomeuta plumbellus
# Ethmia pusiella

The Hyponomeutidae are a small family of worldwide distribution. The moths are small, nocturnal and strongly attracted to light. The larvae of some species live gregariously in dense silken webs. Pupation and the emergence of the adults also takes place communally, the result often being large swarms of moths at the site of their emergence.

*Hyponomeuta cagnatellus* and *Hyponomeuta plumbellus* are representatives of a genus comprising many similar species. The moths are white with black dots, the larvae are yellow spotted with black. The ecology of the individual species, however, shows marked diversity. One of the most common and largest of them all is *Hyponomeuta cagnatellus*, in late spring spindle trees are covered with the white webs of the larvae which strip the shrubs bare with their feeding. They pupate clustered at the base of the shrubs. The smaller *H. plumbellus* likewise lives on the spindle tree. Two to three other similar species are pests of apple and plum trees.

*Ethmia pusiella* is representative of the small family Ethmiidae comprising about 200 species. The variegated larvae, their bodies narrowed at both ends, are extremely agile and mobile, moving with the same speed both forward and back. *E. pusiella* is distributed throughout Europe as far as the Urals and also in Asia Minor. It is a rare species which is encountered in woodland clearings or at the edges of forest paths where grass and herbaceous plants grow in abundance.

Hyponomeuta cagnatellus
Adult:
VI—VIII.
Caterpillar:
IV—VI. Egg overwinters.
Foodplants:
spindle, buckthorn.

1 — adult

Hyponomeuta plumbellus:
Adult:
VI—VIII.
Caterpillar:
IV—VI. Egg overwinters.
Foodplants:
spindle, blackthorn, etc.

2 — adult

Ethmia pusiella:
Adult:
VI—VIII.
Caterpillar:
V—VI. Egg overwinters.
Foodplants:
Boraginaceae; for example gromwell, lungwort.

3 — adult

*Hyponomeuta evonymellus* is another member of the family

# European Grain Moth
*Nemapogon granellus*

## *Scardia boleti*
## *Euplocamus anthracinalis*
## *Euplocamus ophisus*

The family Tineidae includes some 2,000 species with a worldwide distribution. They are generally small, inconspicuous moths very similar in coloration. The larvae feed on dry plant material, seeds, grain, fur, feathers, wool, rotting wood, etc. They are serious storehouse pests that have been introduced to all parts of the world.

The European grain moth is nowadays a cosmopolitan species. It has found its way into storehouses the world over and is common even in homes, where it occurs on dried mushrooms, dried fruit and the like.

*Scardia boleti* is one of the larger members of the family and is found in woodlands. The larvae make tunnels in bracket fungi where they pupate. The adult moths fly off when they emerge but the empty pupal cases remain jutting out of the tunnel openings until they are destroyed by the weather.

*Euplocamus anthracinalis* and *Euplocamus ophisus* are related ornamental species of Oriental origin. The first is widespread in the warmer parts of Europe, the second mostly in the Balkans. The moths are on the wing in the daytime in sunny weather, and are common in suitable habitats. The larvae live in rotting tree stumps.

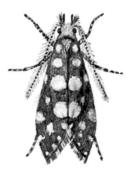

*Euplocamus anthracinalis*

*Nemapogon granellus:*
Adult: IV—IX.
Caterpillar:
throughout the whole year, (hibernates).
Foodplants:
tree fungi, dry plants and mushrooms, rotting wood, corn etc.

1 — adult

*Scardia boleti:*
Adult: VI—VIII.
Caterpillar: IX—V (hibernates).
Foodplants:
tree fungi, mostly *Polyporus igniarius.*

2 — adult

*Euplocamus anthracinalis:*
Adult: IV—VI.
Caterpillar: VIII—IV (hibernates).
Foodplants:
rotting wood of oak, beech etc, tree fungi.

3 — adult

*Euplocamus ophisus:*
Adult: IV—VI.
Caterpillar and food as *E. anthracinalis.*

4 — adult

# Goat Moth
*Cossus cossus*

# Leopard Moth
*Zeuzera pyrina*

## *Dyspessa ulula*
## *Phragmataecia castaneae*

The family Cossidae is distinguished by the fact that it retains a number of primitive characters. It includes some 600 species found mostly in the tropics. Some of the tropical species are among the largest of all moths. The larvae have very large mandibles and bore galleries in wood and in the stems and root-stocks of plants; they are very destructive.

The goat moth is widespread and quite common in Europe and Asia regardless of the climate. The larvae bore in the wood of deciduous trees in much the same way as the larvae of long horn beetles. Trees attacked by the larvae are easily identified by the vinegar-like smell.

The leopard moth has the same range of distribution as the goat moth, and in addition was introduced into North America in the 19th century. In warmer regions the larvae are very destructive to certain fruit trees.

*Dyspessa ulula* is a small Palearctic species of variable coloration as well as size. The larvae live in the ground where they bore into the bulbs of garlic.

*Phragmataecia castaneae* is distinguished by sexual dimorphism. The larger females have a much longer abdomen than the smaller males. The colouring is a sombre brownish hue characteristic of species living in reed beds. The larvae live inside the stems.

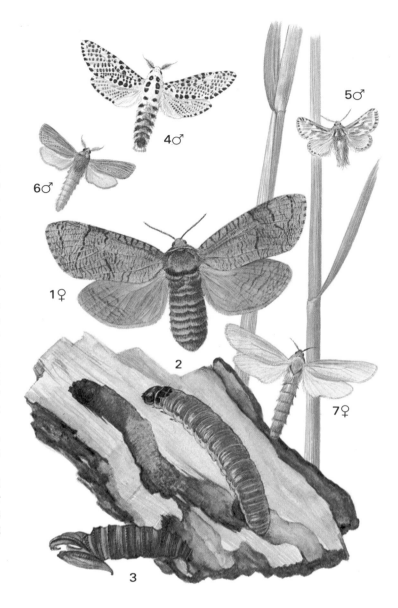

*Cossus cossus:*
Adult: VI—VIII.
Caterpillar:
VIII—V (hibernates twice).
Foodplants: wood of broad-leaved trees.

1 — adult
2 — caterpillar
3 — shed skins of cocoon

*Zeuzera pyrina:*
Adult:
VI—VIII.

Caterpillar:
VIII—V
(hibernates twice).
Foodplants: wood of broad-leaved trees, fruit trees.

4 — adult

*Dyspessa ulula:*
Adult: IV—VII.
Caterpillar:
VI—IV (hibernates).
Foodplants: garlics.

5 — adult

*Phragmataecia castaneae:*
Adult:
V—VII.
Caterpillar:
VIII—VI (hibernates twice).
Foodplant:
reed.

6, 7 — adults

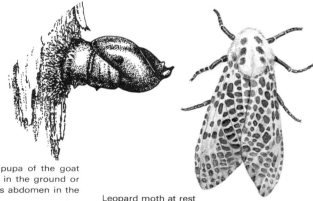

Before the adult emerges, the pupa of the goat moth crawls out of the cocoon in the ground or trunk and remains stuck with its abdomen in the hole.

Leopard moth at rest

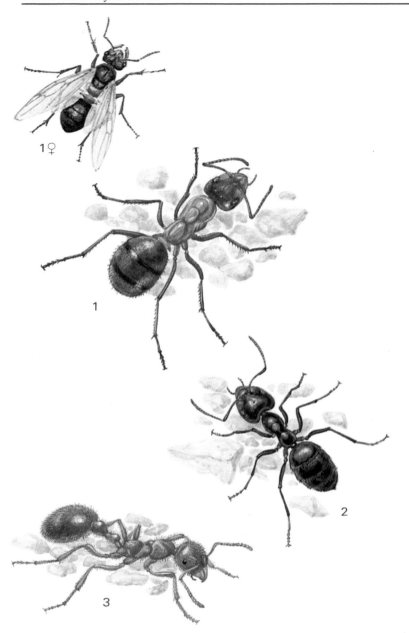

1♀

1

2

3

# Red Wood Ant
# or **Horse Ant** or **Hill Ant**
*Formica rufa*

# Common Ant
*Lasius fuliginosus*

# *Manica rubida*

Ants are socially living insects which form colonies with populations numbering many millions of inhabitants divided into morphologically different castes. The castes include fertile males and females, and workers-females with undeveloped reproductive organs. The workers are the core of the ant colonies: they perform all the work connected with care for the offspring, protection, ant-hill building, etc. The males and females have wings which they discard after swarming. The males die and the females establish a new colony. Ants secrete hormonal substances the composition of which and the frequency of production serve for communication among members of the ant-hill. Within their bodies ants accumulate formic acid which they use for protection.

Ants of the Formicidae family have the thorax connected to the abdomen by just one segment while two segments connect the parts in ants of the Myrmicidae family.

The red wood ants build a nest of dry needles. The females are unable to build a nest alone and therefore they usually move into another nest of the same species or into the nest of *Formica fusca*. At first mixed populations occupy the nest but later the red wood ant population becomes predominant.

The common ants build a paper-like nest of dried rotten matter.

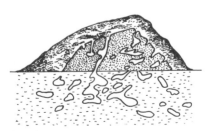

Cross section of the nest of the red wood ant

1 — *Formica rufa:*
Length: 6—11 mm.
Habitat: on the edges of clearings and forest paths in fir forests.
Distribution: Europe, Caucasus, Siberia, North America.

2 — *Lasius fuliginosus:*
Length: 3—5 mm.
Habitat: in hollow trunks and stumps of broad-leaved trees, mainly in oaks growing in clearings.
Distribution: Europe, India, North America.

3 — *Manica rubida:*
Length: 5—9 mm.
Habitat: under stones and in the ground, in sub-mountain and mountainous regions.
Distribution: Europe and northern Asia.

# Biorrhiza Moth
*Biorrhiza pallida*

# Common Oak Gall Wasp
*Cynips quercus-folii*

# *Neuroterus quercus-baccarum*
# Common Rose Gall Wasp
*Diplolepis rosae*

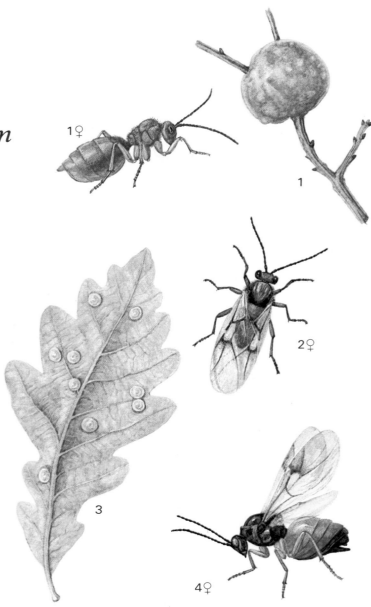

Gall wasps are small insects with a glossy, laterally flattened body. Many species undergo a complex developmental cycle with alternating generations of sexual (winged) and asexual parthenogenetic (wingless) forms. The parthenogenetic generation is formed by females which reproduce without the participation of males. The females lay eggs in the tissue of leaves, buds, etc; the eggs irritate the tissues which respond by forming galls around the eggs. The egg, and eventually the larva and pupa, is isolated within the gall. The shapes of galls are species-specific.

The parthenogenetic generation of the biorrhiza moth forms galls on the roots while the galls of the bisexual generation are formed on the terminal buds on twigs.

Fertilized females of the common oak gall wasp lay their eggs on the underside of oak leaves. Within the galls − 'oak apples' − the parthenogenetic females with wings develop. They lay eggs onto oak buds and in these the males and females develop. *Neurotus quercus-baccarum* has a similar cycle. The common rose gall wasp forms typical galls with several sealed chambers on the common rose.

1 − *Biorrhiza pallida*:
Sexual generation:
    length: 1.7−2.8 mm
    occurrence: June−July
Asexual generation:
    length: 3.5−6 mm
    occurrence: December−February

2 − *Cynips quercus-folii*:
Sexual generation:
    length: 2.3−2.5 mm
    occurrence: May−June
Asexual generation:
    length: 3.4−4 mm
    occurrence: towards end of winter

3 − *Neuroterus quercus-baccarum*:
Sexual generation:
    length: 2.5−2.9 mm
    occurrence: June
Asexual generation:
    length: 2.5−2.8 mm
    occurrence: March

4 − *Diplolepis rosae*:
Length of female: 3.4−4.3 mm;
reproduces parthenogenetically.
Occurrence: spring

Gall of common
rose gall wasp

Gall of common
oak gall wasp

# Hornet
*Vespa crabro*
## *Paravespula germanica*
# Honey-bee
*Apis mellifera*
## *Bombus pomorum*

Wasps, such as *Paravespula germanica,* and hornets are social insects. They form colonies comprising females, males and workers-females with undeveloped reproductive organs. The family is founded by a female that has overwintered, the queen, who builds the basis of the nest and brings up the first generation of workers. The workers then take over all the duties while the queen resorts to laying eggs only. Towards the end of the summer offspring capable of reproduction emerge. In autumn the whole colony dies except for the fertilized females which overwinter. The nests are built from a fibrous paper-like matter which the wasps make from wood they chew. The cells of the nest are open on the underside. The larvae hang suspended, heads down, and the residues of animal food with which they are fed fall out without polluting the cells. The stings of wasps and hornets are smooth which allows repeated use.

Bees and bumblebees or humblebees also live socially. Bumblebees form annual colonies which are always founded by the queen. The queen lays some 200 to 400 eggs during her lifetime. The honey-bee builds wax honey-combs with many six-sided cells. Each colony contains only one queen, several dozen drones and thousands of workers with reproductive organs transformed into a sting with hooks. The workers are short-lived, while the queen can live to be several years old. She mates only once in her life-time, after flying out of the hive.

Nest of the hornet

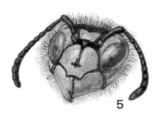

Two closely related *Paravespula* species may be found in similar habitats, namely *P. vulgaris* (5) and *P. germanica* (2).

1 — *Vespa crabro:*
Length: 19—40 mm.
Nest location: hollow trees, sometimes under roofs of buildings, never in the ground.

2 — *Paravespula germanica:*
Length: 10—19 mm.
Nest location: mainly in the ground but also in places sheltered from above, under branches of trees, beams, etc.

3 — *Apis mellifera:*
Length: 14—18 mm.
Nest location: when domesticated in hives, in the wild in the hollows of trees.

4 — *Bombus pomorum:*
Length: female 20—24 mm.
Nest location: underground.

# Common
# or **Green Tiger Beetle**

*Cicindela campestris*

Tiger beetles in Europe represent a family of slender and very active beetles, which are extremely uniform both in shape and in way of life. The common ground beetle is the most abundant species. From the beginning of spring it runs and flies over short distances in sunny fields, across woodland paths, in hedgerows and on sandy slopes. It is an extremely shy beetle and as soon as it senses, usually at a distance of three metres, a human being or an animal approaching, it flies away. It is carnivorous and preys on the larvae and adults of various insects. Despite its large serrated mandibles, it is unable to chew its food and has to break it down beforehand by spitting gastric juices on it. Only when the prey has been turned into liquid form, can it be sucked up and digested.

The eggs, which the female lays in the ground, hatch into larvae that remain underground in deep burrows about 10 to 50 cm long. The larva stays at the entrance of such a tunnel, wedged firmly against one wall, with its broad head and prothorax blocking the entrance. In this position the carnivorous larvae wait for any prey that might crawl past them. When the larva is fully grown it changes into a pupa, which then rests at the bottom of the burrow. The beetle hatches out after one or two winters, although at higher altitudes the developmental process can take as long as 4 years.

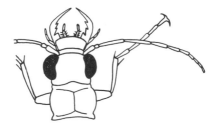

Length: 12—15 mm.
Habitat: lowlands, mountains.
Distribution: whole of Europe, Siberia, north Africa.

Detail of the mandibles and head

Larva

# Calosoma sycophanta

This is one of the handsome ground beetles whose larvae and adults both live in trees. It captures caterpillars and pupae of some moths, particularly pests of the deciduous and coniferous forests, for example, gipsy moths, nun moths, pine lappet moths and others. These beetles are good fliers and first appear in the forests at the beginning of June, when food supplies are sufficient for them and their offspring. They stay in the trees until the end of August, by which time they have consumed an amazing quantity of caterpillars; on average 400 per beetle is a fair estimate. If the amount consumed by the larvae is added to this number, then the importance of this beetle in terms of forest management is evident.

During the course of the season the female will lay over a hundred eggs. At the end of the summer the beetles crawl underground and hibernate there. They reappear the following year, as they usually live between two and three years, which for a beetle is a very long time. The fully grown larvae also hide underground, where they prepare a shelter and pupate. The mature beetles hatch out in the same year, but usually do not emerge above ground until the following summer.

The related *Calosoma inquisitor* stays in the crowns of trees and on roads. It hunts caterpillars. Its larvae are also predatory.

Larva of *Calosoma sycophanta*

Length: 25—35 mm.
Habitat: forests.
Distribution: Europe (locally rare), Siberia, Asia Minor, north Africa, North America (introduced).

*Calosoma inquisitor*

# Carabus coriaceus

This species is one of the large ground beetles of central Europe. The group also includes *C. intricatus*, *C. hortensis* and *C. violaceus*. Like other members of this family, it prefers darkness and hides during the day under fallen leaves, stones or rotting wood. When disturbed it either scurries away or takes up a defensive posture, during which its body remains in an upright position for several moments. The evening is the time when this beetle starts to hunt. It has a voracious appetite and feeds on large slugs, snails, earthworms and the larvae of harmful insects. It is therefore considered a very useful beetle. Its food is predigested by gastric juices before it is eaten, as in the case of other ground beetles.

Like other ground beetles, it cannot fly but instead it is equipped with long legs capable of attaining great speeds. The male can be distinguished from the female by the broader segments of its front legs. This feature is also typical of the rest of the family.

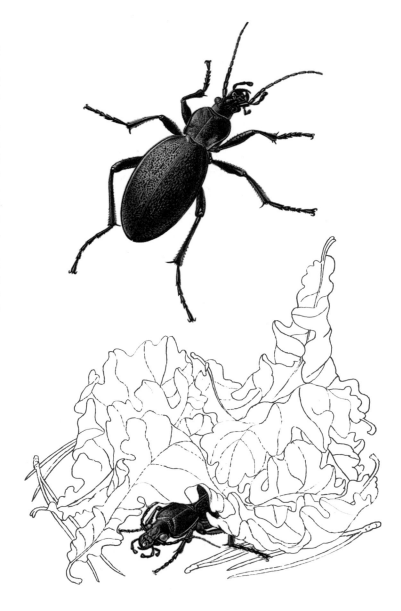

Length: 26—42 mm.
Habitat: submountainous forests.
Distribution: most of Europe except Great Britain.

Topography of a leg of a beetle:
a — tarsal claw, b — tarsus, c — tibia, d — femur, e — trochanter, f — coxa

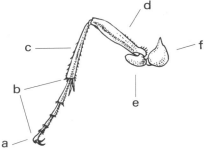

# *Carabus intricatus*

This is one of the largest ground beetles. It differs from the rest of the family in the shape of its elytra. These are usually convex-shaped and oval along their outer margin, but the elytra of this particular species are almost flat, and broad along the back, but sharply pointed at the ends. Their surface under a magnifying glass resembles that of a rugged landscape.

This beetle inhabits woodland regions, where it lives in fallen leaves, under log piles and in moss, although it can also be frequently seen in trees several feet above the ground, where it hides under the bark. It moves very quickly on its long, thin legs, which make up for its inability to fly. It has an insatiable appetite, hunting live slugs and small snails, various caterpillars and insect larvae as well as earthworms, but it will never touch animal corpses. It also likes to sip the sweet resins oozing from injured trees or the juice of ripe fruit. In this way it obtains the necessary quantity of liquid nourishment to sustain its life. This very useful beetle usually hibernates in tree trunks.

Another large species is *Carabus nemoralis*. It lives in woods, forest margins and in gardens.

The larva of *C. nemoralis*

Length: 24—35 mm.
Habitat: forests, gardens.
Distribution: central Europe, the Balkans, Great Britain.

# Carabus cancellatus

From spring to autumn, this handsome beetle can be seen in the stony soil of fields, along river banks and at the edges of forests. It is a carnivorous species which lives on either dead or live animals. It hunts the larvae of the colorado beetle in potato fields and in meadows catches the larvae of the large white butterfly. Thus it has proved very useful to Man.

In late spring the female lays about 45 long, bluntly cylindrical eggs, which are some 4.5 mm long. During the egg-laying process the female extends her abdomen and inserts it into the ground. At the same time she supports herself on her middle and back legs, whilst the front pair stick out into the air. After reproducing, the beetle usually dies and only rarely hibernates to live for a further year. The eggs soon hatch into white larvae, which remain hidden in the ground. Meanwhile the surface of their bodies hardens and assumes a typical dark colouring. During this time the larvae do not receive any food and live only on their fat reserves. After several days they leave the underground shelters and start to hunt. Despite their short legs, the larvae are remarkably nimble and quick. Before pupating, they bury themselves again in the ground and excavate there oval-shaped tunnels, where the adult beetles finally hatch.

Length: 18—26 mm.
Habitat: fields, gardens, damp meadows.
Distribution: Eurasia.

Sculpture on the elytra of the garden ground beetle
(C. hortensis) — left and C. cancellatus — right

The larva of Carabus cancellatus

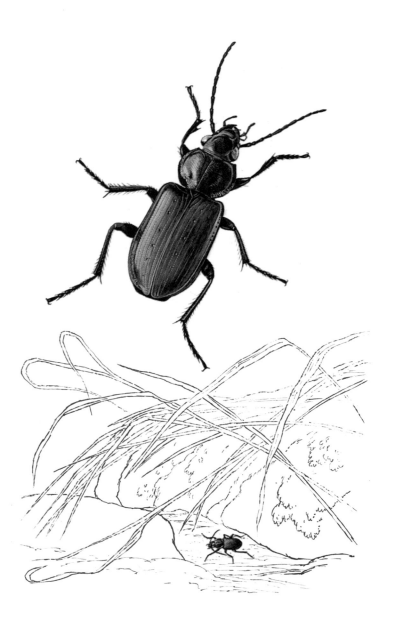

# *Agonum sexpunctatum*

Stones along footpaths and in hedgerows provide a number of beetles with a natural hideout. These include large and small ground beetles, rove beetles and skipjacks. In submountainous regions a small, neat beetle can often be seen among these, which immediately attracts attention because of its glossy green shield and golden-red elytra. It is *Agonum sexpunctatum,* whose genus is represented in Europe by many other species. This one, however, is distinguished from the others by its characteristic colouring and cannot be mistaken for any of them. As with other beetles with a metallic sheen, the precise colouring of this species ranges over a wide variety of shades. Its shield can be blue, whilst its elytra are anything from bronze, blue, blue-violet, or even completely black. Formerly the colouring was used as basis for naming the individual species, but in modern entomology it is no longer employed.

A close examination of this beetle under a strong magnifying glass will disclose a row of six fine dots located on each elytron, close to its central groove. This feature was first utilised by the famous Swedish natural historian, Carl Linnaeus, in naming this species *sexpunctatum* (that is with six dots) more than 200 years ago.

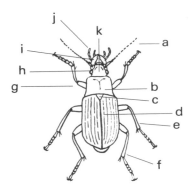

Length: 7—9 mm.
Habitat: footpaths, hedgerows, woodland edges.
Distribution: Eurasia.

Topography of a beetle body:
a — antennae, b — shield, c — scutellum, d — wings,
e — middle legs, f — hind legs, g — front legs,
h — compound (facet) eyes, i — mandibles,
j — maxillary palp, k — head

# Great Diving Beetle

*Dytiscus marginalis*

This beetle, though living permanently in water, still needs fresh air for its existence. It comes up to the water surface and sticks out the end of its abdomen, supporting itself by pressing its hind feet against the water. In this manner it fills its air-storage chamber with air. However, this small amount of air is insufficient for a long time and so the beetle has to repeat these trips to the water surface four to seven times an hour. The male has smooth elytra, whilst those of the female are usually grooved. The best sex-distinguishing features are the sucker-like structures present only in the male which can be seen on the middle and in particular on the front pair of feet, where the roundish sucking pad bordered with a row of bristles is clearly visible. The great diving beetle is carnivorous and apart from eating small aquatic animals it also lives on insect corpses.

The female deposits her eggs in the foliage of aquatic plants. The larvae develop their predatory instinct very early. They are fond of hiding in the foliage of aquatic plants waiting there for their prey, which is then killed by their sickle-shaped mandibles. These, however, are incapable of masticating food, which must therefore be predigested before being broken down by the gastric juices and only then sucked up through the passage in the mandibles. Like the adult beetles, the larvae obtain their necessary air supply from above the water surface. When fully grown, the larvae leave the water for dry land, where they enter the pupal stage.

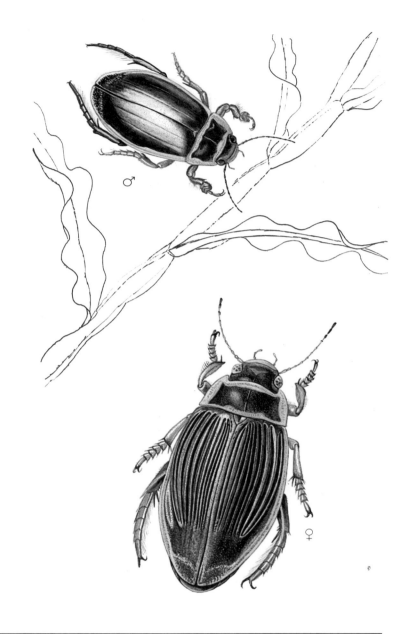

Length: 35 mm.
Habitat: ponds, pools, river creeks.
Distribution: most of Europe (except the Balkans), Siberia, the Caucasus, Japan, North America.

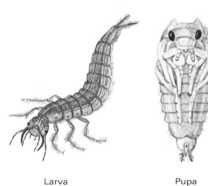

Front legs      Larva      Pupa

# Gyrinus natator

On summer days the surface of slow-running waters presents a vivid scene of activity, swarming as it often does with diving beetles, water beetles, long-legged water boatmen as well as small, silvery whirligig beetles, which usually move about in small shoals. The latter are well adapted to life in water. Their bodies are boat-shaped, smooth and free from any protrusions. The middle and hind pairs of their legs are transformed into paddles and their antennae are short and thick so as not to impede their movement through the water. One of their morphological peculiarities are their eyes, divided into upper and lower sections and therefore giving the appearance of four eyes. The upper section is adapted to see the life above the water surface, whilst the lower section, which is submersed, provides vision in the water.

This beetle is carnivorous and hunts small insects on the water surface. The equally carnivorous larvae live on the bottom and can be easily recognized by their branched tracheal gills, which develop on their abdominal segments and enable them to breathe. When fully grown the larvae swim to the water surface, crawl on to the nearest bank, pupate there and settle in chambers excavated in the earth.

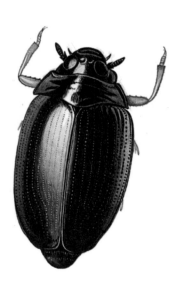

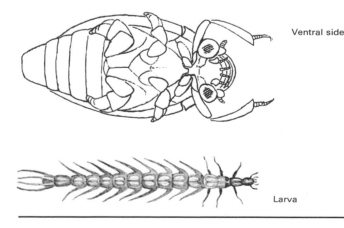

Ventral side

Larva

Leg

Length: 5—7 mm.
Habitat: water surface.
Distribution: most of Europe, Siberia, Mongolia, north Africa.

# Oxyporus rufus

Mushroom pickers are frequently bitterly disappointed to discover in apparently healthy mushrooms a great number of white larvae of various sizes and a network of brown tunnels made by them. These larvae are commonly, but incorrectly, known as maggots. Many beetle species are in fact found in this type of habitat, indeed there are some beetles which undergo all their stages of development in mushrooms and spend their lives there. An example is *Oxyporus rufus*, which is the largest rove beetle living in mushrooms. It first appears in woodlands in May and in ever increasing numbers in July and August, when the mushroom season is at its peak. It usually remains on the underside of the mushroom cap or inside it, where it excavates networks of tunnels with its sizeable mandibles. In this way it searches for the fleshy larvae of other insect species. Its own larvae, however, prefer to feed on the mushroom flesh.

Length: 7—11 mm.
Habitat: mushrooms.
Distribution: most of Europe, Siberia, the Caucasus.

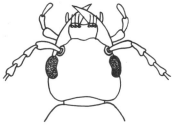

Rove beetles have powerful mandibles on the head

The larvae of the greater rove beetle *(Staphylinus caesareus)* hunt the larvae of other insects in carrion and decaying plant matter

# Burying Beetle

*Necrophorus vespillo*

The burying beetle may be called the pioneer of the beetle sanitary service, as it constantly searches for dead animals and buries them. It is driven to this sort of activity by its instinct to ensure the success of future generations. A small animal corpse is often attacked by many burying beetles, but only the strongest pair ultimately take possession. Then, within a remarkably short period of time, the corpse disappears underground into a slanting tunnel. This is occupied by the female beetle, which proceeds to smooth out the body and gradually transform it into a ball. Finally about ten to twelve eggs are laid in an adjacent tunnel with a nearby opening. Then the female again returns to the body, which she continues to smooth over before finally making a small aperture in it and having her first meal. At the same time she secretes gastric juices which decompose the animal's body tissue and so prepare it for the larvae. These hatch after five days, approach their source of food and wait to be fed by their mother. They grow fast and pupate after a week, the small burying beetles hatching after a further two weeks.

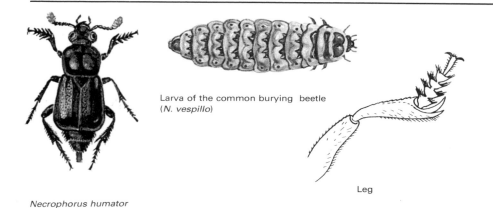

Larva of the common burying beetle
(*N. vespillo*)

Leg

*Necrophorus humator*

Length: 10–24 mm.
Habitat: forests, fields.
Distribution: north of the Tropic of Cancer.

# Glow Worm

*Lampyris noctiluca*

On warm summer nights meadows and fields can be seen swarming with large numbers of tiny blinking lights. These are in fact the male glow worms, which fly about searching for the females which await them on the ground in the grass. Both the winged male and wingless female have complicated phosphorescent organs on the underside of their bodies, covered by a fine transparent skin. These emit light of a 518—656 nm. wave-length. In comparison with artificially produced light, the former is certainly far superior as glow worms produce cold light, which transforms all their energy, without entailing any heat loss. Man's best achievement in this context is equal to only ten per cent of this potential energy. The entire process of light production by these interesting beetles is not known in detail, although apparently it is dependent on the chemical breakdown of complex molecules. An important part in this process is played by oxygen, absorbed by the respiratory organs. It is interesting that this ability is not only a feature of the adult beetles, but is also a characteristic possessed by their larvae.

The glow worm larvae live in the grass and are carnivorous, although the complete range of their diet is not yet fully known.

Length: male 11—12 mm, female 16—18 mm.
Habitat: meadows, edges of forests.
Distribution: most of Europe, the Caucasus, China, Siberia.

Larva

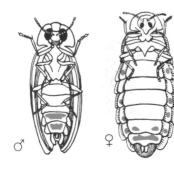

Luminiscent organs on the underside of the body of the lesser glow-worm (*Phausis splendidula*)

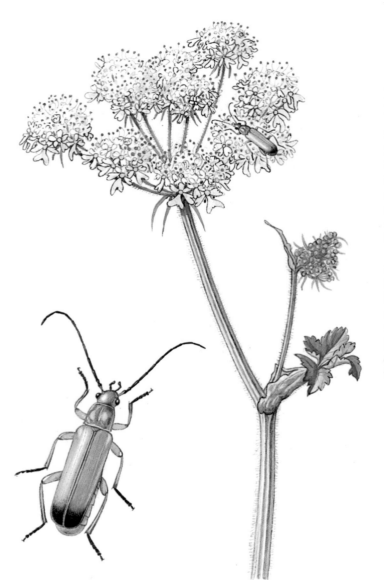

# Black-tipped Soldier

*Rhagonycha fulva*

In late summer the beetle populations of the fields, meadows, forests and gardens begin to decline, some of them dying and the rest preparing for hibernation. However, on the white inflorescences of various umbelliferous plants a hitherto unseen inhabitant suddenly appears, the black-tipped soldier, with its elegant, slender body and soft elytra. In some years it is so prolific that it is difficult to find a single umbel in a meadow without this beetle and indeed most blossoms are swarming with them. In appearance it resembles other species belonging to this genus and differs from them only by the black antennae and black spots at the tips of its elytra.

The black-tipped soldier is carnivorous and specializes in catching various insects occurring on the flowers. Its long antennae, with which it explores its environment, help to find its prey. It is not a fussy eater and is grateful for any food that comes its way, whether this be an aphid or various small insect larvae. The larvae of the black-tipped soldier are also carnivorous. They hibernate and continue to develop the following spring.

Length: 7—10 mm.
Habitat: flowering meadows.
Distribution: Europe, Asia Minor.

# Soft-winged Flower Beetle

*Malachius aeneus*

Some beetles are equipped with a special defence mechanism which in the case of attack can often save their life. For example, some ground beetles are protected by their pygidial glands, which eject an offensive, burning liquid at the enemy. True masters of this art are members of the genus *Brachynus*. Ladybirds, colorado beetles and oil beetles are also endowed with a ready means of defence, although of a rather different nature. In their case the malodorous, poisonous liquid is contained directly in their blood and when danger threatens, fine drops are formed at the joints between the thigh and the shin. The soft-winged flower beetle, illustrated on this plate, has a completely different defence system. On the underside of its body, between the head and thorax and on the thorax itself, there are numerous long, red-orange sacks containing gland openings. These probably emit a repugnant smell, which effectively repels the enemy. However, it is difficult to ascertain the significance of their colouring in this context, as the extent of beetles' vision is as yet unknown to man.

Between spring and autumn, the soft-winged flower beetle can be seen in sunny spots with plenty of flowers, where it not only feeds on the pollen but also catches aphids. Its larvae are carnivorous and live in rotting tree stumps or under bark.

Its relative, *Malachius bipustulatus,* can also be found on flowers, often in large numbers.

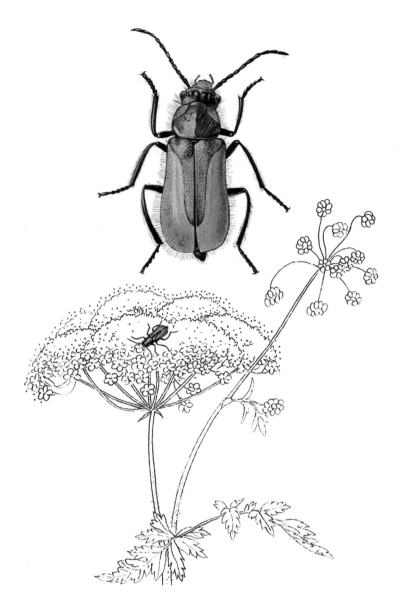

Length: 6—7 mm.
Habitat: flowering plants.
Distribution: most of Europe, Siberia, Asia Minor, Iran, North America.

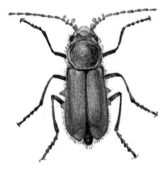

*Malachius bipustulatus* with extended sacs on the antennae and on the sides of the body

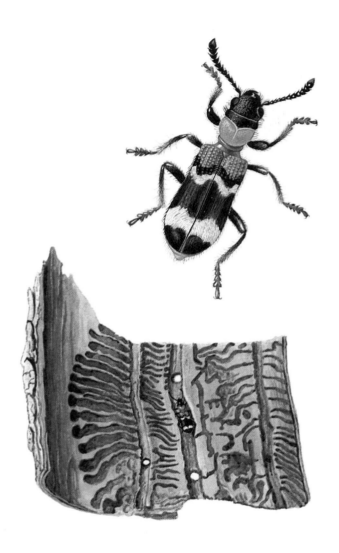

# Ant Beetle

*Thanasimus formicarius*

The specific name of this beetle, *formicarius* (that is relating to ants), can easily give rise to the false idea that this beetle lives with ants or that it preys on them. However, both these suppositions would be incorrect as it is, in fact, the beetle's colouring and also its elongated, slender body that resemble the large wood ant.

From early spring until autumn, the ant beetle can be seen on felled trees which still have their bark intact or even on prepared timbers. It is most frequently found on pine logs, but may also be present on spruce and deciduous trees, where it relentlessly searches for bark beetles, its favourite prey. It has developed an interesting method of catching these beetles. It starts with turning the bark beetle onto its back, then it bites it in half between the front and central part of the thorax and eats the remaining part of the body. Naturally ant beetles are most prolific when bark beetles overmultiply. In spring the female lays 20 to 30 eggs under the bark of a tree. Its larvae hatch often as early as a week later but they grow very slowly and their total development lasts until the autumn. They are at first hairy and feed on various animal remains, but after they have moulted the second time, they feed mainly on the larvae of bark beetles or other insects living under the bark. Both the larvae and beetles hibernate.

Another member of the family Cleridae, which is similar to the ant beetle, the bee-wolf (*Trichodes apiarius*) is often found on the flower heads of the carrot family. Its larvae develop in honey bee hives.

The larva of the ant beetle

Length: 7—10 mm.
Habitat: forests.
Distribution: Europe, north Africa, North America (introduced).

# Mottled Skipjack

*Adelocera murina*

The black elytra and shield of this click beetle are ornamented with fine grey, white, brown and rusty scales: sometimes these are present in such large numbers that they completely obliterate the original colouring of the elytra and shield. The mottled skipjack then seems to be covered with clusters of greyish mould. It appears very early in spring and remains in the open late into the autumn. It lives in lowland areas as well as in submountainous and mountainous regions where it is a typical inhabitant of fields, meadows, forests and gardens. The female habitually lays her eggs in the ground. The thin larvae, three cm in length are covered with a tough, firm skin and continue to live underground. The actual composition of their diet is not yet known in detail and therefore their agricultural value has not yet been fully assessed. On the one hand they are considered dangerous and harmful because it is thought they damage the fine roots of various economically important plants, such as corn and vegetables. However, some scientists consider them useful, because their larvae are carnivorous and their diet also includes the larvae of cockchafers (genus *Melolontha*) and members of the genus *Phyllopertha*.

Length: 11—17 mm.
Habitat: forests, fields, gardens.
Distribution: Europe, the Caucasus, Siberia, North America.

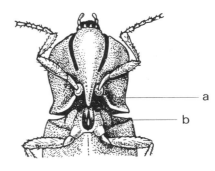

By means of a process (a) and indentation (b) on the under side of the body, the Elateridae or click beetles are enabled to leap into the air with a clicking sound, hence their name.

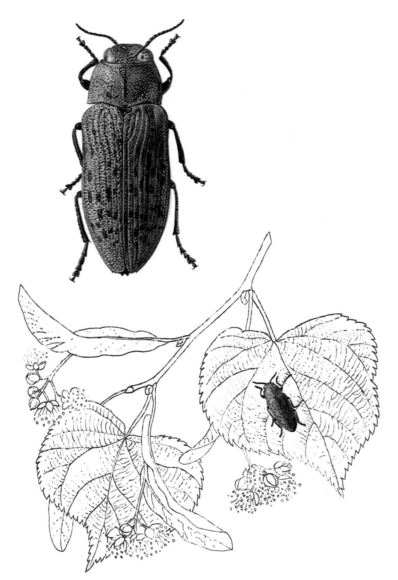

# *Ovalisia rutilans*
# *Anthaxia nitidula*

Members of the Buprestidae family may almost certainly be seen on hot, sunny, windless days. They are very shy, nimble beetles and when disturbed, they fly away immediately. All of them are warmth-loving and the largest and most beautiful species can be found in the tropical and subtropical regions.

Despite its relatively small dimensions, *Ovalisia rutilans* is one of the most beautiful and colourful members of the European beetle fauna. On hot days it can be seen flashing through the air, with its body shining in shades of metallic green, copper and black. It is most abundant from May to July, but sometimes can be come across as late as August in old lime tree trunks. In fact, its favourite habitats are the rows of lime trees, where the females also like to lay their eggs. The entire developmental process lasts two to three years, during which time the flat larvae excavate their characteristic zigzag corridors under the bark. When the larva reaches its full size, it does not leave its shelter but pupates there. The young beetle then bites its way out through the bark.

Out of the 13,000 known species, only several dozen are found in Europe, of which about 20 belong to the genus *Anthaxia*. The most beautiful of these is *Anthaxia nitidula*. In most other beetle species, it is usually the male that is brighter in colour and variable in shape, but in this buprestid species the female has the more attractive colouring of the two. It differs from the green or blue male by its bright red shield. However, populations inhabiting Great Britain have both males and females coloured green.

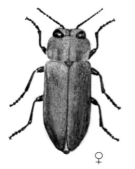

*Anthaxia nitidula* ♀

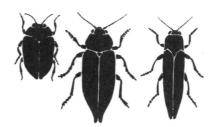

Various body shapes of different members of the Buprestidae family (from left): *Trachys, Dicerca, Agrilus*

*Ovalisia rutilans:*
Length:
12—15 mm.
Habitat: neighbourhood of lime trees.
Distribution: southern and central Europe, the Caucasus, Transcaucasia.

*Anthaxia nitidula:*
Length:
5—7 mm.
Habitat: flowering plants.
Distribution: central and southern Europe, north Africa.

# Great Silver Water Beetle

*Hydrous piceus*

European rivers and ponds are inhabited by more than 300 different beetle species. Some like clear, rapid streams, while others prefer stagnant waters densely overgrown with vegetation. The most abundant among them are water beetles, which are closely followed by the otherwise unrelated diving beetles. However, not all water beetles are typically aquatic species. Some of them inhabit river banks, while others abandoned their aquatic homes long ago for a very different habitat, for example, dung.

Of the truly aquatic species, probably the best-known representative is the great silver water beetle. Its female is known to care for her eggs in an interesting way: the end of her abdomen is equipped with a fibre-excreting apparatus, which she uses to construct a special soft pouch. First of all, she has to find a leaf floating on the water surface. Then she starts to spin the fibres around the tip of her abdomen, thus constructing a basket-like structure into which she subsequently lays about 50 eggs. This 'basket' is finally sealed up and equipped with a chimney-like construction that protrudes above the water surface. The adult beetle inhales the air through its short, club-shaped antennae. In contrast to the adults, the larvae are predatory and live on various aquatic molluscs.

Length: 34—47 mm.
Habitat: stagnant waters.
Distribution: Europe, northern Asia, northern India, Pakistan.

Detail of leg

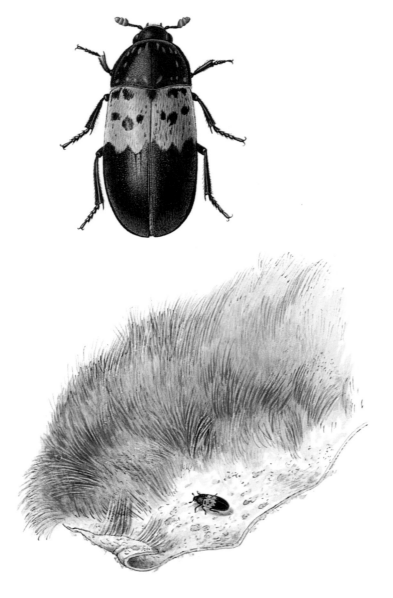

# **Larder** or **Bacon Beetle**
*Dermestes lardarius*

Most human households are occupied by a number of beetle species and although some of these live only on scraps of food, others can often become a real scourge in the house. One such harmful species is undoubtedly the larder beetle, which, although small in size, is still capable of causing considerable damage. There are many species of larder beetles, the most common of which is *Dermestes lardarius*. Its natural habitat is in nests, where it feeds upon moulted fur and feathers. However, human dwellings, besides providing it with safety, also ensure a plentiful and varied supply of food, which includes furcoats, woollen blankets, carpets and various foodstuffs of animal origin such as bacon and ham. Although the larvae are often difficult to detect, when found, they can be easily recognized by their dense, tough bristles which cover the body and the two protrusions on the abdomen. Before pupating, they search out a quiet and safe shelter where they spin a protective web in which to pupate.

The worst enemies of museum and private insect collections are the larvae of *Anthrenus verbasci* which can completely destroy the mounted specimens. The adults live on various flowering plants.

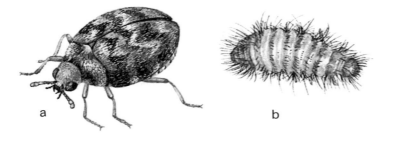

a        b

Length: 7—9.5 mm.
Habitat: human habitation, also in bird's nests.
Distribution: cosmopolitan.

Adult (a) and larva (b) of *Anthrenus verbasci*

# Raspberry Beetle

*Byturus tomentosus*

When picking raspberries and blackberries, we may quite often come across numerous stout, whitish larvae with brown stripes on the back and with the body tapering towards the rear end. These are the larvae of the raspberry beetle. From early spring, the adult beetle spends its time gathering pollen from flowering vegetation, but as soon as raspberry and blackberry bushes start to flower, they soon turn their attention exclusively to these. The females lay about 100 eggs in the flowers and small fruits. After a few days the larvae hatch and bury themselves in the flower centres. Further, relatively slow, development takes place in the fruit. As soon as the larvae are fully grown, they leave their host plants and crawl underground to pupate there. The mature beetles hatch by the autumn of the same year, but they do not leave their shelters before the following spring. Quite often, however, it is the larvae that hibernate and their further development continues throughout the following spring and can therefore take as long as two years.

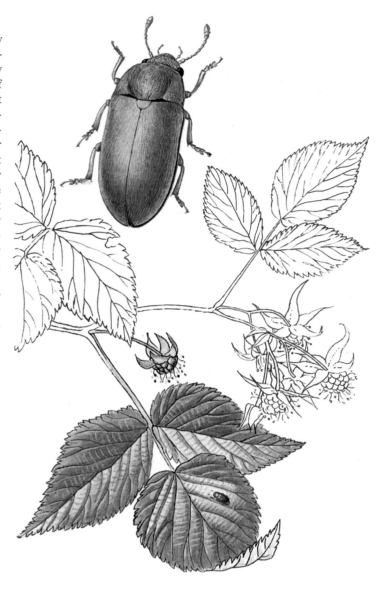

Length: 3.2—4 mm.
Habitat: woodland (on raspberry bushes).
Distribution: most of temperate Eurasia.

Larva

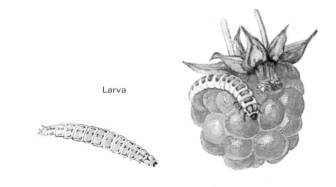

# *Meligethes aeneus*

Early in spring the blossoms of a variety of plants are usually swarming with insect life, particularly sap beetles. These quite small and inconspicuous beetles can be found everywhere in large numbers. They are initially attracted by the pollen and nectar of flowers, supplies of which are soon exhausted and therefore their attention is directed to the members of the cabbage family such as cabbage, turnip and radish. If these plants have not yet started to flower, the beetles creep into their buds, eat them and thus cause considerable damage. This is less serious if these beetles attack a field already in flower, as then they simply search the blossoms for pollen and nectar. During this period the females lay about 150 eggs, which are stuck by ones or twos to the pistils or stamens of the flowers. Larval development is not very long. The small larvae have ample supplies of food and in about four weeks, when they are fully grown, they crawl underground and pupate there. In another two weeks or even less the mature beetles hatch and feed on plants until late summer when they again go underground to hibernate.

Length: 1.5—2.7 mm.
Habitat: meadows, later cabbage fields.
Distribution: temperate Eurasia.

Larva

# Ladybird Mimic

*Endomychus coccineus*

The fungoid growths that cover the bark of old, dead and felled deciduous trees and tree stumps provide a habitat for a number of beetle species which are restricted to this type of environment and cannot be found anywhere else. These beetles are usually very small and inconspicuous, being coloured brown, blackish-brown or yellow-brown. They can therefore be easily overlooked. However, this is not true in the case of the ladybird mimic. This beetle got its scientific specific name after the colour of its elytra and shield, which are red with contrasting black spots. These, however, are occasionally missing in some individual beetles, which have their elytra and shield a uniform red.

The ladybird mimic can be found in spring and autumn, usually in large numbers on beech, oak, birch and other deciduous trees. Both its larvae and adults hibernate.

In central Europe the family Endomychidae is represented by about 20 species, although its world population, inhabiting mostly warm tropical regions, numbers about, 1,400 species.

Length: 4—6 mm.
Habitat: deciduous forests, under bark of trees, in tree fungi.
Distribution: whole of Europe, in the south only at higher altitudes.

Leg

# Seven-spot Ladybird

*Coccinella septempunctata*

The seven-spot ladybird is one of the most common beetles to be found in forests, fields, gardens, by the roadsides or along footpaths from early spring until late autumn. The commonest form has red elytra marked with seven distinct dots. However, this colouring is subject to variation in the vast area of distribution of this beetle, and numerous colour aberrations are known to exist.

This beetle and its larvae are man's invaluable helpers in his fight against insect pests. In fact, it does not hunt all these harmful species, but specializes on the soft, fat aphids, their larvae and some coccids, which it consumes in large quantities.

Like other ladybirds, the seven-spot ladybird pupates on the leaves, the pupae being firmly attached to them head downwards. Before winter sets in, the mature ladybirds search out sheltered places where they might survive the unfavourable weather conditions. They hide, for example, under the bark of trees, in old tree stumps, in moss and under stones. Quite often ladybirds congregate in such places in very large numbers.

Length: 5.5—8 mm.
Habitat: vegetation attacked by aphids.
Distribution: Europe, Asia, north Africa.

Pupa

Adult preying on aphids

# Eyed Ladybird

*Anatis ocellata*

The eyed ladybird is one of the largest ladybirds in the European animal kingdom. Large numbers inhabit coniferous and deciduous forests. As soon as the weather becomes settled, it is awakened by the spring sun and can be seen crawling on the bark and branches of trees in search of food. This predominantly consists of young coccids, scale-insects and aphids and their larvae, as well as the larvae of some important forest pests. For this reason the eyed ladybird, like most other ladybirds, is a very useful species, which rids the forest of many unwanted pests.

The female lays her eggs at the height of summer on the bark of conifers and on the underside of the needles. The larvae emerge within in a few days, and their subsequent development is also rapid. The elongated, yellow-spotted grey-blue larva, which is no less predacious than the adult beetle, is continually on the move in search of food. The pupae remain firmly attached to the underside of vegetation. The beetle, which emerges after a week, is active until the first frost. It hibernates under the bark of spruces, firs and pines as well as in the stumps of conifers.

Length: 8—9 mm.
Habitat: coniferous forests attacked by aphids.
Distribution: Europe, Siberia, North America (introduced).

left — *Propylaea quatuordecimpunctata*
right — *Thea vigintiduopunctata*

Ladybird beetles have a typically vaulted body and their wings are usually brightly coloured. The size, shape and number of dots is usually very variable even among members of the same species.

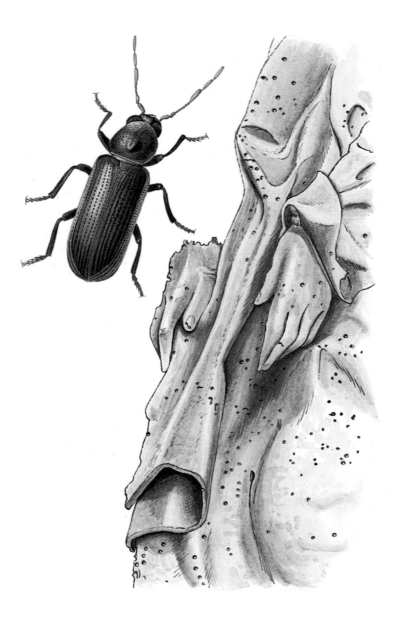

# Furniture Beetle
*Anobium punctatum*

All furniture beetles have similar features, which include the cylindrical body and the shield-covered head. They live in old timber such as rafters, wooden pillars and supports and also in woodcarvings, old furniture and picture frames. In the tunnels which they bore in such wood they emit strange noises resembling the irregular ticking of watches. This ticking noise sounds particularly terrifying during the quiet night hours and therefore the vivid human imagination used to link it with forecasts of a forthcoming and agonizing death. However, this ticking noise is made by the front part of the beetle's shield as it rubs against the tunnel walls, and it probably constitutes a specific signalling system between the two sexes.

The beetles develop in the wood and crawl out through the small apertures, around which the females will later lay their eggs. In this way the small larvae can easily enter the wood, where they then bore their own tunnels. Wood is the only component of their diet and it can be digested only with the aid of special symbiotic organisms. These organisms, bacteria and fungi, are genetically transferred from generation to generation; they live in special sacks in the beetles' guts and facilitate the breakdown of cellulose matter.

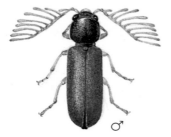

Sexual — dimorphism is especially marked in *Ptilinus pectiniformis,* another member of the family Anobiidae. The male (in the picture) differs from the female in conspicuous antennae.

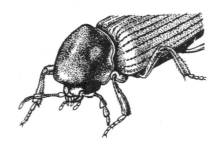

Detail of the shape of the shield in *Anobium punctatum*

Length: 3—5 mm.
Habitat: usually human habitation.
Distribution: Europe, the Caucasus, North America, Australia.

# Oil Beetle

*Meloë proscarabaeus*

This robust beetle with short diverging elytra makes its appearance in spring along footpaths and in meadows. When attacked it defends itself by excreting drops of yellow body fluid at the joints of its limbs. Its colouring as well as the poisonous cantharidin contained in it help to frighten away the attacker. Surprisingly, many animals are immune to this poison. The development of the oil beetle is a complicated process, and only a few larvae usually survive to pupate and develop into mature beetles. Because of this, the females lay several thousand eggs in order to ensure the survival of some of their offspring. The strange larvae, characterized by the three claws on their feet, were originally considered an independent species and named *Triungulinus*. This name was retained even when it was later discovered that these larvae were only a developmental stage of the oil beetle. It even became customary to use this name for young larvae of various other insect genera and species. The full development of the oil beetle larvae is only possible in *Anthophora* bees' nests, where the triungulinus gradually changes into another larval phase, which then develops into a peculiar pupa-like stage. This specific developmental process, which occurs only in the oil beetle and other related species, is an additional stage in the usual development of beetles and has been named hyper-metamorphosis. This stage eventually produces a final larval phase, which pupates.

Length: 13—32 mm.
Habitat: meadows, wood margins.
Distribution: central and southern Europe, the Caucasus.

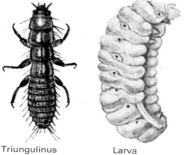

Triungulinus          Larva

# Tumbling Flower Beetle

*Variimorda fasciata*

The pointed end of the abdomen, which is not covered by the elytra, is one of several distinguishing characteristics of this species, which identify it as a member of the family Mordellidae. It has a relatively large, flat head, which can be folded under the shield, and long, strong hind legs as well as a distinctly arched underside of the body. This characteristic helps even amateurs and beginners to identify the beetle readily. However, it does pose some problems during the preparation of such beetles, as specimens usually tend to slip from one side to another. The sharply pointed abdomen and strong legs enable the tumbling flower beetle to perform bizarre jumps or circular movements. This can be easily observed by placing the tumbling flower beetle on the palm of a hand. Another important identifying feature is the number of segments on the beetle's feet. The first and second pairs consist of five segments, whilst the last pair has only four segments.

Generally, members of the family Mordellidae are dark in colour, although this particular species has a lighter, variable pattern on its elytra. The beetle prefers a warm environment and in summer it can usually be seen on the flowers of umbelliferous and composite plants. Its elongated, slender larvae excavate small tunnels in various plants and often also in the branches of plum trees.

The body shape of bristle beetles is distinctive

Length: 6—9 mm.
Habitat: blossoms.
Distribution: most of Europe, the Caucasus, Asia Minor, Iran.

# *Lagria hirta*

The tropical regions of the whole world are inhabited by more than 2,000 species of long-jointed bark beetles, which belong to the family Lagriidae. Some are distinguished by their attractive colouring, others are quite plain and all of them are warmth-loving. In Europe this family is represented by a mere eight species and in central Europe this number is reduced to three, of which only *Lagria hirta* is really abundant. It has the typical body shape, characterized by the narrow shield and soft, fluffy elytra which cover the whole abdomen. The unequal number of foot segments in the first two pairs compared with the last pair of its legs classify this beetle as a member of the group Heteromera. The male can be recognized by the unusually prolonged final segment of his antennae. The beetle is herbivorous and its modest requirements in terms of food enable it to inhabit all types of habitats, where it is quite abundant from spring until late summer. Its larvae are similarly herbivorous, although unlike the mature beetles they live in the shade provided by fallen leaves, on which they also feed. They have elongate, hairy bodies, and their heads are equipped with five, simple eyes. The larvae hibernate.

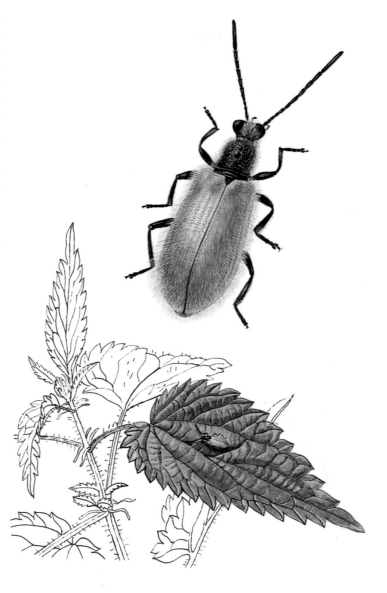

Length: 7—10 mm.
Habitat: damp meadows, blossoms.
Distribution: Europe, Siberia.

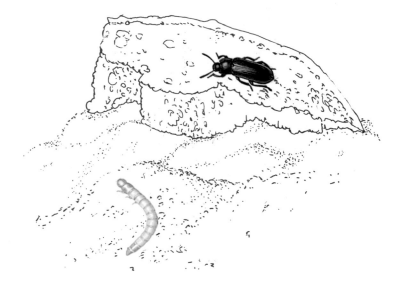

# Mealworm Beetle

*Tenebrio molitor*

Storehouses, bakeries, mills as well as shops and homes regularly house several species of beetles. One of the most common of these is the mealworm beetle, which can be quite easily discovered crawling on a carpet of a room in the middle of summer. This does not necessarily mean that the beetle has hatched in the house. In fact it often flies in accidentally through an open window or may be attracted by an electric light in the evening.

The mealworm beetle spends all its developmental stages in flour and its existence there is at first well concealed. The female lays several hundred eggs in small piles in the flour or in various crevices. She then covers them with a sticky secretion which quickly adheres to grains of flour and thus the eggs are successfully camouflaged. The larvae hatch in one or two weeks, moult several times and develop very quickly. They are also often reared artificially and provide nutritious food for house pets. Surprisingly, such artificially reared larvae sometimes develop wing stumps on the thoracic segments. After six months, but sometimes even considerably later, these larvae change into white pupae. The mature beetle lives only for about three months after hatching.

Larva

Pupa

Length: 15 mm.
Habitat: human habitation.
Distribution: most continents, avoids the tropics.

# Stag Beetle

*Lucanus cervus*

Only a few beetle species are sexually differentiated as conspicuously as the stag beetle. The male's head is adorned with large striking 'antlers', which in fact are his mandibles. However, they do not perform any function during the seizure or biting of food, as is often commonly supposed. The beetle in fact feeds on the sweet sap that oozes from injured oak trees. The mandibles are only used to chase away rivals during the mating season. Such fights are quite a common phenomenon in those areas where stag beetles are found in large numbers.

The stag beetle usually lives in old oak woods, where it develops over a period of five years in old rotting oak trees. However, the life span of the mature beetle is much shorter than that of its larva. The beetle usually hatches in the autumn but remains hidden underground until the spring. It leaves its winter shelter in June, when it can be seen flying about early in the evening, and dies at the end of the same month. Its larva is a robust creature, often as much as nine to ten cm long. Before turning into a pupa, it makes a firm oval bed which serves as protection at first for the pupa and later for the newly hatched beetle. In some countries this beetle is protected by law.

Length: male to 75 mm, female smaller.
Habitat: oak forests.
Distribution: most of Europe, Asia Minor, Syria.

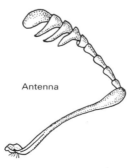

Antenna

Pupa of the male. The sex of the future adult is indicated by the shape of the mandibles

# Cockchafer or May Bug

*Melolontha melolontha*

The cockchafer and its related species can be identified by the characteristic sexual dimorphism in the anatomy of their antennae. The fan which is found at the end of the antenna, is composed of seven long lamellae in the male, whilst the female's consists of six shorter ones. The female is also differentiated from the male by the shape of the front legs, which are adapted for digging. During the egg-laying season she buries herself in the ground and there fulfils her maternal duties. The beetles appear as early as the end of April on the new, tender leaves of oaks, beeches and other deciduous trees. The males die by the end of May, whilst the females continue to lay their eggs until June. Cockchafers tend to overpopulate in certain years. This is in fact repeated every three to four seasons, which corresponds to the lifespan of one generation. The larvae, which moult twice, are white and plump, with a dark head and a fat, dark tip at the rear end of the body. They live in the ground and feed on plant roots, which makes both the beetle and the larva potentially harmful.

Apart from the above-mentioned species, which is the most abundant, another two similar species of stag beetles can be found in Europe, namely *Melolontha hippocastani* and *M. pectoralis*.

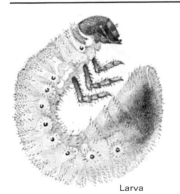

Larva

Pupa

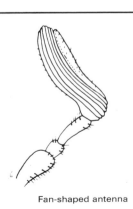

Fan-shaped antenna

Length: 20—30 mm.
Habitat: deciduous forests, fields.
Distribution: most of Europe, absent in the south (Italy, Spain).

# Rose Chafer

*Cetonia aurata*

From the second half of May until the height of summer, the blossoms of wild roses and hawthorns, the white inflorescences of umbelliferous plants and the fragrant blossoms of the common or scarlet-berried elder attract the rose chafer. These appear in such places in full sunshine and fly about like tiny aeroplanes. In comparison with other beetles their flight is somewhat different as they keep their elytra closed, extending underneath them the membranous second pair of wings. They can be frequently found on injured trees or freshly cut tree stumps as they are attracted, like stag beetles, longhorn beetles and many others, by the sweet sap oozing from the wood. The colouring of the rose chafer varies a great deal. Most frequently is it greenish-gold on top and golden-red on the underside of its body. However, certain individuals can also be golden or red-green, bluish, purple or brown.

In comparison with the attractive adult beetle, the fat larvae are plain white. They undergo their development in the old hollow trunks of oak, beech, poplar and willow trees or sometimes in compost heaps and rarely in ant-hills, where the larvae of its relative, *Potosia cuprea,* are much more common. When the larvae have shed their skins twice and have grown to about four or five cm in length, they pupate in a firm cocoon with a smooth inner surface. Their total development takes about one year.

Length: 14—20 mm.
Habitat: flowers of wild rose, hawthorn, elder and umbelliferous plants.
Distribution: Europe, Siberia, Asia Minor and western Asia.

*Potosia aeruginosa* is one of the largest members of the family in Europe

a

b

Larva (a), and pupa (b) of *Potosia cuprea*

# *Geotrupes vernalis*

This species is one of the largest dor beetles known in Europe. Both the beetle and its larvae feed on dung. They live in permanent pairs, which during the mating season build a nest richly supplied with food. In a suitable place under a heap of dung, they excavate a hollow about five cm deep and beneath it dig out horizontal tunnels, each about 20 cm long. Afterwards, both the male and female start filling them with dung. As soon as a sufficient quantity has been stored, further construction work continues. At the bottom of this hollow a vertical tunnel, about half a metre deep, is finally excavated. This terminates in a chamber that serves as a shelter for the larva, pupa and the newly hatched beetle. Dung is also brought to this chamber and moulded into the shape of a cone, in which the female lays a single egg. Subsequently the cone is covered with a layer of sand and soil and some more fresh dung is deposited in the vertical tunnel. As can be seen, the whole developmental process takes place in this dung cone; the egg hatches into a white larva that slowly eats its way through the prepared food supply. When fully grown, the larva pupates underground.

It is worth recording that this dor beetle and other related species are very useful as they bury animal excrement underground and thus help to transform it into compost.

*Sisyphus schaefferi* is another member of the family Scarabaeidae which number more than 14,000 species. It lives on sandy soils of the warm regions of Europe.

*Sisyphus schaefferi*

Types of underground nests of various species of Scarabaeidae

Length: 12—20 mm.
Habitat: in dung.
Distribution: Europe, Asia Minor.

# *Leptura rubra*

Some longhorn beetles, such as the timberman, appear during the first warm days of spring. Unlike these, *Leptura rubra* is a typical summer species which may be found from July to August. The male and the female could easily be taken for two independent species, because they differ not only in body form, but also in colour. The male is smaller and more slender than the relatively stout female. The male's antennae have a pronounced serrated edge and his black shield contrasts with the dirty yellow elytra. The female's shield and elytra are a velvety red-brown. The male can usually be seen on flowers, whilst the female settles on logs and stumps of coniferous trees, where she lays her eggs. There the larvae excavate vertical, zigzag tunnels, which are then filled with crushed material. In this way they promote the decomposition of tree stumps and thus perform a useful service in terms of forestry. However, similar activity when directed at telegraph poles or wooden fences is less welcome. The newly hatched beetle makes a circular hole in the wood to get away. Its whole development probably lasts about two years. Like other longhorn beetles, this species emits sharp, creaking sounds.

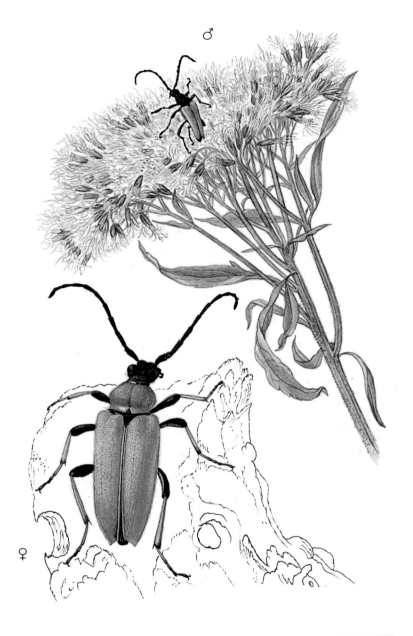

Length: 10—19 mm
Habitat: on flowers, logs of conifers.
Distribution: Europe, Siberia, north Africa.

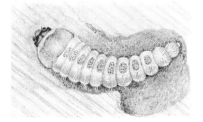

Larva

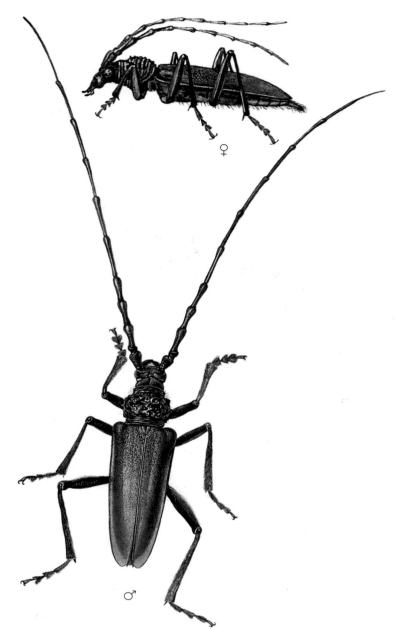

# *Cerambyx cerdo*

As one of the largest longhorn beetles of Europe, it inhabits the original oak forests, occasionally also beech, hornbeam and elm woods mixed with other deciduous trees. The beetles first appear in June and July. They hide from the daylight in tunnels which they made in the trees after hatching in their wood. They favour most of all injured trees as they like to lick the sweet resins that ooze from them. *Cerambyx cerdo,* like many other species, emits very loud creaking sounds, which are produced by rubbing the thick overgrowths on its shield against the grooved plate on the thorax. However, the significance of these noises as well as the whole way of life of this longhorn beetle has not yet been sufficiently explained.

The female lays approximately 80 eggs in groups of 2 to 3 in the bark of oak trees. The larva, which hatches in about two weeks, endeavours to make its way inwards through the hard bark of these old trees, towards the bast and the soft inner wood. This activity takes a long time and is interrupted by the onset of winter. After hibernation it continues to penetrate into the bast, which it reaches by the summer. A year later, when it is already seven to nine cm long, it excavates a relatively long tunnel (several tens of centimetres) in the wood, at the end of which it pupates. The young beetle hatches in the same year and then hibernates in its shelter. Unfortunately, this beetle has recently disappeared from many regions along with the removal of old oaks. As a result, it is now protected by law in some countries.

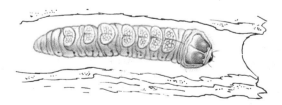

Larva

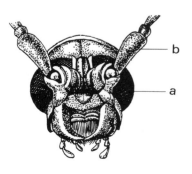

Length: 24—53 mm.
Habitat: oak forests.
Distribution: Europe.

Front view of the head: compound eyes (a) are kidney shaped and embrace the antennae (b)

# *Plagionotus arcuatus*

At a first glance, this longhorn beetle might be mistaken for a wasp on account of its body shape and the combination of black and yellow colours. However, the yellow stripes and patches on the elytra vary in shape a great deal and often blend together to make various patterns.

*Plagionotus arcuatus* is one of the species which do not appear before late spring or the beginning of summer. In May and for almost the whole of June it can be seen on felled oak wood which still has its bark. Less frequently it inhabits beeches, poplars and lime trees. It likes a warm climate and is at its liveliest in full sunshine, when it scurries along the branches of trees and flies quickly about them. The female lays about 30 eggs, which she inserts into the cracks in the bark of trees using her long ovipositor. The larvae often hatch as early as two weeks after this and quickly burrow into the bast, where they excavate several irregular tunnels, which can be anything from several tens of centimetres to as much as two metres long. These are then filled with the crushed wood. The fully grown larva is flat, white and about four cm long, which is roughly double the size of the beetle. The following spring after hibernation it vertically drills the wood of its tree to a depth of several centimetres before finally turning into the pupa.

Length: 6—20 mm.
Habitat: oak forests.
Distribution: Europe, the Caucasus, Asia Minor, north Africa.

Conspicuous colouring, similar to that of wasps, is a warning sign which protects the bearer against enemies — 1 — *Plagionotus detritus*, 2 — *Paravespula germanica* (a wasp)

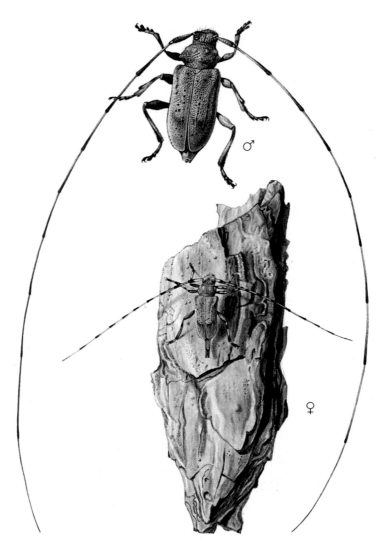

# Timberman

*Acanthocinus aedilis*

The two sexes of this beetle species can be distinguished by the length of their antennae. The male's are from three to five times, and the female's about one and a half times longer than their bodies. The female can also be distinguished by her protruding ovipositor. The timberman is one of the first longhorn beetles to appear in spring. It can be seen as early as March and April and is still about in May, while in some years a second generation is born late in summer. The beetles like to settle on pine logs, where they are very difficult to be spotted, as their grey colouring merges with the colour of the bark.

The female deposits about 40 eggs in pine bark. First of all she gnaws a hollow, into which she inserts her stout ovipositor until she reaches the bast of the tree. The hatched larva lives under the bark of tree stumps and logs, in which it excavates its characteristic irregular tunnels. When it is fully grown, it constructs an oval chamber under the bark and lines it with fine wooden splinters. Here it turns into a pupa, which can be easily recognized by its antennae, which are coiled into loops. The adult beetle hibernates.

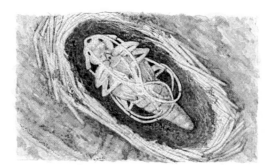

Pupa in its chamber

Length: 12—20 mm.
Habitat: coniferous forests.
Distribution: Europe, Siberia, Korea, Mongolia.

# Cryptocephalus sericeus

Some genera of the leaf-beetle family have a large variability of species. This is especially true of the genus *Cryptocephalus,* which is represented in Europe by several dozen species that range in size from one and a half to nine mm. They may be yellow, red, black or metallic in either a single colour or displaying a variety of colours and patterns. The scientific name of this genus suggests that its members have their heads hidden (it is derived from the Greek words kryptos — hidden, and kephalé — head). In fact the head is covered almost completely by the shield and can be better seen from the side or from below.

One of the most common species is *Cryptocephalus sericeus.* This beetle is most often coloured a metallic green, as shown in the picture, However, its colouring can vary a great deal, from gold to purple and blue, which in the past led to such forms being given individual names. This leaf-beetle can best be observed during the summer months, when hawkweeds, scabious and yarrow are in full bloom. It is found abundantly in meadows, hedgerows and on woodland edges and glades.

Length: 7—8 mm.
Habitat: on flowers.
Distribution: Europe, Siberia, Asia Minor.

The antennae of various chrysomelid species

*Donatia aquatica* looks like a longicorn beetle but it is, in fact, another species of chrysomelids

# Colorado Beetle

*Leptinotarsa decemlineata*

The colorado beetle is one of the newcomers to the European animal kingdom. It was introduced about 100 years ago and, as a result of the large popularity of its host, the potato plant, it soon became widespread in the majority of European countries. The native continent of this beetle is North America, where it originally fed on the leaves of wild-growing nightshades. However, in the second half of the 19th century its diet radically changed as a result of the introduction of potatoes into North America. These began to be grown in such large quantities that the beetle gradually became restricted to this plant. Later it became similarly widespread in Europe.

After hibernation the beetle emerges in spring from its underground shelter. The female soon lays her first eggs and goes on doing this almost continuously throughout the whole summer. These yellowish eggs are stuck in clusters to the leaves of potato plants. The reddish larvae marked with two rows of black dots hatch shortly afterwards. They shed their skin three times and in the process change their colouring to orange, after which they crawl underground to pupate. The young beetle hatches in two weeks and rests another week underground before it emerges and flies away. The colorado beetle usually produces two generations in a year.

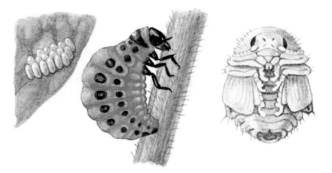

Development of the colorado beetle

Length: 6—11 mm.
Habitat: potato fields, sometimes meadows and forests.
Distribution: originally Greenland, North America, northern Mexico, today cosmopolitan.

# Tortoise Beetle

*Cassida viridis*

Thanks to the green colouring of its three-sectioned shield, this beetle can easily be overlooked when sitting on a leaf. Only when it begins to move, extending its antennae and legs, which otherwise are covered by its shield and elytra, can it be clearly seen. The tortoise beetle is herbivorous and is particularly fond of plants belonging to the mint family; it bites small oval holes in the leaves.

During the egg-laying season the female finds a suitable spot on a leaf and adopts an unusual posture, raising herself on outspread legs and then exuding a drop of white fluid from her abdomen. Then she lays the first egg, which is wrapped in this secretion, and soon adds others to it until a small pile of about 8 to 15 eggs has amassed. These are then covered with a protective layer. She continues this activity throughout the summer until she has finally produced several dozen such piles. The larvae are green and can be recognized by their tough, branched hairs and also by a forked protuberance at the end of their bodies, which can be folded forward along the length of the back. Like the adult beetles, they feed on leaf tissue. The pupa hatches into the beetle after about a week. The mature beetles can be seen on the leaves until autumn, when they retire to hibernate.

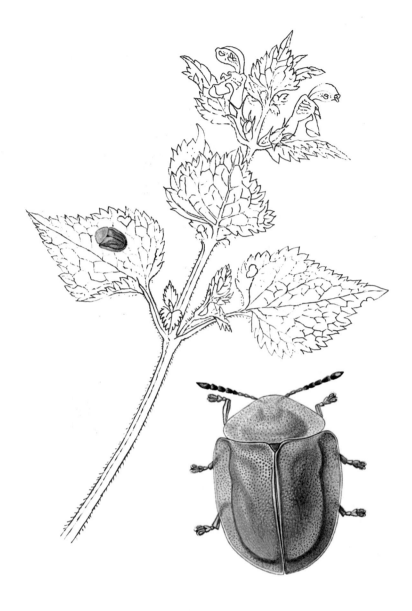

Length: 7—9 mm.
Habitat: on plants.
Distribution: Europe, north Africa, Siberia, Asia Minor, western Asia (Syria), northern China and Japan.

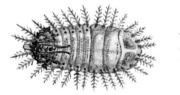
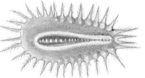

The larvae of *Cassida* species are strange in appearance

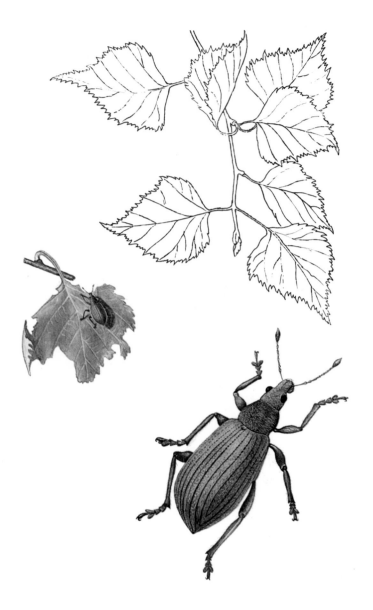

# *Polydrosus mollis*

The Curculionidae family, which is the most abundant as regards the number of species, includes beetles which have an elongated head and usually arched antennae. Many of them are black or generally dark and smooth, although the bodies of some of these beetles are covered with dense rows of fine scales, the arrangement of which determines the actual colouring of the beetle. Young beetles have the most distinctive colouring in green, grey or brown. In older specimens some of these scales either fall or are rubbed off and then the dark colouring of the shield and elytra is displayed.

This group of weevils also includes *Polydrosus mollis,* which usually has copper brown or even greyish-green scales. In spring the beetles stay on the young branches of oaks, beeches, poplars and other trees and shrubs. Each has a pointed head terminating in a pair of mandibles. The beetle uses them to make holes in the leaves in order to reach their soft and juicy centres, which provide it with nourishing food. Young beetles can often be found on new fir and spruce branches. The species generally occurs in almost all European countries.

Length: 6—8.5 mm.
Habitat: predominantly oak, beech and poplar.
Distribution: most of Europe, Siberia.

Heads of various curculionids

# Large Pine Weevil

*Hylobius abietis*

Several species of weevils which damage young and old trees can be found in coniferous forests. Some are harmful as larvae, others as adults. These include the large pine weevil and other related species.

The large weevil lives for about three years and adapts its habits according to the season of the year. In spring the beetles search young trees and are therefore usually concentrated in forest clearings. During this period the main food supply is provided by the bark of young trees, which is systematically consumed all around the trunk of the tree. In this way the young tree is irreparably damaged and dies. In summer the beetles move on to older trees and devour the bark of their new branches in a similar manner. In the autumn they find a suitable shelter for hibernation. They crawl under felled trees or into fallen leaves etc. In summer, the females can be seen on healthy tree stumps, in the roots of which they lay their eggs. The yellow-white larvae with brown heads and two light lateral patches hatch in about two to three weeks. They gnaw out tunnels in the bast and later in the wood itself. The larvae usually hibernate and complete their development in their wooden chambers the following year.

Length: 7.3—13.5 mm.
Habitat: pine forests.
Distribution: Europe, Siberia, Japan.

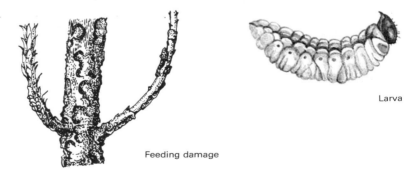

Feeding damage

Larva

# Apple-blossom Weevil
*Anthonomus pomorum*

In some years a great number of rusty brown dry buds occur in the profusion of apple blossoms. These serve as a shelter for the larva, pupa and also the adult of the apple-blossom weevil. It leaves the bud through a small opening and then settles in the foliage of the tree on which it feeds. It has a particular liking for the underside of leaves and is able to shred them completely, leaving only the network of veins. At the end of summer before the fruit-picking season it searches for a suitable shelter for hibernation. It usually crawls under the bark of a tree or into the ground. With the arrival of spring, it again climbs up into the apple trees and feeds on the new shoots and buds, eating the centres and so damaging the blossoms before they even start to flower. More of the blossoms are then damaged by the females and their offspring, as the female lays her eggs directly in the buds. After a short period of time the larva emerges and lives on the inside of the blossom. The ravaged bud naturally fails to open and forms a brown ball instead. The larva lives there for three to four weeks and then pupates. The mature beetle hatches after about a week. Apart from apple trees, this beetle also attacks pear trees.

Length: 3.4—4.3 mm.
Habitat: fruit orchards.
Distribution: Europe, Siberia, north Africa (Algeria), introduced to North America.

Pupa inside a dried up apple tree bud

# Leaf-Rolling Weevil

*Deporaus betulae*

Leaf-rolling weevils, formerly classified with the nut weevils, differ from the latter not only by their straight antennae, but also by many interesting features of their way of life. The females are the first to appear on the young leaves of birches, alders, hazel bushes and beeches towards the end of April and at the beginning of May. They prepare special leaf cornets as nests for their eggs, which hang vertically from the stalks. These interesting constructions are made with great precision, characteristic of the skill of an experienced engineer. The female constructs a cone-shaped nest from a leaf, first by rolling up the leaf tightly, and then, after allowing it to relax, fastening the edges together. She then constructs one or two small, transparent sacs below the leaf cuticle into each of which she lays an egg. The nest is then sealed and the female bites partially through the stem before moving to another leaf. The larva eats only a part of the leaf and the cornet soon becomes dry and falls to the ground. The larva crawls out and retreats underground, where it pupates.

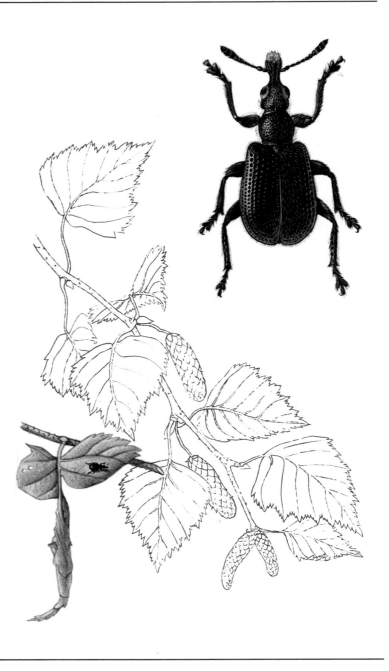

Length: 2.5—4 mm.
Habitat: birch trees.
Distribution: most of Europe, Siberia, Mongolia, north Africa.

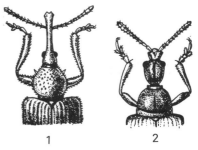

1                    2

Other species of weevil vary considerably in shape, particularly at the head end: 1 — *Rhynchites auratus*, 2 — *Apoderus coryli*

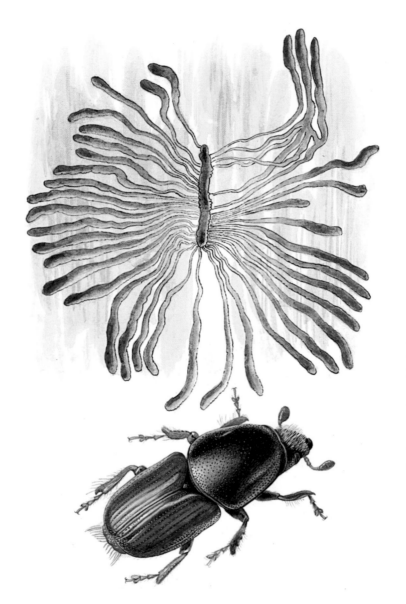

# Large Elm-bark Beetle
*Scolytus scolytus*

Of all bark beetles which damage deciduous trees, the large elm-bark beetle is one of the most common. The female first bites out a mating chamber and after being fertilized, she makes another short (two to six cm) but wide nursery tunnel along the edge of which she lays her eggs. The larvae then bite extensive tunnels, which are much longer than the one made by their mother.

The large elm-bark beetle has two generations in a year. The hibernating larvae produce the first generation of beetles in May. They first fly to the tree tops and feed on the new tender shoots. Shortly afterwards they bury themselves in the lower parts of the broad elm tree trunks, where they produce the second generation, which hatches in August. The large elm-bark beetle can usually be found living together with other related species, such as *Scolytus multistriatus,* which bores into the branches and the slender trunks of trees. Its nest is made up of a distinctive narrow nursery tunnel and a large number of larval tunnels.

The large elm-bark beetle damages elm trees not only by its feeding activities but, along with *Scolytus multistriatus,* it also carries the spores of the fungus *Ophiostoma ulmi,* which causes the drying up of elm trees. This disease, called Dutch elm disease, has had serious economic effects.

To the most dangerous pests of pine woods belongs *Myelophilus piniperda.*

*Myelophilus piniperda*

Length: 3—6 mm.
Habitat: old elms.
Distribution: central Europe.

# Ips typographus

At one time, this cylindrically shaped, relatively large bark beetle was considered a secondary pest, as it attacked old, dying fir trees. If such trees are not available, however, or if the beetle overpopulates, it will attack healthy trees as well. The shelter for the future generation is selected by the male. He makes his way through the thick bark, excavates a chamber within it and then, with the aid of a specific smell, entices two or three females to enter. The size of the chamber differs according to their number, which may be as high as seven. If there are only two females, one of them makes a tunnel about 6 to 15 cm long in one direction from the nesting chamber, whilst the other one excavates a similar tunnel in the opposite direction. When the number of females is higher, the system of tunnels obviously becomes more complicated. As each female prepares her nursery, she gradually lays about 60 eggs in small mounds along its walls. The larvae soon hatch and make their own tunnels, which run at right angles to the nursery. These are five cm long and widen out towards their ends. The white larva has a soft skin, is legless and blind. It gnaws out a chamber at the end of the tunnel and pupates there. Before the hatched beetle leaves the protection of this shelter, it starts feeding on the surrounding wood, thus making an irregular, forked tunnel which is linked with the pupal chamber. Then it makes its own exit or uses an already existing hole and escapes from the wood.

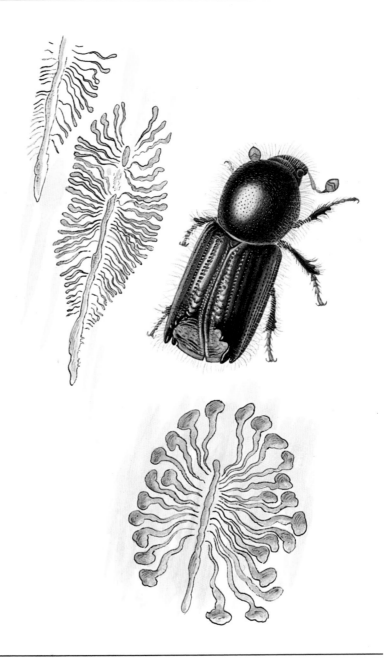

Length: 4.2—5.5 mm.
Habitat: fir forests.
Distribution: Europe, Siberia, northern China.

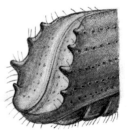

The peculiarly shaped hind end of the elytra

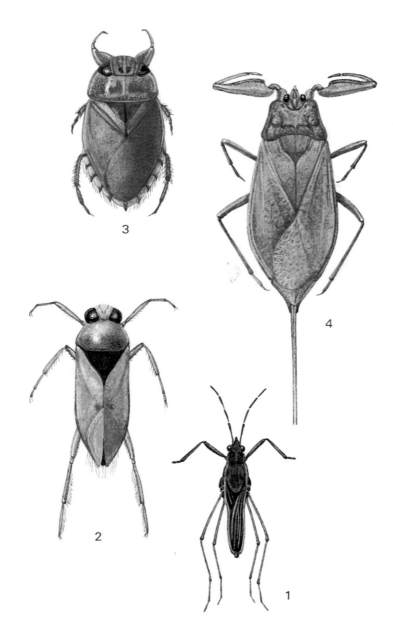

# Common Pond-skater
*Gerris lacustris*

# Backswimmer
*Notonecta glauca*

# Saucer Bug
*Ilyocoris cimicoides*

# Grey Water Scorpion
*Nepa cinerea*

Many species of bugs are confined to water by their way of life. Groups of slim pond-skaters with long legs either stand still or move swiftly on the surface of weed-free or overgrown water without sinking. This is made possible by the dense hair cover on the underside of their feet; the space between the hairs is filled with air thus making them water-resistant. The first pair of legs is for catching and holding objects, the second and third pairs serve for locomotion.

Other bug species live under water yet they breathe atmospheric oxygen, which they take in at the water surface. The first pair of legs of the back-swimmer, or water boatman, are like tongs and are adapted for seizing. The other legs which are beset with long hairs are used as oars. The backswimmer typically swims on its back. It also flies well.

The saucer bug has a powerful tripartite proboscis through which it sucks out its prey. Its front legs are adapted for seizing, the hind legs for swimming.

The grey water scorpion lives in the mud near the banks. The front legs are for seizing, the others are adapted for walking.

Typical posture of *Notonecta glauca* when drawing air at the surface

1 — *Gerris lacustris:*
Length: 8–10 mm.
Distribution: most of Europe, Asia Minor, north Africa.

2 — *Notonecta glauca:*
Length: 14–16 mm.
Distribution: Europe, Caucasus, north Africa.

3 — *Ilyocoris cimicoides:*
Length: 15 mm.
Distribution: most of Europe, Caucasus.

4 — *Nepa cinerea:*
Length: 18–22 mm.
Distribution: most of Europe.

# Common Firebug
*Pyrrhocoris apterus*

# Striped Bug
*Graphosoma lineatum*

# Brassica Bug
*Eurydema oleraceum*

# Green Stink Bug
*Palomena prasina*

# Tarnished Plant Bug
*Lygus pratensis*

The common firebug appears early in the spring on sunlit lower parts of trees. It mates immediately and soon afterwards lays eggs. The female lays about ten batches, each comprising 50 to 80 eggs. The generation which emerges from these eggs mates again, lays eggs and only individuals hatching from this batch overwinter. The common firebug lives mainly on lime tree seed and various organic residues. Originally they developed wings and only secondarily, in the course of evolution, have become wingless.

Insects of the family Pentatomidae have a conspicuous central shield — the visible part of the mesothorax. The striped bug is a warmth-loving species the life cycle of which is the same as that of the common firebug. It also lives in groups.

The green stink bug has stink glands between the front and back trochanter. While feeding on the juices of tree fruits, secretions from these glands are transferred onto the fruits.

The brassica bug and the tarnished plant bug suck the juices of plants — the former often attacks vegetables while the latter attacks mostly fodder plants.

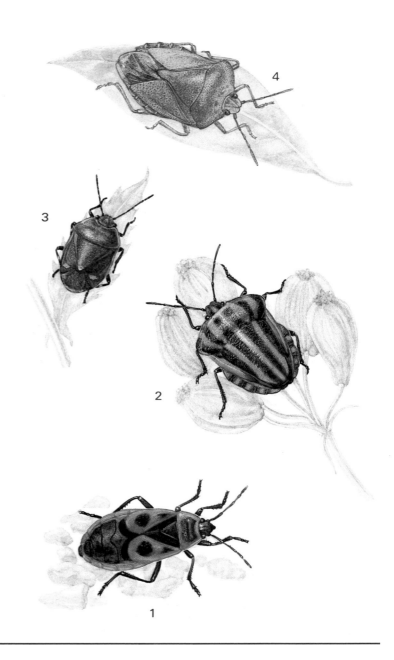

1 — *Pyrrhocoris apterus:*
Length: 7—12 mm.

2 — *Graphosoma lineatum:*
Length: 9—12 mm.

3 — *Eurydema oleraceum:*
Length: 5—7 mm.

4 — *Palomena prasina:*
Length: 12—15 mm.

5 — *Lygus pratensis:*
Length: 5.8—6.7 mm.

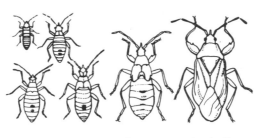

Development — incomplete metamorphosis. Five larval stages and the imago — right

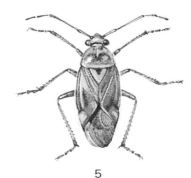

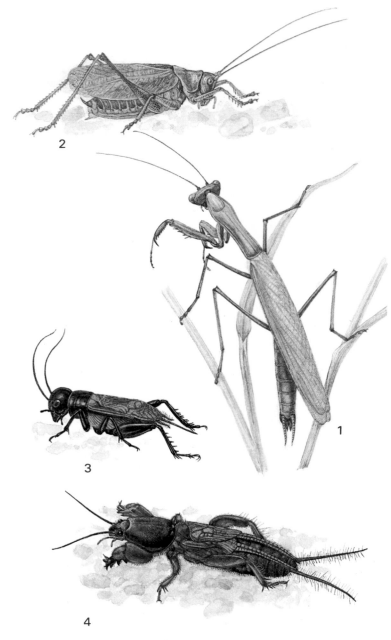

# Praying Mantis
*Mantis religiosa*

# Great Green Bush Cricket
*Tettigonia viridissima*

# Field Cricket
*Gryllus campestris*

# Mole Cricket
*Gryllotalpa gryllotalpa*

The praying mantis has a typically small head with strong jaws and a long prothorax with a pair of raptorial front legs. The meso- and metathorax are joined with the prothorax at an angle which allows the mantis to take up a posture with its thorax raised. The mantids catch their prey with a darting attack of their predacious legs. The female lays eggs onto plants and covers them with a secretion which hardens to form a case (ootheca). The eggs overwinter, the larvae emerge in spring and mature by August.

The great green bush cricket has very long, thread-like antennae consisting of at least 30 segments. The female has a long ovipositor by which she inserts the eggs into the ground. The male has small veins adapted into a stridulatory organ for making the typical chirrup sound while rubbing the wings against each other.

Males of the field cricket have the same stridulatory organ. After mating, the female lays some 300 eggs in a small chamber in the ground.

The stridulatory organ of the mole cricket is also located on the wings. The female has no ovipositor. She lays the eggs into a specially dug out chamber in the ground.

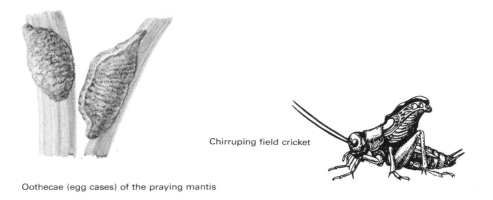

Oothecae (egg cases) of the praying mantis

Chirruping field cricket

1 — *Mantis religiosa:*
Length: 72—75 mm.
Time of occurrence: May—July.

2 — *Tettigonia viridissima:*
Length: 28—42 mm.
Time of occurrence: July—October.

3 — *Gryllus campestris:*
Length: 20—26 mm.
Time of occurrence: May—August.

4 — *Gryllotalpa gryllotalpa:*
Length: 35—50 mm.
Time of occurrence: April—October.

# Red-winged Scraping Grasshopper
*Psophus stridulus*

# Blue-winged Waste-land Grasshopper
*Oedipoda caerulescens*

# Stripe-winged Grasshopper
*Stenobothrus lineatus*

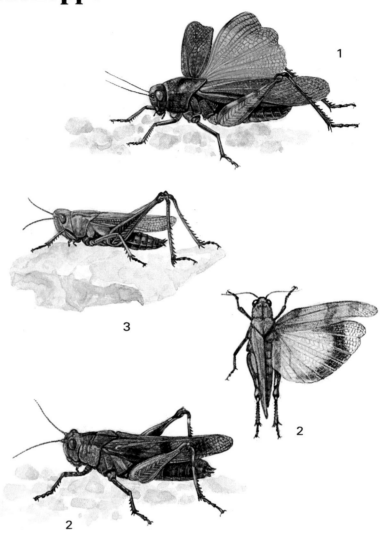

Short-horned grasshoppers are similar to the crickets but for their short antennae. They are exclusively vegetarian, while the crickets and bush crickets are predatory. The males stridulate by rubbing the outgrowths present on the inside thigh of the hind legs against the wing veining.

The red-winged scraping grasshopper has brick-red hind wings visible only in flight; when resting the wings are folded under the wing-covers. In flight the males produce a conspicuous rattling sound. The female has a short ovipositor by which she inserts clusters of eggs, covered in a case of foamy secretion, into the upper layers of the soil.

The blue-winged waste-land grasshopper is a variable species, its colour matches the colour of the environment in which it has developed. Its body is dark, rusty or yellowish, the membranous wings are, as a rule, pale blue with a narrow black stripe, although they may also be yellow-pink to yellowish. The males stridulate inconspicuously. The females, as in the preceding species, have a short ovipositor; they deposit their eggs enclosed with the foamy case into the soil.

The stripe-winged grasshopper is brown or green, the edges of the rear wings are dark. Its way of life does not differ from the other species.

1 — *Psophus stridulus*:
Length: 23—25 mm.
Distribution: large part of Europe, Siberia.

2 — *Oedipoda caerulescens*:
Length: 16—26 mm.
Distribution: Europe (from southern Scandinavia up to the Mediterranean region), Asia Minor and western Asia, Siberia, north Africa.

3 — *Stenobothrus lineatus*:
Length: 16—25 mm.
Distribution: Europe, western Asia, Siberia.

Incomplete metamorphosis of grasshoppers. Several larval stages with gradually growing wing stubs.

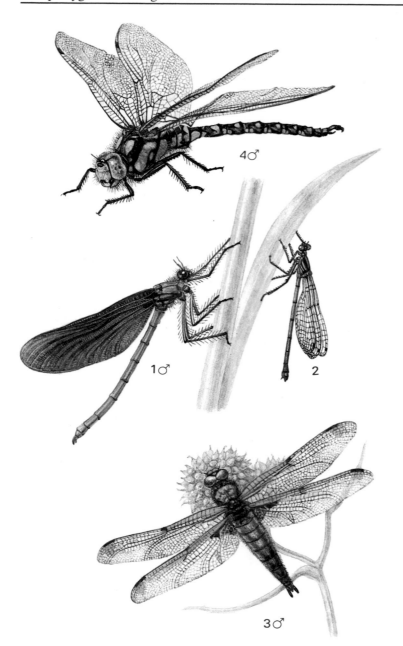

# Calopteryx virgo
# Pyrrhosoma nymphula
# Libellula quadrimaculata
# Aeschna cyanea

The appearance, colour and flight of dragonflies is very conspicuous. They have a long segmented abdomen, densely veined membranous wings and thin seizing legs. They are adapted for hunting moving prey — the head is mobile, it has large eyes and powerful mandibles. They are mostly very good fliers and mate in flight. When mating the male is in front and holds the female with a pair of abdominal nippers. After fertilization the females lay eggs in water or in plants. The larvae are predatory; the lower lip of the mouth is transformed into a "mask" with which they catch their prey. They live in water; they moult up to twenty times before eventually crawling out of water and emerging as the imago.

The Calopterygids and Coenagrionids of the suborder lesser dragonflies or damsel-flies, Zygoptera, have two identical pairs of wings. They are slow fliers. Aeschnids and Libellulids of the sub-order Anisoptera fly quickly, and the front and back pairs of wings differ. Zygoptera rest their wings vertically to the long axis of the body, whereas Anisoptera have them spread out in the horizontal plane.

The larvae of Zygoptera are slim with three tapering caudal gills for locomotion. The larvae of Anisoptera are cylindrical to spindle-shaped; they breathe through a gill chamber formed in the expanded rectal canal.

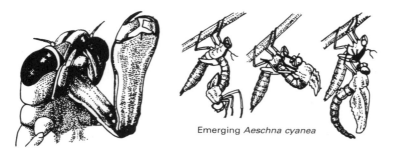

The trapping organ of dragonfly larvae

Emerging *Aeschna cyanea*

1 — *Calopteryx virgo:*
Length: 50 mm.
Wingspan: 70 mm.

2 — *Pyrrhosoma nymphula:*
Length: 35 mm.
Wingspan: 45 mm.

3 — *Libellula quadrimaculata:*
Length: 40—50 mm.
Wingspan: 70—85 mm.

4 — *Aeschna cyanea:*
Length: 65—80 mm.
Wingspan: 95—110 mm.

# Millipede
*Polydesmus complanatus*
## *Iulus terrestris*
# Brown Centipede
*Lithobius forficatus*

The body of a millipede is cylindrical or ventrally flattened; the body segments, with the exception of the first four, are doubled, each with two pairs of legs and two pairs of respiratory openings. On the back the segments are perfectly fused while on the ventral side two plates on each segment are clearly apparent. The tops of the legs are close together, the legs being relatively short and slender. Millipedes move rather slowly and feed mainly on vegetable remains. The body segments of centipedes are flattened, simple, each carrying a single pair of strong, long legs, the tops of which are located close to the edges of the segments. Centipedes are fast runners and they are predacious. Representatives of both orders are active at night. Centipedes are sexually differentiated.

The millipede has the body composed of 19 to 22 segments with lateral appendages. It commonly lives in the dry matter beneath the bark of old broadleaf trees. The females make nests of soil for their eggs.

*Iulus terrestris* has up to 89 pairs of legs. Larvae with three pairs of legs emerge from the eggs and after each moult another pair is added. If disturbed the millipede coils up. The body of the brown centipede has 19 segments of different sizes; the legs are composed of eight segments.

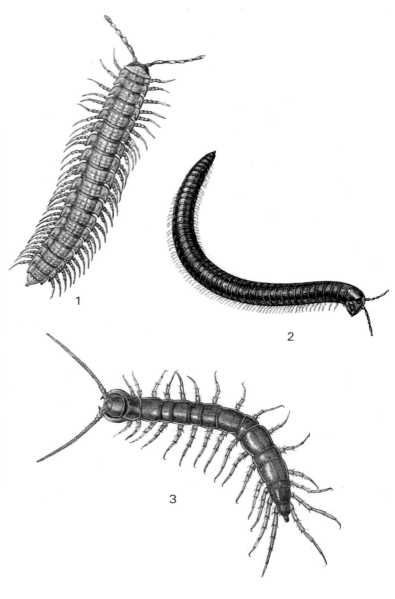

1 — *Polydesmus complanatus:*
Length: 15—23 mm.
Distribution: central Europe.

2 — *Iulus terrestris:*
Length: 17—23 mm.
Distribution: Europe from the Balkan Peninsula north to Scandinavia, Lithuania and Estonia.

3 — *Lithobius forficatus:*
Length: 18—30 mm.
Distribution: cosmopolitan.

Curled up millipede *(Iulus)*

*Polydesmus complanatus* with eggs

1

2

3

# *Porcellio scaber*
# **Wood-louse**
*Oniscus asellus*

# **Pill Bug**
*Armadillidium vulgare*

Small isopod crustaceans, *Porcellio scaber* and the wood-louse, live in damp fallen leaves and under stones in forests, but also in association with Man, in cellars, glass-houses, sheds and so on. Both species feed on decaying vegetable matter. The body is arched on the dorsal side and broad and considerably flattened on the ventral side. It is protected by a case (cuticle) strongly encrusted with calcium carbonate, so the surface of the body segments is densely granular. The head is fused with the first segment of the thorax to form the cephalothorax. Under the head shield there are two pairs of antennae — the first is stunted, the second, which is segmented, is clearly visible. The wood-louse has a triangular head lobe, *Porcellio scaber* has it strongly turned up. The thoracic legs of both species are adapted for walking. Those of the females bear fine appendages forming a pouch (marsupium) in which the eggs are carried. The abdominal legs are transformed into respiratory organs for air-breathing.

*Armadillidium vulgare,* in contrast to the former species, loves dry places to live in. It is commonly encountered under stones in dry, sunlit places, on sun-facing slopes, behind wall plasters, etc. It is able to curl up into a ball. The abdominal end is broadly cut and curved; it has a triangular flat spot in the centre of the forehead.

*Armadillidium vulgare* curled up into a ball

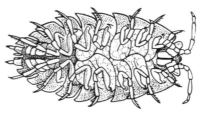

*Porcellio scaber* from below

1 — *Porcellio scaber:*
Length: 11—16 mm.
Distribution: cosmopolitan.

2 — *Oniscus asellus:*
Length: up to 18 mm.
Distribution: large part of Europe, North America.

3 — *Armadillidium vulgare:*
Length: 12—17 mm.
Distribution: almost worldwide.

# *Asellus aquaticus*
# *Triops cancriformis*
# **Crawfish** or **Crayfish**

*Astacus astacus*

*Asellus aquaticus,* an amphibious member of the order Isopoda, is a typical inhabitant of still waters. It crawls skilfully among plants, in the mud and under stones. It lives on plant remains. In contrast with its terrestrial kin both pairs of antennae are developed. The abdominal segments are fused into a single shield, the pleotelson.

In areas periodically flooded by rivers, *Triops can-criformis* may be encountered from spring until autumn. It swims or crawls on the river bed. Its body consists of 32 to 35 segments with 45 to 57 pairs of legs. The related species, *Lepidurus apis,* is found in flood waters only early in spring. The terminal segment of the abdomen is extended into a gill between the spinal bristles. Both species lay eggs in the mud and then die. The eggs must dry up with the mud, otherwise they cannot develop in the spring of the following year.

The body of the crawfish is covered by a hard crust; as it grows the crawfish moults each time replacing the old crust with a new one. The new crust is soft at first and then is encrusted by chitin and calcium carbonate. The abdomen is made up of six segments and a telson, and may bend under the cephalothorax allowing the crayfish to swim tail first. The female carries the eggs on the underside of the abdomen. The young hatch in June and July; they moult about five times in the first year of their life.

1 − *Asellus aquaticus:*
Length: female 8 mm, male 12 mm.
Distribution: north and central Europe.

2 − *Triops cancriformis:*
Length: up to 100 mm (including terminal appendages).
Distribution: cool, temperate regions in the northern hemisphere.

3 − *Astacus astacus:*
Length: 120−160 mm.
Distribution: central Europe (up to the south of Scandinavia).

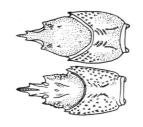

The shape of the rostrum in *A. astacus* (top) and *A. leptodactylus* (bottom)

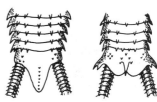

The shape of the last abdominal segment of *Lepidurus apis* (left) and *Triops cancriformis* (right)

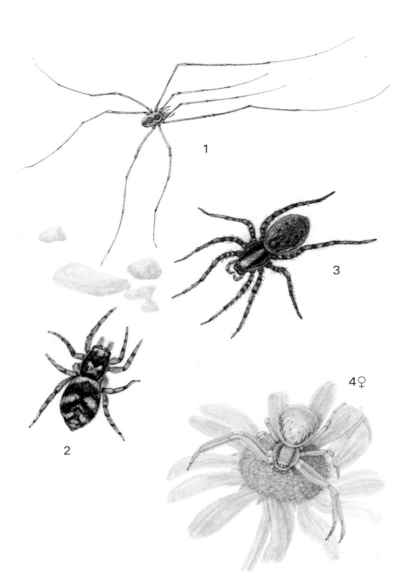

# Daddy Longlegs
*Phalangium opilio*

## *Salticus scenicus*
## *Pardosa lugubris*
# Flower Hunting Spider
*Misumena vatia*

The Opilionids may be distinguished from the spiders, Araneae, at a glance. The abdomen of spiders is not segmented and it is connected to the cephalothorax by a very narrow waist, whereas the abdomen of Opilionids is segmented and connected to the cephalothorax by the whole width of the segments. Their legs are much longer than their bodies and while walking the tarsus coils around plant stalks. The daddy longlegs remains hidden in daytime and hunts small arthropods, worms and the like at night.

Spiders of the following families do not make webs; they hunt their prey actively. Despite this they use web-weaving as a safeguard, for building shelters, cocoons and so on. The Salticidae have the best eyesight of all. *Salticus scenicus* lies in wait for its prey, creeps after it and catches it by jumping at it — its jump is several times longer than the length of its body.

*Pardosa lugubris* hunts its prey on the ground. Females carry their eggs in a cocoon attached to the underside of the abdomen. After hatching the young crawl up onto their mother's back where they stay for some time.

On the underside of composite plants (Asteraceae) the females of *Misumena vatia* wait for their prey. They seize it with two extended pairs of legs. Females are able to change colour.

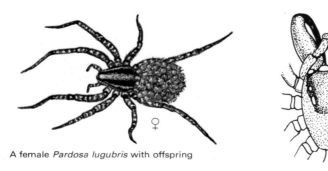

A female *Pardosa lugubris* with offspring

The cephalothorax of a male *Salticus scenicus*. The differences in the size of the eyes are conspicuous.

1 — *Phalangium opilio*:
Length:
6—9 mm.

2 — *Salticus scenicus*:
Length:
4.5—7.5 mm.

3 — *Pardosa lugubris*:
Length:
6—8 mm, male is smaller with relatively longer legs.

4 — *Misumena vatia*:
Length:
male 4 mm, female 10 mm.

# *Pholcus opilionoides*
# **House Spider**
*Tegenaria domestica*
# *Argiope bruennichi*
# *Euscorpius carpathicus*

Members of the Pholcidae, Agelenidae and Araneidae families catch their prey in webs of varying complexity. *Pholcus opilionoides* usually sits on the underside of an inconspicuous and thinly woven web. By biting its prey it injects it with highly active digestive enzymes. Through the same perforation it then sucks out the liquidized contents so perfectly that the prey, at the end of the process, maintains its original body shape. The female spins a thin cocoon for her eggs which she carries around until the young have hatched.

The house spider is a markedly domestic species; records about its occurrence in nature are not available. Its web is made of two layers — the basis is a thick net of nonadhesive fibres and immediately above that is a thin web, the actual prey trap. The webs are usually situated horizontally across a room corner and in the corner itself the fibres join to form a tube in which the spider hides.

*Argiope bruennichi* places its large circular web with a white centre of a thickly woven strands and vertical stabilizers about 30 cm above the ground.

*Euscorpius carpathicus* has the typical scorpion body shape with a poisonous gland at the abdominal end and large claw-like pedipalps with which it hunts various arthropods; it only rarely uses its sting.

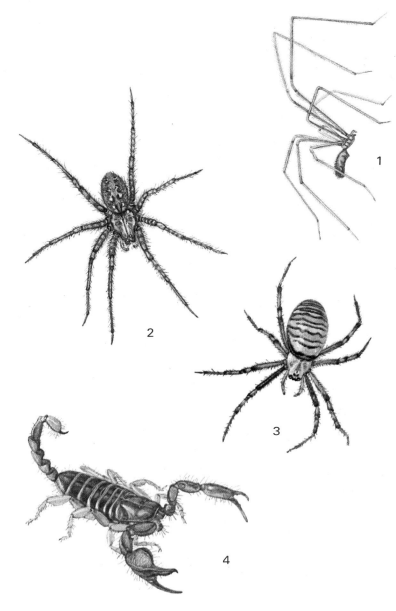

1 — *Pholcus opilionoides:*
Length:
4—5 mm.

2 — *Tegenaria domestica:*
Length: 12—18 mm, the male is smaller with longer legs.

3 — *Argiope bruennichi:*
Length:
male 3 mm, female 10 mm.

4 — *Euscorpius carpathicus:*
Length:
40 mm.

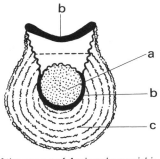

Cross section of the cocoon of *Argiope bruennichi:* a — mass of eggs, b — densely woven region, c — cushion of greatly expanded fibres

The head of *Tegenaria domestica* showing huge chelicerae

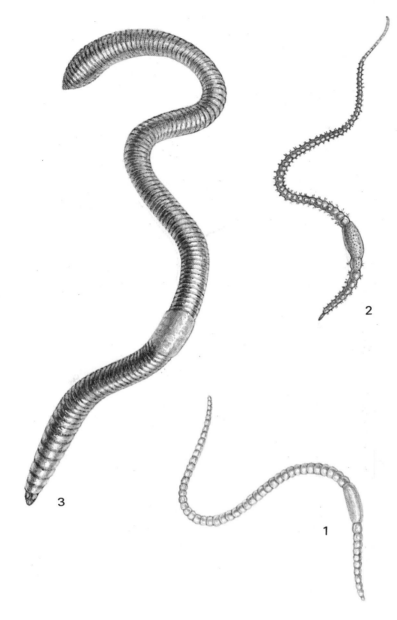

## *Enchytraeus albidus*
## *Tubifex tubifex*
# Earthworm or Dewworm
### *Lumbricus terrestris*

Members of all these families belong to the order Oligochaeta. They have a worm-like body, conspicuously segmented both inside and out; each segment, except the first one, carries at least four clusters of bristles. On the front part of the body several segments are swollen to form a belt (clitellum) which at the time of reproduction produces a kind of mucus which turns into a jelly cocoon. Members of the order Oligochaeta are hermaphrodite.

The Enchytraeidae are small, slender annelids frequently found from April to early summer in the upper layers of soils rich in humus.

Tubificids are aquatic annelids which often occur in large numbers. They live in vertical burrows, in mud, with their heads downwards.

The earthworm or dewworm is a large annelid with a body diameter of six to nine mm; its belt is on the 32nd to 37th segment. It moistens its skin with mucus which assists respiration and decreases friction between its body and the soil. By contracting the powerful muscles beneath the epidermis and by the pressure of its body fluids the earthworm stiffens the front part of its body into a wedge and can penetrate between soil particles. It eats soil and digests the organic components contained within it.

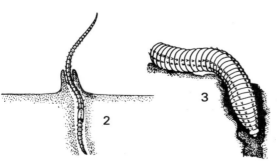

1 — *Enchytraeus albidus:*
Length:
20—35 mm.
Habitat:
in humid soil and rotting plant remains.
Distribution:
cosmopolitan.

2 — *Tubifex tubifex:*
Length: 25—40 mm.
Habitat:
the mud of shallow, still or slow-flowing waters.
Distribution:
North America, Europe, Asia,
and Australian region.

3 — *Lumbricus terrestris:*
Length: 90—300 mm.
Habitat:
forest soils and those rich in organic matter,
but avoiding dry or acid soils.
Distribution:
cosmopolitan, not indigenous everywhere.

# Coat-of-mail shell

*Chiton olivaceus*

## *Lepidochitona cinereus*

*Chiton olivaceus* is one of the most primitive existing molluscs. This is borne out not only by the body structure and internal arrangement but also by the primitive type of larva.

The shell covers only the animal's upper surface. It is unusual in construction and differs from the shells of other molluscs in that it consists of a series of eight convex plates which articulate and overlap rather like the tiles of a roof. They enable the animal to curl up when danger threatens.

The shells are extremely variable in colour, and may be yellow-brown to olive-grey; sometimes also black, red, orange or yellow. On the upper surface they have transverse as well as longitudinal stripes. The second and seventh plates are usually of a different colour. This mollusc lives firmly attached to stones and rocks in the splash zone. It feeds on the minute algae that form a surface film on rocks. This species is not found in Britain.

*Lepidochitona cinereus* is a smaller species, about 12 mm long. Its shell is not as colourful and is generally green or brown. Its way of life and habitat are similar to that of *Chiton olivaceus*. It is probably the commonest chiton on the shores of Great Britain, and much of western Europe.

1 − *Chiton olivaceus:*
Length:
30−40 mm.
Habitat:
under rocks and stones.

2 − *Lepidochitona cinereus:*
Length:
12−25 mm.
Width:
8−16 mm.
Habitat:
under rocks and stones.

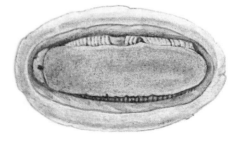

*Chiton olivaceus* from below

# Ormer or Sea Ear
*Haliotis tuberculata*

*Haliotis tuberculata* belongs to a group of very primitive gastropod molluscs. The shell is flat and shallow, the whorls widening so abruptly that the overall effect is to appear like a human ear. This resemblance is the reason not only for the animal's scientific name but also for the name by which it is known in the various languages, for example, "Orechia di San Pietro" (Ear of St Peter) in Italian.

The exterior of the shell is dark grey with dark brown marbling and distinct transverse and longitudinal grooves. Inside it is lined with a thick layer of mother-of-pearl. At the outer edge are a series of holes through which the exhalant current escapes.

*H. tuberculata* is abundant in European seas, especially in the Mediterranean. It is commonly found below the littoral zone, where it adheres firmly to rocks, the underside of stones, harbour constructions, and the like. It feeds on the algal covering of rocks.

In the Mediterranean it is commonly gathered for the valuable mother-of-pearl, used in making fancy goods and souvenirs. In the Channel Islands it is also gathered for food.

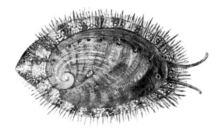

*Haliotis tuberculata* with foot extended

The shell of *Haliotis tuberculata* is usually covered with layers of algae

Length:
up to 85 mm.
Shell:
ear-like.
Habitat:
mainly below low-water mark, on stones and rocks.

# Common River Snail
*Viviparus viviparus*

## *Viviparus fasciatus*

Members of the family Viviparidae are freshwater prosobranch snails with a single gill in front of a single heart chamber. They have a short, stout body, a broad foot and a head extended into a snout. Their two long arrow-shaped tentacles cannot be withdrawn. The eyes are located below them. They feed on detritus and algae, which they grate using a tongue-like organ, the radula, which has up to seven spine-like teeth in each transverse row. The lid of the shell is permanently attached to the dorsal side of the foot, and is used to seal the shell when the foot is withdrawn. Around the nucleus of the lid concentric growth-rings are apparent. Members of the family are bisexual, the right tentacle of the male is thickened and it serves as a copulatory organ. The female holds the fertilized eggs in a cavity within the shell until they hatch and then lays the live young with a tiny shell covered by various sculptures.

The shell of the common river snail is fragile with thin walls which are finely and irregularly grooved. The apex is pointed. The shell is usually covered with mucus and detritus. The common river snail is widespread in Europe.

*Viviparus fasciatus* has a strong-walled shell with a bluntly curved apex. The whorls are slightly and quite regularly arched. It lives in larger rivers of most of Europe and Great Britain.

1

2

1. *Viviparus viviparus:*
Height: 30—45 mm.
Width: 25—35 mm.
Habitat:
muddy bottom of overgrown stagnant waters at low altitudes.

2. *Viviparus fasciatus:*
Height: 28—35 mm.
Width: 22—24 mm.
Habitat:
among stones on the bottom of larger rivers and adjoining reservoirs.

The common river snail extended from its shell

# Periwinkle or Common European Winkle

*Littorina littorea*

The shell of this species is up to 30 mm high, thick, ovate and with a pointed apex. There are six to seven slightly rounded whorls. The surface bears the characteristic sculpture of rugged spiral lines crossed with transverse growth bands. The colour is quite variable, generally greyish with brown lines.

*Littorina littorea* lives in the upper regions of the intertidal zone, on marine plants, stones and harbour constructions. At low tide the animal withdraws into its firm shell and closes the aperture with an operculum. It can live for some time out of water, frequently foraging for food on dry land. This is made possible by the mantle lining being richly supplied with blood capillaries, which enable the animal to absorb oxygen from the air. The gills are correspondingly reduced.

*L. littorea* feeds on seaweed and organic debris. It is widely distributed along the European coast of the Atlantic and is of great commercial value for it is an edible species that is very popular, especially along the coast of Britain.

The small periwinkle, *L. neritoides,* is a related species which lives in narrow crevices higher up the shore in the splash zone.

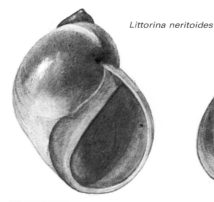

*Littorina neritoides*

*Littorina littorea:*
Height:
up to 30 mm.
Width:
up to 20 mm.
Shell:
thick, ovate, apex pointed; 6–7 whorls.
Habitat:
rocky shores, between the tide-marks.

*Littorina neritoides:*
Height:
up to 6 mm.
Width:
up to 3 mm.
Shell: ovate, appex pointed, 6–7 whorls.

# Common Wentletrap

*Clathrus clathrus*

*Clathrus clathrus* has a turret-shaped shell with a large number (12—15) of markedly convex whorls, regularly increasing in size and separated by a deep suture. Often they do not even touch. The exterior of the shell is strengthened by ridges that regularly cross each whorl, joining vertically to form almost continuous bands. The shell is about 30 mm high and 12 mm in diameter. The aperture is closed by an operculum. The colour is very delicate, usually white or pale pink, the bands are sometimes reddish or marked with horizontal streaks. The loose coiling, unusual surface sculpturing and pale coloration make the shell look like a piece of alabaster filigree work. Large tropical species were at one time highly valued and sold for fantastic prices.

*C. clathrus* is a predatory gastropod mollusc. It is found on sandy and muddy bottoms, often at depths of as much as 100 metres. It has a scattered distribution, however, and does not reproduce in large numbers.

Its home is the Mediterranean and the west European coast of the Atlantic, its range extending northwards as far as the North Sea.

The related *C. turtonis* has fewer, broader ridges on the whorls of the shell.

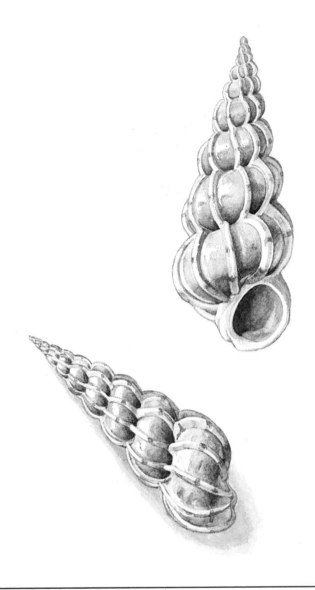

Height:
up to 37 mm.
Width:
up to 13 mm.
Shell:
loosely coiled, 15—16 whorls.

*Clathrus turtonis*

# Netted Dog Whelk

*Nassarius reticulatus*

The shell of this species is firm, conical to ovate, and composed of eight to nine whorls separated by a very shallow suture. It grows to a length of 32 mm and a breadth of 18 mm. The surface is conspicuously marked by a large number of broad, flat ribs that form a spiral pattern. The colour is very variable, ranging from pale yellow to dark brown. Pale shells are patterned with dark brown stripes.

*Nassarius reticulatus* is a carnivorous species and an important member of the sea's "sanitation force", feeding chiefly on the flesh of various dead animals such as worms, molluscs, cephalopods and fish. With its radula it rasps out pieces of the animal's flesh.

It lives buried in sand, leaving its hideout, however, as soon as it scents prey. These gastropod molluscs will converge on a piece of flesh from as far away as 20—30 metres. Their greatest enemy is the starfish. When they wish to put a safe distance between themselves and a predator they do so by a reflex action consisting of eight to nine violent leaps in rapid succession.

*N. reticulatus* is widely distributed and plentiful along the coast of Europe from Norway to the Mediterranean and as far as the Black Sea.

1

2

*Nassarius* crawling under the surface of the sand

Height:
up to 32 mm.
Width:
up to 18 mm.
Shell:
conspicuously ribbed, 5—7 whorls.
Habitat:
lower shore and shallow seas; on sand and mud.

1 — Empty shell
2 — Empty shells often serve as hiding-places for various animals, such as hermit crabs

# Great Pond Snail
*Lymnaea stagnalis*

# Dwarfed Limnaea
*Lymnaea truncatula*

Members of the Lymnaeidae family are typical lung bearing snails. They live in water yet they breathe air through lungs by extending a siphon tube above the water. They have eyes at the base of a single pair of tentacles which cannot be withdrawn (hence the Latin name of the order: Basommatophora). They have no lid on the dorsal side of the foot. Members of this family crawl over water plants or move, shell downwards, on the underside of the surface film. They live on detritus, algae, and aquatic vegetation. They are hermaphrodite and lay their eggs on water plants.

*Lymnaea truncatula* together with the related *L. stagnalis* lives in the cooler parts of North America and Eurasia. *L. truncatula* has a strongly arched shell with step-like whorls divided by a deep suture. *L. stagnalis* has a shell with a sharply pointed spire and its whorls are not step-like. *L. truncatula* is an intermediate host of the liver fluke which lives parasitically in the bile ducts of cattle, sheep and goats. If the parasite is to develop, its eggs must get into water. The larvae (miracidia) which emerge from the eggs enter the lung and liver of *L. truncatula*. After several developmental stages they abandon this host and settle on plants which are grazed by cattle.

2

1

1 – *Lymnaea truncatula*:
Height:
7–14 mm.
Width:
3.5–6 mm.
Shell:
conical, irregularly grooved, slightly glossy, translucent, right-handed with 5 to 5.5 whorls. Its mouth is eliptical with a blunt horn on the top.
Habitat: mainly small fresh-water sources, humid places outside water.

2 – *Lymnaea stagnalis*:
Height:
45–60 mm.
Width:
22–34 mm.
Shell:
elongate and ovate, fragile, thin-walled, very finely and regularly grooved, with 7 to 7.5 whorls. Body whorl is distended – more than two thirds the shell height.
Habitat:
stagnant fresh-water or brackish waters in the lowlands.

The great pond snail extended from its shell

# Great Ramshorn

*Planorbarius corneus*

In warm ponds and in river backwaters members of the Planorbidae family are the most common aquatic lung snails. They can be found crawling along stems and leaves of water plants. Their diet consists of green algae which cover objects submerged in the water. The shell is horizontally coiled in a spiral so when viewed from the side the shell seems to be flat. A crawling specimen, however, carries its shell erect, and vertical. When the snail is crawling the shell gives the impression of being right-handed but members of the family Planorbidae have their reproductive and respiratory openings on the left side.

The shape of the shell mouth, the growth of whorls and the shell dimensions vary considerably. The shell of young animals is conspicuously grooved along its length. The grooves are covered with evenly distributed bristles which disappear with age. The shell surface of adults is conspicuously grooved only on the first whorls while on later ones the grooving has disappeared.

The body and head are small, the head carries one pair of narrow tentacles with eyes at their base. Haemoglobin has been found in the blood of the members of this family, while red blood cells of most other molluscs contain haemocyanin instead. Planorbids are hermaphrodite. They stick their eggs contained in a gelatinous case to water plants.

The great ramshorn inhabits almost all of Europe, the Caucasus, Siberia and Asia Minor.

Height:
10—13 mm.
Width:
25—33 mm.
Shell:
Thickly disc-like with concave centre and a slightly arched lower side, firm, finely and irregularly grooved, often with sculptures; 5 to 5.5 well arched whorls. The mouth is slightly oblique, widely kidney-shaped.
Habitat:
overgrown stagnant or slow-flowing waters in lowlands; absent at higher altitudes.

# Large Amber Snail

*Succinea putris*

Members of the Succineidae family are also lung snails. Their eyes (ommatophores), however, are located on the distal ends of the first pair of withdrawable tentacles (order Stylommatophora). The lower pair of tentacles is shorter and used as feelers. The foot of the large amber snail is short with a rounded hind end. Since its body has a high water content it cannot completely hide in the shell. Only after drying up a little can the animal withdraw into its shell completely and seal the shell mouth with a mucous membrane. The shell is quite typical — the whorls grow in quick succession so the last one conspicuously dominates the others. The last whorl is flat to slightly curved below the suture.

Amber snails feed on the soft parts of plants. They are hermaphrodite; after mating each individual lays about 100 eggs on moist soil. Unfavourable periods of the year are spent inside the shell in various clefts or under organic debris.

The large amber snail is abundant in the temperate zone of Europe and in west and north Asia. It is dependent on water and it can therefore be found mainly on plants close to banks or crawling along the leaves of plants just above the water surface. It occurs less frequently on the grass of flooded meadows far from water.

Height:
16—22 mm.
Width:
8—12 mm.
Shell:
pointedly ovate, thin, highly translucent with an irregularly grooved surface. 3 to 4 whorls; the last one is very swollen. The mouth is ovate with a conspicuous sharp horn on the top. Great variability in position and size of the whorls. The whorls more or less overlap, making the shell either compressed with a low disc or high and slender.
Habitat:
banks overgrown with vegetation close to water sources, lowland forests.

# *Arion rufus*

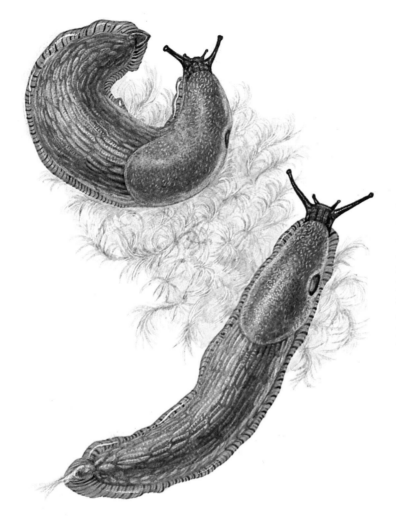

The order Stylommatophora also includes the robust, shell-less slugs of the families Limacidae and Arionidae. Their bodies are bare, and the internal organs are located inside the foot. The mantle on the dorsal side of the body forms a shield with a respiratory opening on its right-hand side. The Arionidae have a rough skin, the foot is broad, with a blunt hind end and without the dorsal keel. The shield is rounded and the respiratory opening is located in its front half. The foot of the Limacidae is slim, pointed at the back and bearing a sharp keel along the long axis of the body. Their shield is loose in the front and with the respiratory opening located towards the rear.

*Arion rufus* lives in western and central Europe, Great Britain and Iceland. Its vivid orange, red, brown or black colours are very conspicuous. Its back, sides and shield are of one colour, the rim of the foot is almost always reddish, and striped in a darker colour. The shield is granular, with the sides and back deeply grooved; their papillae contract if irritated and become raised. The mucus on the top part of the body is orange in reddish slugs; in others it is colourless. The mucus on the foot is colourless in all forms. *Arion rufus* is omnivorous. It is hermaphrodite, and lays about 500 eggs into cracks in bark, under stones etc.

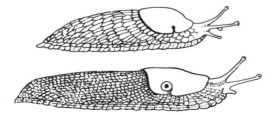

Typical shape of Arionidae (top) and Limacidae (bottom)

Length:
120—150 mm.
Width:
17—20 mm.
Shell:
rudimentary, in form of numerous calcareous grains under the skin of the shield.
Habitat:
damp places in broadleaved or mixed forests and tree avenues; it avoids deep coniferous forest.

# Roman or Edible Snail

*Helix pomatia*

The roman snail is the most common snail of western, central and south-eastern Europe, southern Scandinavia, Great Britain and the Baltic states. It is a vegetarian; it grates its food by forward movements of its tongue-like organ, the radula, which moves against the upper jaw. The radula is also covered with some 40,000 tiny teeth leaning backwards. The food is further decomposed by secretions of the powerful mucous glands which open into the mouth. The shell is composed of three layers which are secreted by glands in the swollen edge of the mantle. The spirally coiled visceral mass containing most of the internal organs is located inside the shell. The body is covered by mucus secreted by the epidermal glands as well as by a powerful mucus gland with an opening located beneath the mouth. The mucus decreases friction and allows the snails a smooth, skidding movement over a rough substratum. If disturbed, while resting or during unfavourable conditions the snail closes its shell with a mucous cover which hardens to form a solid membrane. When preparing for hibernation the animal blocks the shell mouth with a calcareous porous lid which is discarded when the winter is over. The roman snail is hermaphrodite; special calcareous arrowlike formations are created in its reproductive organs. These arrows are then stuck into the bodies of their partners during mating. After fertilization about 60 spherical eggs are laid in the ground. The newly-hatched offspring have an organic shell with few whorls.

Shell closed by a mucus lid

Height:
38—40 mm.
Width:
38—40 mm.
Shell:
dextral, mono-chamber, spherical with a cylindrical disc, very hard, lengthwise irregularly ribbed. 4.5 to 5 whorls, the last being conspicuously larger. The mouth is slightly oblique, rounded, more high than broad.
Habitat:
light broad-leaved forests and park land in warm regions mainly on lime. Secondarily introduced to many places by man.

Detail of the radula

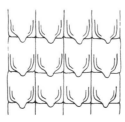

A clutch of eggs

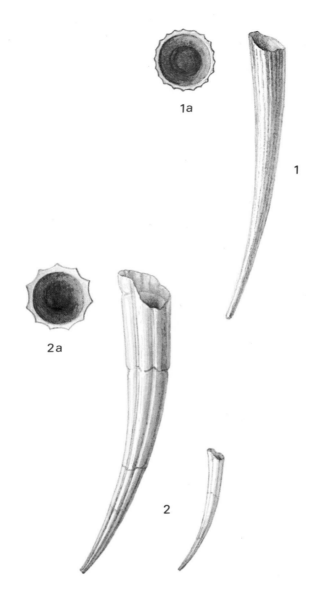

# Common Tusk Shell
*Dentalium dentale*

## *Dentalium vulgare*

*Dentalium dentale* has a large, slightly curved shell resembling a small elephant tusk. The surface is marked by 18—20 longitudinal grooves. The colour is generally white, sometimes with reddish bands.

On each side of the head is a tuft of long filaments with club-shaped ends, which serve as tactile organs and are also used for capturing food. The radula is capable of crushing the shells of small molluscs, crustaceans, foraminiferans and the like.

This species lives on muddy or sandy bottoms, sometimes also in fine gravel, buried in the ground with only the hind end projecting. It is a fairly active animal that ploughs through the mud and sand of the sea bed. It is found from the lower shore to depths of several hundred metres.

*Dentalium vulgare* has a narrower shell. The surface is marked with very fine longitudinal grooves and is a mat milky white. The body structure, way of life and method of capturing and digesting food is the same as in *D. dentale. D. vulgare,* however, has a more limited vertical distribution, generally inhabiting waters closer to the shore, mostly at depths of about 30—70 metres.

Diagram showing a cross section of a tusk shell

1 — *Dentalium dentale:*
Height: 30—50 mm.
Width: 4—6 mm.
Shell: tapering, cylindrical, slightly curved.

1a — Cross section

2 — *Dentalium vulgare:*
Height: up to 60 mm.
Width: 4—6 mm.
Shell: as *D. dentale.*

2a — Cross section

# Swan Mussel

*Anodonta cygnea*

The swan mussel can be found almost all over Europe, in Siberia, and North America. The body of this mussel is concealed between two identical valves which are joined on the back by an elastic ligament. From the inside, the two valves are drawn together and closed by two strong muscles acting perpendicularly to the hinge axis and counteracting the resistance of the ligament. The outermost layer of the shell (periostracum) is of organic origin; the middle layer (ostracum) is strong, and calcareous; the internal layer (hypostracum) is mother-of-pearl, which is smooth and with a typical bluish-green sheen and iridescence. The layers are secreted by glands on the outer layer of the mantle throughout the life of the animal. The mantle is closely attached to the internal layers of the valves. It has two lobes, its margins are very close to each other and they embrace the true body of the mussel which is soft, headless and unsegmented. In the more rounded and broader part of the valves there is an opening in the mantle cavity through which the foot can be extended. On the opposite side there are two siphons in the mantle cavity. Water is drawn into the lower one and it supplies the body with oxygen and bits of organic matter on which the mussel lives. The food is sieved through a ciliary system located on numerous gills so that only pure water enters the gill ducts. The upper siphon is for excretion. Mussels are bisexual, in isolated reservoirs they become hermaphrodite. From the eggs hatch larvae known as glochidia, which live parasitically for some time on the skin of fish.

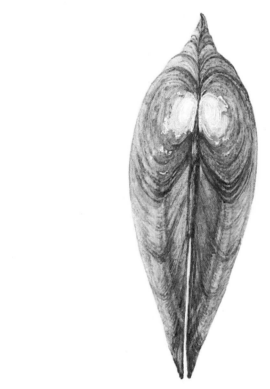

Height:
75—120 mm.
Width:
50—60 mm.
Length:
150—200 mm.
Shell:
longish ovate, the lower margin is straight to concave, the back part is pointed, the fore part rounded. The walls are thin, fragile and layered. The outer organic layer bears concentric growth-lines. The shell contour varies according to whether the shell lives in stagnant or running water.
Habitat:
soft bottoms of deeper stagnant or slow-flowing waters.

Glochidium

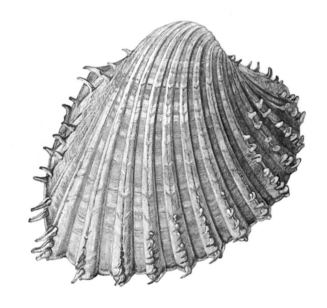

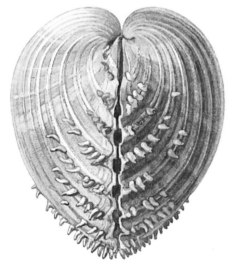

# Spiny Cockle

*Acanthocardia aculeata*

This is an interesting cockle with a large, fairly thin, heart-shaped shell, which grows to a length of about 80 mm, a height of 75 mm and a thickness of 50 mm. Both valves are markedly convex.

The shell is highly ornamented. The prominent radiating ribs (20—22) are furrowed lengthwise on top, and these spines are generally broken off, only the strongest and youngest remaining. The ribs as well as the broad flat furrows between them are crossed by fine transverse growth lines.

The coloration consists of delicate pastel hues. The ground colour is usually yellow-brown to red with a more pronounced pattern of similarly coloured spiral bands of varying width.

*Acanthocardia aculeata* is a common species of cockle found in large numbers on soft muddy bottoms of the littoral and sublittoral zones. An edible species, it is widely gathered both on the European coast of the Atlantic and in the Mediterranean. The shells are often used to make ornaments.

Stages in the movement of a spiny cockle when in flight from an attacker (for example a starfish)

Height:
60—75 mm.
Width:
40—50 mm.
Length:
60—80 mm.
Shell:
thin, heart-shaped, with prominent radiating ribs.
Habitat:
muddy bottoms in littoral and sublittoral zones.

# Common Cuttlefish

*Sepia officinalis*

In most of the existing members of the class Cephalopoda the shell is greatly reduced, enclosed by the side folds of the mantle and located on the dorsal side of the trunk.

A good example of such a shell is that of the common cuttlefish, *Sepia officinalis*. It is spoon-shaped with a thin, horny layer on the dorsal side. Of the original shell partitions, all that remain are the thin calcareous plates running obliquely from the horny layer down to the underside of the body. Shells often cast up on the sandy shores are the well-known "cuttle-bones" gathered by bird fanciers for their pets to peck at since they are a rich source of calcium. The cuttlefish grows to a length of 40−50 cm. It lives near the bottom at shallower depths and has a preference for marine growths such as seaweed. It spends most of the time, however, floating in the water, for it is an excellent swimmer. It propels itself through the water by the undulating motion of the narrow fins extending on either side. Frequently, however, it makes use of the thrust produced by the rhythmical, powerful ejection of water from the mantle cavity through the pedal funnel. When in danger, it uses this method to escape with rapid leaps. The cuttlefish is an edible species harvested in large numbers especially in the Mediterranean.

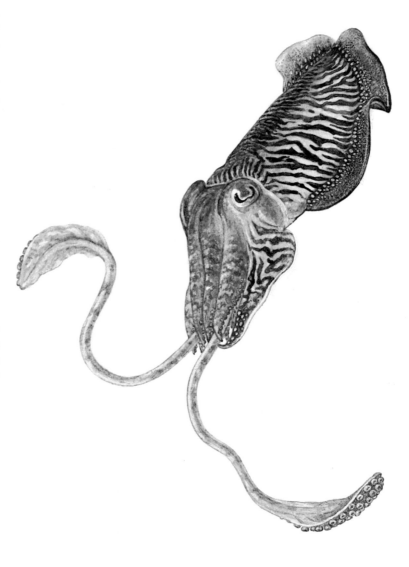

Length:
 400−500 mm.
Shell:
much reduced, enclosed by the mantle.
Habitat:
near the bottom at shallow depths, often in marine growths.

"Cuttle-bones"

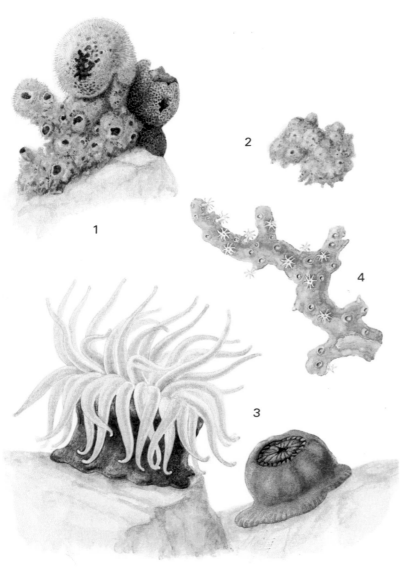

# Bath Sponge
*Spongia officinalis*

# River Sponge
*Ephydatia fluviatilis*

# Beadlet Anemone
*Actinia equina*

# Red Coral
*Corallium rubrum*

The bath sponge often lives in large colonies. Its skeleton is formed by spongy, densely-woven horny fibres; spicules of silica are absent. Water with dispersed food particles enters the inside of the sponge through holes in the spongy network. Sponges reproduce both sexually and vegetatively. The fertilized egg develops into a swimming larva, known as planula — the mobile stage of the sponge, which settles after only a few hours.

The river sponge forms amorphous coverings on submerged objects. It usually has an unpleasant smell. Its skeleton is made of spicules of silica interwoven with horny fibres into bundles. It may also reproduce by gemmules, that is brownish bodies formed in clusters on the underside towards the end of the summer. In this way the species overwinters.

The beadlet anemone has a gelatinous body without a hard skeleton. Around its mouth, it has five to six circles of extensible tentacles bearing stinging cells with which they catch their prey. Beadlet anemones are dioecious; the young develop in the body of the parent which releases them after they are fully developed.

The red coral forms poorly branched colonies which reproduce vegetatively. The red skeleton is made up of calcareous needles.

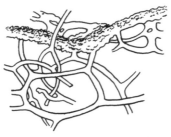

Spongin fibres

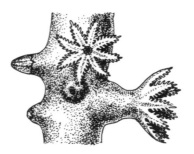

Polyp on a branch of a coral

1 — *Spongia officinalis:*
Size:
up to 200 mm in diameter.
Distribution:
the Mediterranean Sea.

2 — *Ephydatia fluviatilis:*
Size: up to 200 mm.
Distribution:
most fresh-waters of Europe,
the Baltic Sea.

3 — *Actinia equina:*
Base diameter: 10—60 mm.
Height:
up to 70 mm.
Distribution:
eastern Atlantic coastline
from North Cape to south
Africa and the Mediterranean.

4 — *Corallium rubrum:*
Height:
200—400 mm.
Distribution:
the Mediterranean Sea.

# Bibliography

Attenborough D.: *Life on Earth,* Collins & BBC, London 1979.

Barnes R. D.: *Invertebrate Zoology,* Saunders, Philadelphia 1974.

Bellairs A. d'A.: *Life of Reptiles,* Weidenfeld & Nicolson, London 1965.

Campbell A. C.: *Hamlyn guide to the seashore and shallow seas of Britain and Europe,* Hamlyn, London 1976.

Crook J. H.: *Social Behaviour in Birds and Mammals,* Academic Press, New York 1970.

Dorst J.: *Life of Birds,* 2 vols., Weidenfeld & Nicolson, London 1974.

Dorst J. & Dandelot P.: *A field guide to the larger mammals of Africa,* Collins, London 1972.

Fitter R., Heinzel H. & Parslow J.: *The Birds of Britain and Europe,* Collins, London 1972.

*Grzimek's Animal Life Encyclopaedia,* vols. 1–13, Van Nostrand Reinhold, London and New York 1975.

Harrison Matthews L. S.: *Life of Mammals,* Weidenfeld & Nicolson, London, Vol. 1. 1969; Vol. 2. 1971.

Herald E. S.: *Living fishes of the world,* Hamish Hamilton, London 1961.

Krebs C. J.: *Ecology,* Harper and Row, New York 1978.

Marshall N. B. *Life of Fishes,* Weidenfeld & Nicolson, London 1965.

Russel Hunter W. D.: *The Life of Invertebrates,* Collier Macmillan, New York 1979.

Sanderson I. T.: *Living Mammals of the World,* Hamish Hamilton, London 1955.

Schmidt K. D. & Inger R. F.: *Living Reptiles of the World,* Hamish Hamilton, London 1957.

Wigglesworth V.: *Life of Insects,* Weidenfeld & Nicolson, London 1964.

Wilson E. O.: *The Insect Societies,* Belknap, Cambridge, Mass. 1971.

# Index of Common Names

315

# Index of Latin Names